ENGINEERING RADIATION HEAT TRANSFER

John A. Wiebelt

Oklahoma State University

Holt, Rinehart and Winston

New York – Chicago – San Francisco – Toronto – London

Preface

This book is an attempt to assemble and classify a portion of the literature, both past and present, of infrared energy transmission. Infrared or thermal radiation activities have been so stimulated by space applications that the literature is growing very rapidly. For this reason the book attempts to lay a foundation as a guide for further study, rather than to treat comprehensively more sophisticated design characteristics.

In general, the field of electromagnetic theory is introduced in concepts. Most of the classical thermodynamics laws are introduced in order to inform the reader of the limiting conditions that they impose upon any theoretical results.

Since many engineering problems today involve energy-exchange calculations, two chapters have been devoted to this area. The energy exchange procedures in general use, excluding Monte Carlo techniques, are introduced and examined for compatibility. As a logical extension, the solution of practical problems by the digital computer is also introduced.

Energy exchange when participating gases are present is considered in Chapter 7. The author feels that the solution of such problems under the simplifying assumption of isothermal gas is possible presently only with certain fairly restrictive assumptions. For this reason the discussion includes both the gray gas approximations as originally introduced by H. C. Hottel and a nongray gas approximation method introduced by D. K. Edwards. The case of nonisothermal gases is presented briefly, and radiation from luminous flames is discussed. This material is primarily the engineering approximation material as developed by Hottel.

Chapter 8 is designed primarily to introduce the techniques used in radiation measurements and radiation property evaluations—not for the person involved in radiation research, but rather for the person interested in the basic ideas of radiation measurement. Also included is a discussion of property measurement apparatus presently in use. None of the apparatus has been standardized for testing of radiation properties, however, because the area of radiation property measurement is still developing and many new instruments are presently being examined.

iii

Each of the first seven chapters includes problems or exercises. The total number of exercises should be sufficient for a three-hour semester course. In the latter chapters very extensive algebraic calculations must be carried out in order to obtain any sort of solution to the problems. For those schools where digital computer equipment is available, it would be worthwhile to write simple programs to carry out these numerical solutions. The programs can be generalized if required, and an example of such a program is included in Appendix 5. This program was written for use on an IBM 1620 computer, and has been used in several semesters of work.

Acknowledgements usually involve only people directly associated with the author. However, I would like to acknowledge certain persons, not closely associated with me, who have contributed much to this text and to other texts. Max Jakob, R. J. Grosh, E. R. G. Eckert, H. C. Hottel, R. V. Dunkel, D. K. Edwards, and Frank Kreith have made many significant contributions to my understanding of radiation heat transfer.

Among the close associates who have helped with the preparation of the text, I would like to acknowledge J. D. Parker, J. H. Boggs, J. Edward Sunderland, and Eric K. Farber. Finally, I would like to thank Mrs. Mildred Avery, Mrs. Norma Monday, Mrs. Sara McMath, Mrs. Eugenia Brann, and my wife, who helped so much in the preparation of the manuscript.

J. A. WIEBELT

Stillwater, Oklahoma
January 1966

Contents

v

Chapter 7   Energy Transfer in Absorbing and Emitting Media

CHAPTER 1

Introduction

Historical Background

1.1 Identification of Infrared Radiation

Early research work by physicists, primarily interested in visible light phenomena, indicates the presence of thermal energy in sunlight beyond the red
region of the visible spectrum. In 1666, Sir Isaac Newton discovered that
white light, when passed through a prism, is split into the various colors of
the visible spectrum. This discovery led other physicists to experiments that
substantiated the presence of infrared or below-red radiation. Infrared radiation was identified in these experiments as being of the same nature as
visible light and later was shown to obey exactly the same physical laws of
reflection, refraction, polarization, and interference. For these reasons a
study of infrared radiation is closely associated with the science of optics.
Because of this close association, the work in this area was for many years
conducted primarily by physicists.

1.2 Basic Optics

Since the study of infrared radiation involves the study of optics, a few
of the basic concepts of optics should be reviewed. (Newton, in his treatise
Opticks, presented the first comprehensive discussion of the subject.) The
laws of reflection and refraction as presented by Willebrod Snell are illustrated in Figure 1.1.

The laws of reflection and refraction from the interface may be expressed
as $\phi_1 = \phi_1'$ for reflection and $\sin \phi_1 / \sin \phi_2 = n_{21}$ for refraction, where n_{21} is
the index of refraction for medium 2 with respect to medium 1. In the example
shown, n_{21} would be larger than one, resulting in $\phi_2 < \phi_1$, or a bending of
the incident ray toward the normal. Snell's law is applicable only when the
interface between medium 1 and medium 2 is optically flat. If the surface is

1

rough, and the average roughness is of the order of magnitude of the wavelength of the incident ray, the law is no longer useful. This is caused by the phenomena called *diffraction* and *interference*. When these occur it is no longer possible to identify the reflected ray.

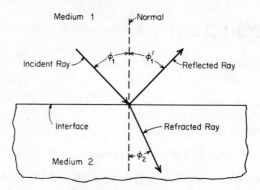

Figure 1.1   Snell's Law.

In order to describe diffraction effects it is necessary to consider the rays of Figure 1.1 (which represent plane waves) as spherical wavefronts, and use electromagnetic wave theory, or, for geometrical construction, the principle of Christian Huygens. Huygens' principle was developed before electromagnetic theory and does not give the more complete explanation possible from the Maxwell equations, but it does present information of value in visualizing physical phenomena. Interference effects are discussed later when the subject of coherence is examined.

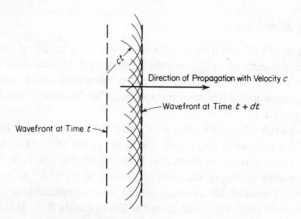

Figure 1.2   Huygens' Construction for the New Position of a Wavefront after a Time Interval *dt*.

1.3 Huygens' Principle

Huygens' principle is based on a geometrical construction in which all points in a wavefront are considered as sources of spherical waves. The new position of the wavefront after a time t will be the surface represented by the fronts of the spherical waves. For example, see Figure 1.2, which depicts a plane wave at times t and $t + dt$. As indicated, the velocity of light in the medium is c.

The construction of wavefronts using Huygens' principle results in Snell's laws of reflection and refraction. An advantage of the Huygens principle is that the phenomena of diffraction is predicted from this construction. This is illustrated in Figure 1.3, where a two-dimensional aperture is shown, for

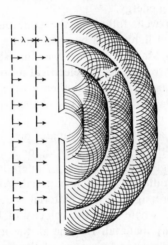

Figure 1.3   Diffraction by a Slit of Width Equal to the Wavelength λ of an Incident Plane Wavefront.

which the width is in the order of magnitude of the wavelength. In order to avoid wave propagation in both the forward and reverse direction, Augustin Fresnel determined that the intensity of the wave should vary as $(\cos \phi) + 1$, in which ϕ is the angle measured between the normal to the wavefront and the point in question on the wavelet (see Figure 1.2) [5]†. This results in a maximum intensity for the forward direction ($\phi = 0$, so $\cos \phi + 1 = 2$) and zero intensity in the reverse direction. When the Huygens construction is used, a plane incident wave becomes a spherical wavefront if the slit is a circular hole. Such an effect cannot be explained from the ray concept.

Another advantage of the Huygens construction is in visualizing light as

---

† Bracketed numbers refer to the bibliography at the end of the chapter.

wavefronts. With this concept, electromagnetic theory becomes more acceptable as a physical explanation.

1.4 Wave Theory Development

Following the development of the " dynamical theory " of heat (1789) by Count Rumford (Benjamin Thomson) and others, the wave theory was extended. In this development a medium for the transport of waves, *ether*, was postulated. In the thinking processes of the physicists, the transfer of energy by a wave-like system was obvious; however, the transfer was thought of as being similar to sound waves and, as such, required a medium of transfer. The ether postulated for this theory did not have density, compressibility, molecular structure or any property of matter except the property of containing and transferring energy.

In 1862, James Maxwell, following the concepts of Michael Faraday, showed analytically that light could be considered a transverse wave phenomenon. Verification of Maxwell's theory was furnished in 1887 by Heinrich Hertz. Hertz was able to produce by electrical means very long wavelength infrared radiation. Maxwell's classical theory of electromagnetic waves is accepted and used today to explain many of the experimental phenomenon of optics.

This theory leads to a model that postulates propagation of the transverse waves in free space at the velocity of light c_o, or 3×10^8 meters per second, with waves of wavelength λ and frequency f interrelated by $\lambda f = c$. Furthermore, the velocity is different in each material. As defined in optics, the velocity of the wave propagation in a material is described by the index of refraction n: $n = c_o/c_m$, where c_o is the velocity of light in free space, and c_m is the velocity in any material. In general, the index of refraction for a given material depends on the frequency of the waves. As the waves pass through the material, the wavelength is determined by $\lambda_m f = c_m$. In passing from one medium to a second medium, the frequency remains constant; but, since the velocity changes, the wavelength will change.

Electromagnetic Waves

1.5 Method of Production

Electromagnetic waves are produced by oscillations of the electric fields around charges. As shown in elementary electrical theory, electric charges have forces of attraction or repulsion. Charles Augustin Coulomb, in the 18th century, showed that these forces were related to charge and distance by the proportionality

$$\text{Force} \propto \frac{q_1 q_2}{r^2}$$

in which q_1 and q_2 are the charges of two spheres located a distance r apart. In order to investigate changes in the force field produced by a charge, the field concept is introduced. In this case the force field is a vector field, and is associated with a charge q by assuming a unit positive charge placed at a distance r from q. The resulting force upon the unit positive charge is the value of the field at the point in question. Since this force has magnitude and direction, a vector field is indicated. This field is described as the electric field due to the charge q.

When the charge q moves, a disturbance is produced in the field. The disturbance is propagated through the field at the speed of light, that is, the disturbance is not immediately felt by a charge at a distance r from the original charge. When the charge oscillates, a series of disturbances are propagated. These disturbances are electromagnetic waves. By extending Ampere's law, Maxwell showed that the electric field disturbance would be accompanied by a magnetic field disturbance, that is, the electric field wave would create a magnetic field with a wave accompanying the electric field wave. Because of this, the wave is called an *electromagnetic* wave.

1.6 Maxwell's Equations

The characteristics of electromagnetic waves are described analytically by the Maxwell equations. A somewhat simplified representation of these equations for the case of isotropic homogeneous materials is given in [4] as

$$q_v = \mathscr{E} \operatorname{div} \mathbf{E} \tag{1.2}$$

$$0 = \operatorname{div} \mathbf{H} \tag{1.3}$$

$$-\mu \frac{\partial \mathbf{H}}{\partial t} = \operatorname{curl} \mathbf{E} \tag{1.4}$$

$$\sigma \mathbf{E} + \mathscr{E} \frac{\partial \mathbf{E}}{\partial t} = \operatorname{curl} \mathbf{H} \tag{1.5}$$

where q_v is the net electric charge
$\mathbf{E}$ is the electric field vector
$\mathscr{E}$ is the absolute permittivity
$\mathbf{H}$ is the magnetic field vector
μ is the absolute permeability
σ is the electrical conductivity.
A complete, easily followed derivation of the Maxwell equations in an integral form is presented in [2].

The concept of electromagnetic waves and their characteristics may be obtained from Equations 1.2–1.5 as follows (this derivation follows the work in [4]): Equation 1.4 may be changed to

$$-\mu \frac{\partial}{\partial t} (\text{curl } \mathbf{H}) = \text{curl curl } \mathbf{E}$$

by taking the curl of both sides. From the vector identity

$$\text{curl curl } \mathbf{E} = \text{grad div } \mathbf{E} - \nabla^2 \mathbf{E}$$

this becomes

$$-\mu \frac{\partial}{\partial t} (\text{curl } \mathbf{H}) = \text{grad div } \mathbf{E} - \nabla^2 \mathbf{E}$$

Substitution of Equation 1.5 into the left-hand part gives

$$\mu\sigma \frac{\partial \mathbf{E}}{\partial t} + \mu\mathscr{E} \frac{\partial^2 \mathbf{E}}{\partial t^2} = \nabla^2 \mathbf{E} - \text{grad div } \mathbf{E} \tag{1.6}$$

Starting with Equation 1.5 and proceeding in a similar manner gives

$$\text{curl curl } \mathbf{H} = \text{curl } \sigma\mathbf{E} + \text{curl } \mathscr{E} \frac{\partial \mathbf{E}}{\partial t}$$

or

$$\text{grad div } \mathbf{H} - \nabla^2 \mathbf{H} = \sigma \text{ curl } \mathbf{E} + \mathscr{E} \text{ curl } \frac{\partial \mathbf{E}}{\partial t}$$

After substitution from Equations 1.3 and 1.4 this becomes

$$\nabla^2 \mathbf{H} = \mu\sigma \frac{\partial \mathbf{H}}{\partial t} + \mu\mathscr{E} \frac{\partial^2 \mathbf{H}}{\partial t^2} \tag{1.7}$$

Equations 1.6 and 1.7 describe an electromagnetic wave in any homogeneous isotropic medium, and are useful for demonstrating wave characteristics.

1.7 Wave Solution for Nonconducting Media

The various media that concern engineers include electrical conducting media, semiconductors, and nonconducting media. To examine electromagnetic wave propagation, these can be divided into nonconducting and conducting media by considering semiconductors to be a special case of the conducting media. The ideal nonconducting media with no charge would have $q_v = 0$ and $\sigma = 0$. In this case Equations 1.6 and 1.7 become

$$\nabla^2 \mathbf{E} = \mu\mathscr{E} \frac{\partial^2 \mathbf{E}}{\partial t^2} \tag{1.8}$$

and

$$\nabla^2 \mathbf{H} = \mu\mathscr{E} \frac{\partial^2 \mathbf{H}}{\partial t^2} \tag{1.9}$$

Equations 1.8 and 1.9 are for the general three-dimensional wave. If the wave is considered to be a plane wave propagating in the x direction, Equation 1.8 can be written for the two components of the vector $\mathbf{E}$ as

$$\frac{\partial^2 E_z}{\partial x^2} = \mu\mathscr{E}\,\frac{\partial^2 E_z}{\partial t^2} \tag{1.10}$$

and

$$\frac{\partial^2 E_y}{\partial x^2} = \mu\mathscr{E}\,\frac{\partial^2 E_y}{\partial t^2} \tag{1.11}$$

Of course similar equations could be written from Equation 1.9 for the magnetic field; however, Equations 1.10 and 1.11 are satisfactory for illustration without considering the magnetic field.

The solution to Equation 1.11 may be written

$$E_y = E_{y_o} \cos\left[\omega\left(t - \frac{x}{c}\right)\right] \tag{1.12}$$

where ω is defined as 2π times the frequency of the wave and c is the velocity of propagation, $(\mu\mathscr{E})^{-1/2}$. The solution (Equation 1.12) consists of a sinusoidal wave traveling with a velocity c. This is illustrated in Figure 1.4, in

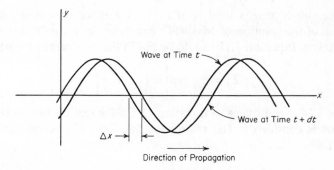

Figure 1.4   A Traveling Sine Wave.

which two waves are shown, at times t and $t + \Delta t$. As indicated, the wave has advanced a distance Δx during Δt such that $\Delta x = c\,\Delta t$. A similar solution can be found for the z component of the plane wave E_z. The vector addition of the two components E_y and E_z at any location x gives a space curve that describes the magnitude of the vector $\mathbf{E}$ for the plane wave.

Waves in an electric field as represented by these solutions are accompanied by waves in a magnetic field. This is illustrated in Figure 1.5 in which the electric field wave E_y is plotted along with the accompanying magnetic field wave component H_z. Since magnetic fields are always associated with an

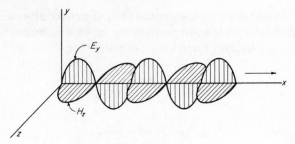

Figure 1.5   The Relationship between the Electric Vector Wave E_y and the Magnetic Vector Wave H_z at Any Time.

electric field, it has become standard practice to discuss the electric field alone, with the realization that magnetic fields will be present in a definite relationship.

An important observation to be made from Equation 1.12 is that $c = (\mu\mathscr{E})^{-1/2}$, that is, velocity of propagation is related to electrical properties. From this relationship the index of refraction of a material is given by

$$n = \frac{c_o}{c} = \left(\frac{\mu\mathscr{E}}{\mu_o\mathscr{E}_o} \right)^{1/2} \tag{1.13}$$

where the subscript o is used to indicate free space conditions. Before a discussion of the solution of Maxwell's equations for a conducting medium is undertaken, Equation 1.12 should be put in the exponential form:

$$E_y = E_{y_o} \exp\left[i\omega\left(t - \frac{nx}{c_o} \right) \right] \tag{1.14}$$

Equation 1.14 is equivalent to Equation 1.12 if the real portion of the right-hand part is considered. The reason for this form will become evident in Section 1.8.

1.8 Wave Solution for Electric Conductors

When Equation 1.6 is applied for a conducting media that has no charge ($q_v = 0$), the following equation is obtained:

$$\mu\sigma \frac{\partial \mathbf{E}}{\partial t} + \mu\mathscr{E} \frac{\partial^2 \mathbf{E}}{\partial t^2} = \nabla^2 \mathbf{E} \tag{1.15}$$

Specializing this for the y component of the plane wave propagating in the x direction gives

$$\mu\sigma \frac{\partial E_y}{\partial t} + \mu\mathscr{E} \frac{\partial^2 E_y}{\partial t^2} = \frac{\partial^2 E_y}{\partial x^2} \tag{1.16}$$

Equation 1.16 may be solved by assuming a solution in the form $E_y = F(x)e^{i\omega t}$, in which $F(x)$ may be complex. Substitution into Equation 1.16 gives

$$E_y = E_{y_o} \exp(i\omega t - Ax) \qquad (1.17)$$

where

$$A = (i\omega\mu\sigma - \omega^2 \mathscr{E}\mu)^{1/2}$$

By convention [4] A is frequently written as

$$A = \frac{i\omega}{c_o}(n - ik)$$

in which

$$n = \left[\frac{\mathscr{E}\mu}{\mathscr{E}_o\mu_o}\right]^{1/2}\left[1 + \left(\frac{\sigma}{\omega\mathscr{E}}\right)^2\right]^{1/4} \cos\left\{\frac{1}{2}\left[\arctan\left(\frac{\sigma}{\omega\mathscr{E}}\right)\right]\right\} \qquad (1.18)$$

$$k = \left[\frac{\mathscr{E}\mu}{\mathscr{E}_o\mu_o}\right]^{1/2}\left[1 + \left(\frac{\omega\mathscr{E}}{\sigma}\right)^2\right]^{1/4} \sin\left\{\frac{1}{2}\left[\arctan\left(\frac{\omega\mathscr{E}}{\sigma}\right)\right]\right\} \qquad (1.19)$$

When the defined expression for A is used, Equation 1.17 becomes

$$E_y = E_{y_o} \exp\left(i\omega t - \frac{i\omega n x}{c_o} - \frac{\omega k x}{c_o}\right)$$

or

$$E_y = E_{y_o} \exp\left(\frac{-\omega k x}{c_o}\right)\exp\left[i\omega\left(t - \frac{nx}{c_o}\right)\right] \qquad (1.20)$$

Equation 1.20 is the same as Equation 1.14, the previous solution, except for the damping factor $\exp(-\omega k x/c_o)$ which mutliplies the other term. Since the second term is a traveling sine wave, it is easily seen that the solution for a conducting medium is a damped sine wave. The variable k in the damping term is frequently called the *absorption coefficient*. Both n and k—as defined by Equations 1.18 and 1.19—depend on the frequency or the wavelength of the waves. When $\sigma \ll \omega\mathscr{E}$ or $\sigma \ll 2\pi f$, the equations specialize to the solution for a nonconducting medium. When $\sigma \gg \mathscr{E}$,

$$n = k = \left(\frac{\sigma\mu}{2\mathscr{E}_o\mu_o}\right)^{1/2} = c_o\left(\frac{\sigma\mu}{4\pi f}\right)^{1/2}$$

and the absorption characteristics of the medium depend on σ.

1.9 Electromagnetic Power Flow

An important characteristic of the electromagnetic vector is the energy carried with it. John H. Poynting expressed the instantaneous power associated with an electromagnetic wave as

$$\mathbf{P} = \mathbf{E} \times \mathbf{H} \qquad (1.21)$$

The vector **P** represents the instantaneous power associated with the traveling wave and points in the direction of propagation. For the case of a plane wave, as examined in the preceding sections, the power vector points in the x direction and has the magnitude $(E_y)(H_z)$. This expression for the power assumes that for the plane wave $E_z = 0$. Using the solution for E_y for the nonconducting medium as an example gives

$$E_y = E_{y_o} \cos\left[\omega\left(t - \frac{x}{c}\right)\right]$$

and, from Equation 1.4

$$-\mu \frac{\partial H_z}{\partial t} = \frac{\partial E_y}{\partial x}$$

or, since

$$H_z = H_{z_o} \cos\left[\omega\left(t - \frac{x}{c}\right)\right],$$

$$\mu\omega H_{z_o} \sin\left[\omega\left(t - \frac{x}{c}\right)\right] = \frac{\omega}{c} E_{y_o} \sin\left[\omega\left(t - \frac{x}{c}\right)\right]$$

thus

$$\mu H_{z_o} = \frac{1}{c} E_{y_o}$$

or

$$H_z = \frac{1}{\mu c} E_{y_o} \cos\left[\omega\left(t - \frac{x}{c}\right)\right]$$

From this expression for H_z the instantaneous power flow in the x direction is

$$P_x = \frac{1}{\mu c} E_{y_o}^2 \cos^2\left[\omega\left(t - \frac{x}{c}\right)\right] \qquad (1.22)$$

The average power flow past a given location x during several cycles would be

$$\overline{P}_x = \frac{1}{\mu c} E_{y_o}^2 \frac{1}{\Delta t} \int_t^{t+\Delta t} \cos^2\left[\omega\left(t - \frac{x}{c}\right)\right] dt$$

or

$$\overline{P}_x = \frac{1}{2\mu c} E_{y_o}^2 \qquad (1.23)$$

Equation 1.23 indicates the important fact that the power flow associated with a wave is proportional to the electric vector squared. Thus, the energy associated with electromagnetic waves at any location could in principle be expressed from the solutions of Maxwell's equations.

1.10 Emission from Solid Surfaces

The discussion up to this point has considered a field produced by a single charge. Actually, the more usual discussion would be of electric dipoles. Electric dipoles are two charges, one positive and one negative, located some distance apart. The concept of electric dipoles is convenient in a discussion of energy emitted from a real surface.

Typically, the molecules that make up a real surface are considered to be configured such that a dipole exists. Considering the molecules to be vibrating due to their temperature, we can conceive of oscillating electric fields associated with each molecule. As the individual molecule vibrates with some frequency f, a train of waves are emitted. This train of waves, with a unique frequency, propagate away from the molecule, along with other wave groups.

In general, the number of waves of unique frequency emitted by an individual molecule depend on the time of residence at any energy level for the molecule. At a given frequency, several million waves are emitted as a wave train or group. The energy emitted away from a surface at temperature T during a time Δt consists of all the wave-group energies from the molecules on the surface and below the surface—if the effects can propagate through the material.

Since the molecules have many different energy levels, the frequencies of the wave groups will be many. Actually, for normal temperatures, there are so many frequencies present that all possible frequencies are normally considered to be present. In other words, the frequency spectrum is considered to be continuous for a solid substance at normal temperatures (well above absolute zero). Of course, the number of wave groups at each frequency is not the same, and the distribution of the number of groups at any given frequency are examined in detail later.

1.11 Polarization

It is common practice to describe by polarization the type of electromagnetic wave that is propagating. If the electric vectors for a plane wave propagating in the x directions are aligned with the y axis, the wave is said to be plane polarized in the y direction. That is, the direction of plane polarized waves is described by the direction of the electric vector.

When the electric vector components E_y and E_z are equal at each time and position, the result of their vector addition is an electric vector that oscillates with time in a plane inclined at 45 deg to the yx or zx planes.

Another specific case occurs when E_y and E_z are specified by equations such as Equation 1.12, modified to indicate the phase angles. For example

$$E_y = E_{y_o} \cos\left[\omega\left(t - \frac{x}{c}\right) + \delta_y\right] \tag{1.24}$$

where δ_y is an arbitrary angle indicating the phase of the y component. A similar equation for the z component would be

$$E_z = E_{z_o} \cos\left[\omega\left(t - \frac{x}{c}\right) + \delta_z\right] \tag{1.25}$$

Physically, these two equations can be considered, at an instant in time, to represent sine waves in the yx and zx planes that are not in phase (that is, the maxima do not occur at the same value of x). The phase difference between the waves could be represented as $\Delta\delta = \delta_y - \delta_z$. Now, when $\Delta\delta = \pi/2$, the vector addition of E_y and E_z results in a vector that rotates when examined at any location x. In the case where $E_{y_o} = E_{z_o}$, the rotating vector has a constant magnitude. The head of this vector when examined at any time describes a helix around the x axis. In this case the plane wave is described as being *circularly polarized*.

In a case similar to the circularly polarized case, where $E_{y_o} \neq E_{z_o}$, the rotating vector has a magnitude variation that is elliptical in shape, that is, if the vector at a specified value of x is examined, the vector head describes an ellipse. Of course, this elliptically polarized wave has the major and minor axes aligned with the y and z directions. It should be noted that elliptically polarized waves can occur if $\Delta\delta$ is not exactly $\pi/2$. In this case an ellipse is described by the vector head, but the major and minor axes are not aligned with the x and z directions.

Natural or unpolarized light occurs when many waves are emitted with arbitrary polarization. When the many waves are examined, the electric vectors, on the average, have the same magnitude in all directions around the direction of propagation. In the case of natural light propagating as plane waves in the x direction, all possible y and z plane directions are found. The vectors, when averaged, all have the same magnitude.

1.12 Coherence

Electromagnetic waves are said to be coherent when the phase difference is a definite quantity. Strictly speaking, coherent waves are emitted from several molecules only when the change in energy levels occurs at precisely the same time. (A present-day device that emits coherent waves is the *laser*.)

In the study of waves that are coherent, a single source may be used. One procedure by which coherent waves may be obtained is to collimate the emission from a single source. The collimated beam is directed onto slits or apertures for which a is in the order of λ (see Section 1.3). This procedure results in coherent spherical waves propagating away from the pair of apertures. The waves are coherent since each individual wave originates at the same time from the single source.

If the waves from the source are essentially of a single wavelength, that is, monochromatic, observable destructive and constructive interference occurs: for example, an alternate light and dark pattern would appear on a screen. When the electric vectors are in phase, constructive interference occurs; when they are out of phase by 180 deg or π radians, destructive interference occurs.

Note that energy from two separate sources would not be coherent and, therefore, interference would not occur. If the energy from the source is not monochromatic, alternate bright and dim spectra occur.

For energy transfer expressions used in the following chapters, alternate bright and dim images represent variations in the power incident upon a surface. The possibility of such an effect occurs only when the energy incident on a surface comes from a single source. In this case detailed examination for power variations due to interference is feasible.

1.13 Electromagnetic Spectrum

Electromagnetic waves are unique in that they cover such a wide range of frequencies or wavelengths. The range of wavelengths and the typical method of producing these waves are shown in Figure 1.6. Very short-wavelength

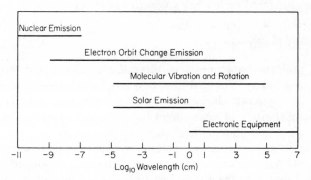

Figure 1.6   Electromagnetic Spectrum Based on the Source of Emission.

electromagnetic waves are emitted from the nuclei of atoms. These waves are called *gamma rays* and result from the decomposition of the nuclei. Even shorter-wavelength waves occur in nature as *cosmic rays*. Relatively longer-wavelength electromagnetic waves are emitted by atoms when the electrons in the orbits change from orbits of high energy to orbits of lower energy. These waves go from the short x rays to waves that have wavelengths somewhat longer than visible light. Flourescent light is a common example of electromagnetic waves emitted due to electronic changes.

When molecules vibrate, electromagnetic waves may be emitted. This phenomenon occurs only when the molecules have an electric dipole. For molecules with electric dipole moment, energy is emitted with a wavelength ranging from the short-wavelength visible region well into the longer-wavelength infrared. Normally, most instances of energy transfer by radiation come from molecular vibration or rotational energy transitions. As indicated in Figure 1.6, this energy has wavelengths in the order of 10^{-4} cm to 10^4 cm. It is common practice to refer to the wavelengths in this region in terms of microns rather than centimeters (1 $\mu = 10^{-6}$ meters). In terms of microns, the portion of the electromagnetic spectrum of most concern in heat transfer is the approximate range 0.1–100 μ. In the visible light region, which is approximately 0.4–0.7 μ, the typical unit of wavelength is a millimicron or 10^{-3} μ. For the shorter wavelength region, or ultraviolet region, the angstrom Å is the normal unit of measure (1 Å $= 10^{-8}$ cm $= 10^{-4}$ μ). Where electromagnetic waves of longer wavelength, such as radar or radio emissions, are concerned, the measure of wavelength is usually millimeters or meters.

There is a very wide range of electromagnetic wavelengths. Fortunately, the same general concepts of electromagnetic wave theory apply throughout this range. Because of this fact, the research work in many varied scientific fields can be correlated within any given area of study.

Basic Definitions

A major problem for students of thermal radiation lies in acquiring a meaningful vocabulary. Thermal radiation has been a subject of study for many years by physicists, chemists, and heat transfer engineers. During this period, a parallel study of visible light has been developed by scientists in the field of optics and illumination.

The results of the various areas of study are equally applicable to the study of thermal radiation. As would be expected, each group developed a different set of symbols and units for a wide variety of defined quantities. The subject has been confused to the point where very few engineering textbooks use a consistent system. In order to avoid such a difficulty, this section will be devoted to the explicit definition of basic terms.

1.14 Thermal Radiation

Thermal radiation is defined as *energy transferred by electromagnetic waves that originate from a system because of the temperature of the system.* This energy is normally associated with the vibration and/or rotation of the molecules of a system; as such, it depends on the substance and temperature of the system. With this definition, phosphorescence or chemoluminescence do not classify as thermal radiation, although the energy emitted by these phenomena is often of a wavelength similar to thermal radiation. In monochromatic energy-exchange calculations, energy is classified by specified wavelengths. For these calculations, energy from any type of source may be considered, even though the amount of energy emitted may not depend on the temperature of the source.

1.15 Total Emissive Power, $E(T_1, system)$

Total emissive power is *the total thermal radiation energy emitted by a surface element into the entire volume above the surface per unit time per unit area*. In terms of electromagnetic waves, total emissive power is the sum of all of the energy carried by the wave groups emitted from a unit area of the surface during a relatively long time interval. Since this energy is associated with incoherent unpolarized electromagnetic waves emitted from molecular vibrations, the examination of the process on a microscopic (time and space) scale would be very difficult. For this reason total emissive power is defined mathematically in terms of radiant power, which is the sum of the time-averaged value of the energy carried by each wave

$$E(T_1, system) = \lim_{\Delta A \to 0} \left[\frac{\text{radiant power}}{\Delta A} \right]$$

and, therefore, is a point function. That is, the total emissive power of a finite surface may vary from point to point since the temperature may vary from point to point. Thus, for a surface of finite size

$$\bar{E}(T_1, system) = \frac{\int_{\Delta A} E(T_1, \text{point } xy)}{\int_{\Delta A} dA}$$

where $\bar{E}$ is used to indicate the average value over the finite surface element area ΔA. This definition does not specify the direction in which the emitted energy leaves the surface, but rather includes all energy leaving the surface element regardless of direction. The typical engineering units for E or $\bar{E}$ are Btu per hr-ft^2.

Some other names and symbols applied to total emissive power are *total hemispheric emissive power, emissive power*, and *radiant flux density*; other symbols frequently encountered are W or e [1, 3].

1.16 Total Irradiation, G, H

The total irradiation of a system is defined as *the total power incident or incoming to the surface of the system per unit of area of irradiated surface*. As in the definition of total emissive power, the direction from which the waves come to the surface does not matter. That is, the waves may be incoming to the surface from all directions over the surface, or coming from one speci- fied direction. The total irradiation is incoming power per unit area, or the local flux in Btu per hr-ft^2; so far as energy effects are concerned, the system is insensitive to direction. Another way of specifying this is to define G as a scalar quantity rather than a vector quantity. (Another symbol used for total irradiation is H.)

1.17 Total Radiosity, J

Radiosity is defined as *the total radiant power leaving the surface of a system per unit area of the surface.* This quantity is different than total emis- sive power in that radiosity includes both energy emitted from a system and energy reflected from a system. Total radiosity does not depend on direction, and is a point function as is total emissive power. Total radiosity is an energy flux, and is normally expressed in Btu per hr-ft^2 by engineers. In some texts the symbol R is used for radiosity.

1.18 Intensity of Radiation, I

Intensity of radiation is defined in engineering work for an idealized diffuse surface emitter. Within the concepts of electromagnetic theory already developed and Huygens' principle, a diffuse surface can be described as follows:

Consider a small surface element ΔA which has many dipole oscillators on the surface. Let all the energy emitted into space over the surface come from these dipole oscillators. Each of the oscillators will produce electro- magnetic waves, and the waves from the several oscillators will have ran- dom phase angles. Since the phase angles are random, no interference will occur, and the concept introduced in Huygens' principle may be used.

From this concept a small area ΔA will emit spherical wavefronts into space over the area. This is illustrated in Figure 1.7 in which a small area ΔA is shown. For the purpose of this discussion the radius of the wavelets is taken to be much larger than the characteristic dimension of ΔA. This is not to imply that the dimensions of ΔA are less than the wavelength; rather, it is to avoid complication by using too many wavefront positions.

Examination of Figure 1.7 for the intensity of energy at some angle ϕ away from the surface normal indicates that the energy becomes less as ϕ increases. This observation comes from two facts: (1) As ϕ increases, fewer wavelets contribute to the energy; (2) the intensity of any wavelet is greatest in the forward propagation direction. Careful consideration of the variation of the energy intercepted by a surface element Δa as $\Delta \phi$, Δa, and ΔA approach zero (within the limits of a continuum) leads to Lambert's cosine law. This

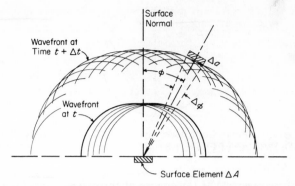

Figure 1.7   Lambert's Law.

law states that the energy intercepted by *da* from an area *dA* will vary as the cosine of ϕ. It is obvious from electromagnetic theory that the Lambert cosine law must involve many point sources or many oscillators. That is, $\Delta A \to dA$, where dA is not in the order of size of a single oscillator.

In engineering terms this variation may be described by replacing the small area Δa by a detector, as shown in Figure 1.8. When the detector is directly above ΔA, or $\phi = 0$, a maximum signal S_M is obtained. As the angle ϕ is

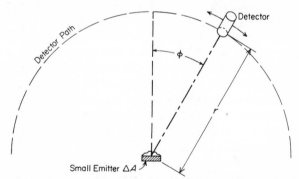

Figure 1.8   Engineering Application of Lambert's Law.

increased, the signal decreases. According to Lambert's cosine law, the value decreases such that the signal S is related to the maximum signal S_M by $S = S_M \cos \phi$.

This variation is plotted on polar coordinates in Figure 1.9. The energy in the spherical wavefronts moving away from the area ΔA are continually spread over the area of a larger and larger sphere. Because of this, if the detector is moved toward or away from the surface ΔA holding ϕ constant,

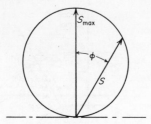

Figure 1.9   **Polar Coordinate System Plot of the Signal Resulting from the Detector of Figure 1.8.**

the signal varies inversely as the square of the distance from the detector to ΔA; that is

$$\frac{S_1}{S_2} = \frac{r_2^{\,2}}{r_1^{\,2}}$$

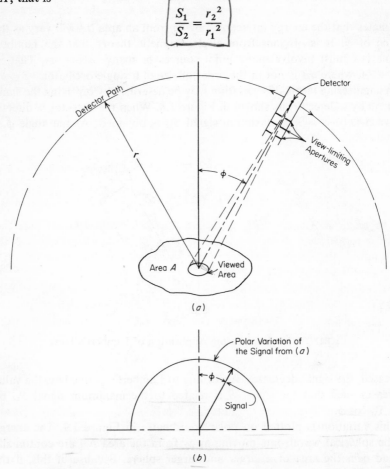

Figure 1.10   **An Engineering System that Reacts to Intensity.**

The more usual method of indicating this variation is to use solid angles. From spherical trigonometry, a solid angle is defined from a sphere as $\omega = A/r^2$, where A is an area on the surface of a sphere of radius r. Using solid angles

$$\frac{S_1}{S_2} = \frac{(\text{area of detector in position 1})/r_1{}^2}{(\text{area of detector in position 2})/r_2{}^2}$$

or $S_1/S_2 = \omega_1/\omega_2$, which is exactly the same as $S_1/S_2 = r_2{}^2/r_1{}^2$ since the detector has the same area Δa in each position.

The conclusion resulting from the foregoing analysis is that the intensity for a diffuse emitter should be described in terms of the area seen by the detector and the solid angle. That is, if intensity is to depend on emitter characteristics and not upon its size or location relative to the detector, the intensity should be described as power per solid angle per unit area of the emitter, projected normal to the line of view from the detector to the surface element. With this definition, the intensity is seen to be constant over the hemisphere above a diffuse surface. A physical system that would react in this manner is shown in Figure 1.10a. A detector with a limited viewing angle is focused on a large area A. This detector reacts to the energy from the large area in the manner indicated in Figure 1.10b, since the detector "sees" the same projected area in any position through the same solid angle. The signal remains constant for variations of angle ϕ.

System Properties

1.19 Reflectance-Reflectivity, ρ

The terms *reflectance* and *reflectivity* appear in heat transfer literature without regard to a difference. As suggested by A. G. Worthing [6], the term reflectivity will be used in this text for systems with a single reflecting interface for which Snell's and Fresnel's equations are valid.

As indicated, Snell's equations are valid when the incident and reflected rays are identifiable. This occurs for surfaces that are optically smooth and uncontaminated. For this type of interface between two dielectric media, Snell's relations are (see Figure 1.1)

$$\phi_1 = \phi_1{}' \tag{1.28}$$

and

$$n_1 \sin \phi_1 = n_2 \sin \phi_2 \tag{1.29}$$

For the case of two dielectric materials, the Fresnel equations are given in terms of two principal planes. These two planes are described as the plane of *incidence*, which is the plane containing the incident and reflected ray, and the plane *normal* to the plane of incidence.

In Figure 1.1 the plane of incidence or p plane is the plane of the paper.

The normal plane or s plane is normal to the plane of the paper and usually consists of the plane containing the ray. For incident s plane, the ray and the plane normal to the paper describe the s plane.

With the s and p planes defined, Fresnel's equations for two dielectric media are

$$r_p = \frac{n_2 \cos \phi_1 - n_1 \cos \phi_2}{n_2 \cos \phi_1 + n_1 \cos \phi_2} = \frac{\tan(\phi_1 - \phi_2)}{\tan(\phi_1 + \phi_2)} \tag{1.30}$$

and

$$r_s = \frac{n_1 \cos \phi_1 - n_2 \cos \phi_2}{n_1 \cos \phi_1 + n_2 \cos \phi_2} = \frac{\sin(\phi_1 - \phi_2)}{\sin(\phi_1 + \phi_2)} \tag{1.31}$$

where r_p and r_s are the ratios of the amplitudes of the incident wave and reflected wave for the p and s planes respectively. Since the power carried by the waves is proportional to the square of the amplitudes, the reflectivity values for power are

$$\rho_p = (r_p)^2 \tag{1.32}$$

$$\rho_s = (r_s)^2 \tag{1.33}$$

When ρ_p and ρ_s are calculated from Equations 1.30–1.33, the reflectivities obtained are a function of the angle ϕ_1. A plot of the typical variation is shown in Figure 1.11. If unpolarized energy or natural light, for which

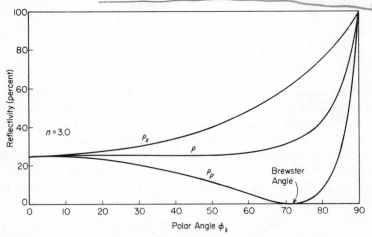

Figure 1.11   Fresnel's Equation of Reflectivity for a Nonconductor with $n = 3.0$.

$I = I_p + I_s$ and $I_p = I_s = I/2$, is incident upon a dielectric interface, the energy leaving the surface is polarized or partially polarized for all angles of incidence other than 0 deg or 90 deg. For the case of unpolarized energy incident, the reflectivity ρ is equal to $\rho_p/2 + \rho_s/2$, as shown in Figure 1.11.

At the particular angle where $\rho_p = 0$, the energy reflected away from the interface is completely polarized in the s plane. This angle is called the *Brewster angle*.

Fresnel's equations for an interface between a dielectric and conducting material are much more complicated. However, in the particular case for waves incident from free space ($n_1 = 1$, $k_1 = 0$) onto a conductor—for which n_2 and k_2 are defined by Equations 1.18 and 1.19—and for a zero angle of incidence, Fresnel's equations become

$$\rho = \rho_p = \rho_s = \frac{(n_2 - 1)^2 + k_2^{\,2}}{(n_2 + 1)^2 + k_2^{\,2}} \tag{1.34}$$

For any angle of incidence other than the normal, the equations for ρ_p and ρ_s have a variation similar to that shown in Figure 1.12.

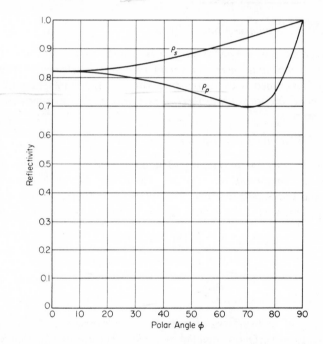

Figure 1.12 **Fresnel's Equation of Reflectivity for a Conductor** with $n = 0.5$, $k = 3.0$.

Reflectance for a system is defined in terms of the energy G incident upon the surface from outside systems. The irradiation G is all the energy incoming to a particular elemental area, and is expressed as Btu per hr-ft². A portion of this energy is reflected away from the surface. Considering that the energy leaving can be divided into two parts—(1) energy emitted by the system, and (2) energy reflected from the irradiation—we define reflectance as the ratio of reflected energy to the original irradiation. It should be noted that reflectance is a function of location, just as is irradiation.

So long as the irradiation of a surface element is a scalar quantity, the foregoing reflectance description is satisfactory. In the normal case, energy incoming to a surface element is directed, and this energy is more correctly described as a vector quantity. A similar situation exists for energy reflected from the surface. If irradiation is considered to be a vector quantity, the description of reflectance in terms of scalar quantities is unsatisfactory. It has become conventional in the literature to describe reflectance expressed in terms of scalars as *hemispherical reflectance*. When irradiation must be considered a vector, other terms are used. The definitions of these terms are discussed in Section 3.10, *Goniometric Definitions*.

1.20 Absorptance-Absorptivity, α

The absorptance of a system surface is defined as *the fraction of energy absorbed from the total energy incoming to a surface element*. Once again, since this is concerned with energy flow through the hemisphere above the surface element, the term *hemispherical absorptance* is sometimes used.

1.21 Transmittance-Transmissivity, τ

The transmittance for a system is defined as that *fraction of the incoming energy transmitted through the system*. Again, the energy is considered as coming to the system element over the entire hemisphere.

An energy balance for the system surface element is $G = \alpha G + \rho G + \tau G$, or

$$\alpha + \rho + \tau = 1 \text{ (for any system)} \qquad (1.35)$$

$$\alpha + \rho = 1 \text{ (for an opaque system)} \qquad (1.36)$$

1.22 The Black Body

In the study of real surfaces or systems it is convenient to define an ideal surface. The ideal surface is defined as a *black* surface or *black body*. For a black body all energy incident upon the body is absorbed, regardless of direction, wavelength, or any other identifiable energy characteristic. Since all of the energy is absorbed, $\alpha = 1$, $\rho = 0$, and $\tau = 0$.

The black body has another important characteristic which is not obvious from the preceding definition. This is the characteristic of being a perfect radiator of radiant energy. The equivalence of a perfect absorber and a perfect radiator is shown in Chapter 2; however, for this discussion the black body will simply be defined as both a perfect absorber and a perfect radiator. With this definition, the total emissive power of a black body must be a function of the temperature, and the symbol $E_b(T)$ will be used for the total emissive power of a black body at the absolute temperature T.

1.23 Emittance or Emissivity, ε

The total emissive power of a real surface is described in terms of an idealized black surface. In general, any real surface emitting thermal radiation at temperature T has a total emissive power less than the total emissive power of a black surface. The ratio of the total emissive power of a real surface at temperature T to the total emissive power of a black surface at the same temperature T is the emittance.

$$\varepsilon\,(T,\text{system}) = \frac{E(T,\text{system})}{E_b(T)} \tag{1.37}$$

Equation 1.37 indicates that the total emittance of a system is a function of the absolute temperature of the system. This is illustrated in Figure 1.13 for two characteristically different materials, white paint (a nonconductor) and stainless steel (an electric conductor). Although the values indicated by Figure 1.13 are not from actual emittance measurements (they were obtained

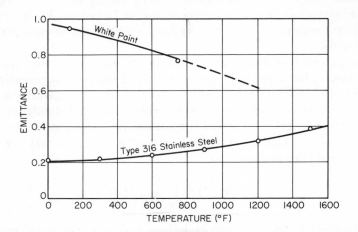

Figure 1.13   Total Emittance as a Function of Absolute Temperature

(Adapted from Gubareff, Janssen, Torborg, *Radiation Properties Survey*).

by reflectance measurements), the trend of variations is typical. That is, the total emittance of nonconductors tends to decrease with temperature, while the total emittance of conductors tends to increase with temperature.

1.24 Monochromatic Quantities, subscript λ

As indicated previously, the radiant energy of interest to engineers consists of electromagnetic waves with many frequencies or wavelengths. In certain cases it becomes necessary to analyze energy transfer in narrow wavelength regions. All of the system properties defined are required in so-called "non-gray" analysis, but only for small wavelength intervals. When a property is defined for a wavelength interval λ to $\lambda + d\lambda$, the term *monochromatic* or *spectral* is used to indicate this fact. In this text the word monochromatic will be used exclusively, and the symbols will be the same as defined for total values except for subscript λ.

The quantities used in defining system properties—monochromatic emissive power, radiosity, irradiation, and the monochromatic emissive power of a black body—are related to total values as follows:

$$E(T,\text{system}) = \int_0^\infty E_\lambda(T,\text{system}) \, d\lambda \qquad (1.38)$$

$$E_b(T) = \int_0^\infty E_{b\lambda}(T) \, d\lambda \qquad (1.39)$$

Equation 1.38, as shown, could be described as having quantities that depend on the system and the system temperature T. In Equation 1.39, the system is specified; therefore, the only independent variable is the temperature of the black body.

The equation relating total irradiation to monochromatic irradiation must involve the temperature and character of the entire surroundings for an elemental area of a system. Since this would lead to an impossibly complex expression, the surroundings may be represented symbolically as an external system by the hypothetical temperature $T_s{}^*$. (This temperature can be approximated in certain simple cases, but, in general, it is very difficult to obtain.) With this nomenclature

$$G(T_s{}^*) = \int_0^\infty G_\lambda(T_s{}^*) \, d\lambda \qquad (1.40)$$

Relationships between monochromatic emittance and total emittance may be developed as follows:

$$\varepsilon(T,\text{system}) = \frac{E(T,\text{system})}{E_b(T)} \qquad (1.37)$$

or, from Equations 1.38 and 1.39

$$\varepsilon(T,\text{system}) = \frac{\int_0^\infty E_\lambda(T,\text{system})\,d\lambda}{\int_0^\infty E_{b\lambda}(T)\,d\lambda}$$

since

$$\varepsilon_\lambda(T,\text{system}) = \frac{E_\lambda(T,\text{system})}{E_{b\lambda}(T)} \tag{1.41}$$

$$\varepsilon(T,\text{system}) = \frac{\int_0^\infty \varepsilon_\lambda(T,\text{system})E_{b\lambda}(T)\,d\lambda}{\int_0^\infty E_{b\lambda}(T)\,d\lambda} \tag{1.42}$$

By reasoning similar to this, the relationships between monochromatic absorptance or reflectance and total absorptance or reflectance can be obtained as follows:

$$\alpha(T,T_s^*,\text{system}) = \frac{\int_0^\infty \alpha_\lambda(T,\text{system})G_\lambda(T_s^*)\,d\lambda}{\int_0^\infty G_\lambda(T_s^*)\,d\lambda} \tag{1.43}$$

$$\rho(T,T_s^*,\text{system}) = \frac{\int_0^\infty \rho_\lambda(T,\text{system})G_\lambda(T_s^*)\,d\lambda}{\int_0^\infty G_\lambda(T_s^*)\,d\lambda} \tag{1.44}$$

Equations 1.43 and 1.44 indicate why monochromatic values rather than total values are used in certain cases. The added complexity of the surrounds hypothetical temperature T_s^* in absorptance and reflectance frequently necessitates nongray or monochromatic analysis.

Exercises

1.1 Show that Huygens' construction for a plane wave incident upon an interface between two media results in Snell's laws.

1.2 For the purpose of describing reflection from conducting media, a complex index of refraction A' may be defined. Compare Equations 1.14, 1.17, and

$$A = \frac{i\omega}{c_0}\left(n - ik\right)$$

From this information how would the complex index of refraction be defined?

1.3 By equating real and imaginary parts of the defined quantity A following Equation 1.17, show that n and k are given by Equations 1.18 and 1.19.

1.4 Consider a plane wave propagating in the x direction such that the y and z components of the electric vector are given by Equations 1.23 and 1.25. Let $E_{y_0} = E_{z_0}$ and $\delta_y - \delta_z = \pi/4$. Describe the path of the vector head in the yz plane located at $x = 0$. This should be complete, including direction of rotation.

1.5 The equations of two mutually perpendicular electric field potentials moving in the x direction are

$$E_y = E_{y_0} \cos \left[\omega \left(t - \frac{nx}{c_0} \right) + \delta_y \right]$$

$$E_z = E_{z_0} \cos \left[\omega \left(t - \frac{nx}{c_0} \right) + \delta_z \right]$$

where E_y and E_z are the electric field potentials in the y and z directions respectively; δ_y and δ_z are the phase angles in the y and z directions respectively. Develop the following general equation of the electric field motions, which indicates that the general motion is elliptic:

$$\left(\frac{E_y}{E_{y_0}} \right)^2 + \left(\frac{E_z}{E_{z_0}} \right)^2 - 2 \frac{E_y E_z}{E_{y_0} E_{z_0}} \cos \theta = \sin^2 \theta$$

where $\theta = \delta_y - \delta_z$.

1.6 The Maxwell electrical field curl equation describes the maximum circulation per unit area of an electric field intensity as equal to the time rate of change of the magnetic flux density at a point. If the electric field intensity is described by $E = 800(\sin x \cos ct)\mathbf{k}$ in free space, what is the equation for a time-varying magnetic field?

1.7 An electromagnetic wave is incident upon the interface between two dielectric materials. The waves proceed from a medium for which the index of refraction is n_1 to a medium for which the index of refraction is n_2. (a) Using Fresnel's equations and Snell's law, derive an equation where the Brewster angle can be calculated directly, knowing only the values of n_1 and n_2. (b) Calculate the Brewster angle for

(1)	$n_1 = 1.0$	$n_2 = 2.0$
(2)	$n_1 = 2.0$	$n_2 = 3.0$

1.8 A small circular diffusely emitting area ΔA has an area of 1 sq in. and an intensity $I = 100$ Btu per hr per ft^2 per steradian. Consider a 1-ft-radius hemisphere over ΔA. (a) Determine the total radiant power in Btu per hr passing through the hemisphere. Assume that ΔA is very small compared to the size of the hemisphere. (b) Determine the total radiant power in Btu per hr passing through that portion of the hemisphere intercepted by right circular cones with axes along the normal to ΔA and cone half-angles of 30 deg and 60 deg.

1.9 A small diffuse radiant source and a small detector of equal area are mutually parallel at a distance h perpendicular to each. If the detector displaces along a straight line in its own plane a distance s, how far (in terms of h) must it be displaced to reduce the radiant power incident on the detector due to the emitter, to one half of the value in the original position?

1.10 A very small plane circular emitter has an intensity I of 100 Btu per hr per ft² per steradian. Assume that the emitter obeys Lambert's cosine law and behaves as a perfect diffuse emitter. The area of the emitter is 1.44 in.² Determine the total radiant power that impinges on the following conditions: (a) A circular cylinder of radius 0.500 ft and infinite length. The cylinder is perpendicular to the plane of the emitter and extends to an infinite height but always has an open end. (b) A plane wall placed 1.00 ft from the emitter and perpendicular to the plane of the emitter. The wall is infinite in all directions. (c) A plane wall placed 1.00 ft from the emitter and perpendicular to the plane of the emitter with one edge in the plane of the emitter. The wall extends 1.00 ft in the z direction (perpendicular to the emitter's plane). It extends 1.00 ft on either side of the x axis and is rectangular.

1.11 A particular surface has a monochromatic reflectance and irradiation as given below. Determine the total reflectance for $T_s{}^* = 500°$, $3000°$R.

Reflectance

$$\rho_\lambda = 0 \qquad \lambda \leq 1$$

$$\rho_\lambda = \frac{\lambda}{10} \qquad 1 < \lambda < 10$$

$$\rho_\lambda = 1.0 \qquad \lambda > 10$$

Irradiation

$$G_\lambda = \frac{T_s{}^*\lambda - 400}{\lambda^3} \qquad \lambda > 0.8$$

1.12 A particular surface element has a monochromatic reflectance and irradiation as given below. Determine the total reflectance (approximately) as a function of $T_s{}^*$ using the approximation $e^x = 1 + x + (x^2/2!) \ldots$ (use only two terms).

Reflectance

$$\rho_\lambda = 0 \qquad \lambda \leq 0.2$$

$$\rho_\lambda = \frac{\lambda}{24.8} - \frac{0.2}{24.8} \qquad 0.2 \leq \lambda \leq 25$$

$$\rho_\lambda = 1.0 \qquad \lambda \geq 25$$

Irradiation

$$G_\lambda = 0 \qquad \lambda \leq 0.2$$

$$G_\lambda = \frac{c_1 \lambda^{-4}}{\exp\left[\left(\dfrac{c_2}{\lambda T_s{}^*}\right) - 1\right]} \qquad \lambda \geq 0.2$$

References

1. ECKERT, E. R. G., and ROBERT M. DRAKE, JR., *Heat and Mass Transfer*. New York: McGraw-Hill, Inc., 1959.
2. HALLIDAY, DAVID, and ROBERT RESNICK, *Physics for Students of Science and Engineering, Part II*, 2nd ed. New York: John Wiley & Sons, Inc., 1962.
3. JAKOB, MAX, *Heat Transfer*, vol. 1. New York: John Wiley & Sons, Inc., 1950.
4. KRUSE, P. W., L. D. McGLAUCHLIN, and R. B. McQUISTAN, *Elements of Infrared Technology*. New York: John Wiley & Sons, Inc., 1962.
5. MORGAN, JOSEPH, *Introduction to Geometrical and Physical Optics*. New York: McGraw-Hill, Inc. (1953), p. 186.
6. WORTHING, A. G., "Temperature Radiation Emissivities and Emittances," *Temperature, Its Measurement and Control in Science and Industry*. New York: Reinhold Publishing Corporation, 1941.

CHAPTER 2

Thermal Radiation Laws
from Thermodynamic Laws

In the study of thermal radiation, both classical thermodynamic (macroscopic) laws and quantum mechanical (microscopic) laws are important. This chapter examines the macroscopic laws that are a guide to the results obtained from microscopic laws.

This chapter presents the laws of thermal radiation attributed to Kirchhoff, Stephan, Boltzmann, and Wien. The laws introduced by Kirchhoff are examined first, followed by the Stephan-Boltzmann relationship and Wien's distribution law. The latter two laws, which are basic expressions resulting from classical thermodynamics, are used as guides for the expressions of Planck's distribution discussed in Chapter 3.

Kirchhoff's Laws

2.1 Prevost's Law

Historically, the first step in obtaining Kirchhoff's laws was made by Prevost [4]. Prevost's law is stated as follows: *Two or more bodies continue to emit radiation even when in thermal equilibrium.*

Proof of this law may be shown as follows: Consider an evacuated enclosure with walls that have a reflectance of one, as shown in Figure 2.1.

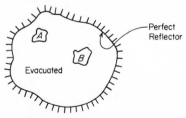

Figure 2.1 **Prevost's Law.**

A and *B* are two test bodies in the enclosure. In case 1 the temperature of
A has been increased an amount ΔT above the temperature of *B*. In case 2
the temperature of *B* is the same as in case 1, but *A* has been decreased below
the temperature of *B* an amount ΔT.

In case 1 we notice a tendency for the temperature of *B* to increase, which
indicates that energy is flowing from *A* to *B*. In case 2, the temperature of *B*
tends to decrease, indicating that energy is flowing from *B* to *A*. The temperature of *B* is the same in case 1 and 2, and nothing is changed concerning test
body *B*. Since the only change is in test body *A*, the conclusion must be that
test body *B*, which obviously is radiating energy to *A* in case 2, is also radiating energy to *A* in case 1. Thus, energy is being emitted from body *B* regardless of the condition of body *A*.

The basic conclusion resulting from this is that the energy $E_B A_B$ emitted
from body *B* is a function of the temperature of the body. Since A_B is not a
function of temperature, E_B is a function of temperature, or $E_B(T)$. This
result was stated in Section 1.15.

2.2 Properties of Isothermal Enclosures

One of the important concepts that result from thermodynamic considerations is the *hohlraum*, or isothermal enclosure. The properties of an enclosure
with walls and all contents at a single temperature are important, not only
for analytical reasoning, but also for experimental analysis.

The first property to be examined is monochromatic irradiation. Consider
an isothermal enclosure in which a test object is placed (Figure 2.2). The
test object and the walls of the enclosure are of uniform and equal temperature. The test object *A* is assumed to have the characteristics shown in
Figure 2.3; that is, $\alpha_\lambda = 0$ except in a small range $\Delta\lambda$. As is shown in Figure
2.2, the test object will be considered in two positions.

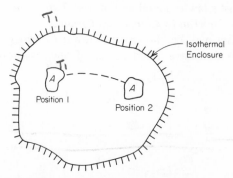

Figure 2.2   Kirchhoff's Law.

In position 1, the energy balance for the test object will be as follows (*energy absorbed = energy emitted*):

$$\int_{\Delta\lambda} \alpha_\lambda(T)[G_\lambda(T_s^*)]_1 A\, d\lambda = [E(T)]_1 A \qquad (2.1)$$

where $[G_\lambda(T_s^*)]_1$ is the monochromatic irradiation for the test object in position 1.

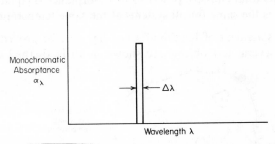

Figure 2.3 Special System Characteristics for the Derivation of Kirchhoff's Law.

In position 2, the energy balance for the test object will be as follows:

$$\int_{\Delta\lambda} \alpha_\lambda(T)[G_\lambda(T_s^*)]_2 A\, d\lambda = [E(T)]_2 A \qquad (2.2)$$

Equations 2.1 and 2.2 are related, since $[E(T)]_1 = [E(T)]_2$ by Prevost's law. This results in

$$\int_{\Delta\lambda} \alpha_\lambda(T)[G_\lambda(T_s^*)]_1\, d\lambda = \int_{\Delta\lambda} \alpha_\lambda(T)[G_\lambda(T_s^*)]_2\, d\lambda \qquad (2.3)$$

If we consider the integrands on each side of the equality of Equation 2.3, we have for the case $\Delta\lambda \to d\lambda$

$$\alpha_\lambda(T)[G_\lambda(T_s^*)[_1 = \alpha_\lambda(T)[G_\lambda(T_s^*)]_2 \qquad (2.4)$$

The original consideration was that the test object be located in a hohlraum at temperature T; therefore, T_s^* in Equation 2.4 is equal to the hohlraum temperature, and we have

$$[G_\lambda(T)]_1 = [G_\lambda(T)]_2 \qquad (2.5)$$

Equation 2.5 states the proof that the monochromatic irradiation in a hohlraum at temperature T is independent of location, that is, has a constant value.

In a similar manner, the total irradiation in a hohlraum can be proved to be constant and independent of location.

2.3 Proof of Kirchhoff's Laws

We will consider the statements of Kirchhoff as four separate laws. Actually all of the laws are interrelated, but the use of four separate statements will aid in clarification.

Law 1. When a system is in thermal equilibrium with its surroundings, the ratio of its total emissive power to its absorptance is equal to a constant, which is the same for all systems at the same temperature.

The preceding statement of Kirchhoff's first law may be proved as follows: In Figure 2.4 several test objects are shown in an isothermal enclosure at

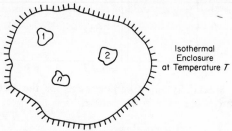

Figure 2.4   Kirchhoff's Law.

temperature T. The following energy balances for the test bodies must be satisfied in the isothermal enclosure:

$$E_1(T)A_1 = G_1(T)\alpha_1(T)A_1$$

$$E_2(T)A_2 = G_2(T)\alpha_2(T)A_2$$

$$\vdots$$

$$E_n(T)A_n = G_n(T)\alpha_n(T)A_n$$

Notice in these expressions that α is shown as a function of the temperature T, rather than $T_s{}^*$ and T as in previous equations. This is because $T_s{}^* = T$ for the isothermal enclosure, and the functional variation of α is only T. From the considerations for an isothermal enclosure, $G_1(T) = G_2(T) \cdots = G_n(T)$. Thus,

$$\frac{E_1(T)}{\alpha_1(T)} = \frac{E_2(T)}{\alpha_2(T)} = \cdots = \frac{E_n(T)}{\alpha_n(T)} = f(T) \tag{2.6}$$

From Equation 2.6 we can write

$$\frac{E_i(T)}{\alpha_i(T)} = f(T) \qquad \textit{(for an isothermal enclosure)} \tag{2.7}$$

Thus, for any given T_j

$$\frac{E_i(T_j)}{\alpha_i(T_j)} = \text{constant}$$

Law 2. The irradiation within an isothermal enclosure is equal to the total emissive power of a black body at the temperature of the enclosure.

This statement can be proved from Equation 2.7 by examining the range of values possible for $\alpha_i(T)$. Since absorptance is a fractional quantity, the range of values mathematically possible would be all points from zero to one. However, the value of zero was not considered in the derivation of Equation 2.7; therefore, the set of numbers from values larger than zero to one should be considered. For this set, all values of $E_i(T_j)/\alpha_i(T_j)$ must have the same value. This value can be obtained by considering the particular point when $\alpha_i(T_j) = 1.0$. In this case

$$\frac{E_i(T_j)}{1} = G(T_j)$$

but, when $\alpha_i(T_j) = 1.0$, we have by definition

$$E_i(T_j) = E_b(T_j)$$

therefore

$$G(T_j) = E_b(T_j) \tag{2.8}$$

in an isothermal enclosure at T_j. Equation 2.8 must be valid for all of the points in the set $0 < \alpha_i(T_j) \le 1.0$. The particular point $\alpha_i(T_j) = 0$ is meaningless for the derivation of Equation 2.7; therefore, we conclude that Equation 2.8 must be valid for all real cases.

Law 3. The absorptance for a system in an isothermal enclosure is equal to the emittance of the system.

In general we define emittance as follows:

$$\varepsilon(T,\text{system}) = \frac{E(T,\text{system})}{E_b(T)} \tag{1.37}$$

Equations 2.7 and 2.8, along with the derivation of Equation 2.7, result in

$$\frac{E_i(T)}{\alpha_i(T)} = E_b(T)$$

or

$$\alpha_i(T) = \frac{E_i(T)}{E_b(T)} = \varepsilon_i(T) \tag{2.9}$$

Equation 2.9 should be considered critically, since the improper use of this expression can result in gross errors. It may be preferable to write this equation as follows, but only when $T_s^* = T_i$:

$$\alpha_i(T_i, T_s^*) = \varepsilon_i(T_i) \tag{2.10}$$

Equation 2.10 points out explicitly that the emittance and absorptance are equal only when the surrounds have a temperature equal to the system temperature. Of course, this is valid for the condition described.

Law 4. In an isothermal enclosure, monochromatic emittance is equal to monochromatic absorptance for a specified frequency of radiation.

This statement may be proved as follows: Consider a thin test body in a hohlraum, which has the properties of monochromatic absorptance, reflectance, transmittance, and emittance constant over the entire test system. For the case under consideration, the symbols $\alpha_f(T)$, $\rho_f(T)$, $\tau_f(T)$, and $\varepsilon_f(T)$ will be used to indicate that the monochromatic property is for the frequency interval f to $f + df$. (Such a system is shown in Figure 2.5.) From

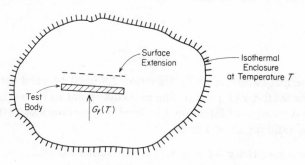

Figure 2.5   Proof of $\alpha_f(T) = \varepsilon_f(T)$.

the previous proof that $G_\lambda(T)$ is constant in a hohlraum, we imply that $G_f(T)$ is also constant. If the surface extension shown is considered, the energy passing through the extension in a direction away from the test body (this is the radiosity) will consist of $E_f(T) + \rho_f(T)G_f(T) + \tau_f(T)G_f(T)$, where $E_f(T)$ and $G_f(T)$ are described in terms of the test body surface area. Since the viewpoint from the surface extension indicates this energy to be the irradiation of the extension, we can write

$$G_f(T_s^*) \text{ extension} = E_f(T) \text{ test body} + \rho_f(T)G_f(T_s^*) \text{ test body}$$
$$+ \tau_f(T)G_f(T_s^*) \text{ test body} \tag{2.11}$$

if the surface extension is considered very close to the test body such that areas are equal and energy does not escape between the extension and test body. For this condition, the specification of surface extension and test body are not required. Writing Equation 2.11 for the monochromatic emissive power of the test body gives

$$E_f(T) = G_f(T_s^*) - \rho_f(T)G_f(T_s^*) - \tau_f G_f(T_s^*)$$

or

$$E_f(T) = G_f(T_s^*)[1 - \rho_f(T) - \tau_f(T)] = \alpha_f(T)G_f(T_s^*)$$

But $E_f(T) = \varepsilon_f(T)E_{b_f}(T)$. Thus

$$\varepsilon_f(T)E_{b_f}(T) = \alpha_f(T)G_f(T_s^*)$$

In the hohlraum $G_f(T_s^*) = G_f(T)$ and $G_f(T) = E_{b_f}(T)$. From this we obtain

$$\varepsilon_f(T) = \alpha_f(T) \qquad (2.12)$$

A question that frequently arises concerning equation 2.12, or its equivalent for an opaque test body $\varepsilon_\lambda(T) = \alpha_\lambda(T)$, is whether or not the temperature of the surrounds T_s^* has any effect on the relationship. Of course, the answer to this is obvious when the functional relationship is considered; that is, both ε_λ and α_λ are functions of the temperature of the system for which they are defined.

Fortunately, most materials used in engineering have small variations for these quantities over the usual engineering temperature ranges. The magnitude of errors expected by assuming α_λ constant over the rather large temperature variations can be implied for several engineering materials from [1]. The results from this work indicate that the major problem in using monochromatic data for a surface at a low temperature, when the surface has a high temperature, is probably oxidation, or other changes that occur in the surface itself. Of course, this is equivalent to using data obtained for one specified system for an entirely different system. For example, data for steel at room temperature would not be equivalent to data for steel that had been given a thermal treatment and then returned to room temperature.

Although the angular variation of properties has not been described at this point, the more general form of Equation 2.12 will be given. As presented in [2], Kirchhoff's laws for the general case may be written

$$\varepsilon_p(\phi, \theta, T, \lambda) = \alpha_p(\phi, \theta, T, \lambda)$$

$$\varepsilon_s(\phi, \theta, T, \lambda) = \alpha_s(\phi, \theta, T, \lambda)$$

$$\varepsilon_\Phi(\phi, \theta, T, \lambda) = (\alpha_\Phi\phi, \theta, T, \lambda) \qquad (2.13)$$

$$\varepsilon(\phi, \theta, T, \lambda) = \alpha(\phi, \theta, T, \lambda)$$

In Equation 2.13, the angles ϕ and θ describe the polar and azimuth angles. The subscripts p, s, and Φ describe the directions of polarization.

The Stephan-Boltzmann Equation

2.4 The Relationship Between I_b and E_b for a Diffuse Black Surface

To determine the relationship between I_b and E_b, we shall consider a small element of a black diffuse surface dA enclosed by a hemisphere, as

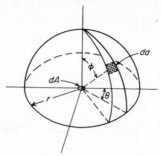

Figure 2.6   Geometry of the Solid Angle $d\omega$.

shown in Figure 2.6. The power that leaves dA and passes through da is

$$I_b \cos \phi \, dA \, d\omega$$

But $d\omega = da/r^2$, and $da = (rd\phi)(r \sin \phi d\theta) = r^2 \sin \phi \, d\phi \, d\theta$, or $d\omega = \sin \phi \, d\phi \, d\theta$. Then the total power leaving dA and passing out through the hemisphere is

$$P_{\text{tot}} = dA \int_0^{2\pi} \int_0^{\pi/2} I_b \cos \phi \sin \phi \, d\phi \, d\theta$$

or, if I_b is constant, as it is for a black body

$$P_{\text{tot}} = I_b \, dA \int_0^{2\pi} \int_0^{\pi/2} \cos \phi \sin \phi \, d\phi \, d\theta$$

$$P_{\text{tot}} = I_b \, dA \, \pi$$

But
$$\frac{P_{\text{tot}}}{dA} = E_b(T) = \pi I_b(T) \tag{2.14}$$

Equation 2.14 gives the relationship between energy and intensity for the total emissive power of a black body, and also indicates that the intensity from a black body surface is a function of the temperature of the surface. A similar derivation for a system that emits diffusely but is not black would result in

$$E(T,\text{system}) = \pi I(T,\text{system}) \tag{2.15}$$

One additional relationship can be given from this derivation for a system that emits diffusely and reflects diffusely. In this case

$$J(T, T_s^*, \text{system}) = E(T, \text{system}) + \rho(T, T_s^*, \text{system})G(T_s^*)$$

and

$$J(T, T_s^*, \text{system}) = \pi I(T, T_s^*, \text{system}) \tag{2.16}$$

Equation 2.16 indicates that the intensity from a surface in an enclosure energy exchange problem may be considered constant for diffuse surfaces. This result is used in many calculations for energy exchange in diffuse systems.

2.5 Energy Density in a Hohlraum

An important quantity for the determination of additional physical laws for thermal radiation is the energy density in a hohlraum. The symbol u is used to represent energy per unit volume. In order to determine energy density, consider the spherical isothermal enclosure with a small volume inside shown in Figure 2.7.

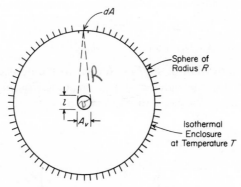

Figure 2.7   Evaluation of Energy Density.

The power incident on v from an elemental area dA of the spherical wall is $I_b(T) \cos \phi \, dA \, d\omega$. The solid angle $d\omega$ can be written in terms of the projected area of the volume A_v as

$$d\omega = \frac{A_v}{R^2}$$

The power incident on the volume v will require a time $dt = l/c$ to pass through the volume if the volume is small. Thus, the total energy in the volume v due to emission from dA during dt is

$$I_b(T) \cos \phi \, dA \, \frac{A_v}{R^2} \frac{l}{c}$$

Integrating over the entire sphere surface area gives the total energy in v at any time:

$$E_{\text{tot}} = \int_{\text{sphere}} \frac{I_b(T) \cos \phi \, A_v l \, dA}{R^2 c}$$

Since volume v is arbitrarily small and located a relatively long distance from dA, $\cos \phi$ may be considered equal to one. Using this, the total energy can be obtained as

$$E_{\text{tot}} = \frac{I_b(T) A_v l}{R^2 c} \int_{\text{sphere}} dA = \frac{4 \pi I_b(T) A_v l}{c}$$

but $A_v l$ is equal to v for a small volume, so

$$E_{\text{tot}} = \frac{4 \pi I_b(T) v}{c}$$

The energy density $u = E_{\text{tot}}/v$; therefore, $u = [\pi I_b(T)]/c$, and

$$u = \frac{4 E_b(T)}{c} \tag{2.17}$$

2.6 Boltzmann's Derivation of Stephan's Law

The following derivation of $E_b(T)$ is similar to the derivation that Boltzmann used in verifying Stephan's empirical equation. Consider an isothermal enclosure with a piston for one wall, as shown in Figure 2.8. From preceding

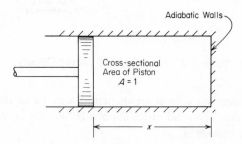

Figure 2.8   Derivation of the Stephan-Boltzmann Equation.

sections we have the following preliminary facts: (1) $G = E_b(T)$, (2) energy density $u = [4E_b(T)]/c$; therefore, $u = f(T)$.

From electromagnetic theory, the pressure exerted by radiation in a hohlraum is given as $P = u/3$. We will use classical thermodynamic laws and assume that any property is a function of two other properties. The first law of thermodynamics expressed for a quasistatic system is

$$dQ = dU + P\, dV$$

since $dV = d(Ax)$ and $A = 1$,

$$dV = dx$$

$$dQ = d(uV) + P\, dx$$

or

$$dQ = u\, dV + V\, du + P\, dx \tag{2.18}$$

Substitution of $P = u/3$, $dV = dx$, and $V = x$ into Equation 2.18 gives

$$dQ = \frac{4}{3} u\, dx + x\, du \tag{2.19}$$

From $u = u(T)$,

$$du = \frac{du}{dT}\, dT$$

Thus

$$dQ = \frac{4}{3} u\, dx + x\, \frac{du}{dT}\, dT \tag{2.20}$$

The entropy of the system can be written as $S = S(V, T) = S(x, T)$ or, for a reversible system change,

$$dS(x,\ T) = \frac{dQ}{T}$$

Therefore

$$dS(x,T) = \frac{4}{3} \frac{u}{T}\, dx + \frac{x}{T} \frac{du}{dT}\, dT \tag{2.21}$$

The quantity $dS(x, T)$ can be considered an exact differential; therefore

$$dS(x,T) = \left(\frac{\partial S}{\partial x}\right)_T dX + \left(\frac{\partial S}{\partial T}\right)_x dT \tag{2.22}$$

Comparing the coefficients of Equations 2.21 and 2.22 gives

$$\left(\frac{\partial S}{\partial x}\right)_T = \frac{4}{3} \frac{u}{T} \qquad \left(\frac{\partial S}{\partial T}\right)_x = \frac{x}{T} \frac{du}{dT}$$

Since $dS(x, T)$ in Equation 2.21 is an exact differential,

$$\frac{\partial^2 S}{\partial x \partial T} = \frac{\partial^2 S}{\partial x \partial T}$$

or

$$-\frac{4}{3} \frac{u}{T^2} + \frac{4}{3} \frac{1}{T} \frac{du}{dT} = \frac{1}{T} \frac{du}{dT}$$

or

$$\frac{du}{dT} = 4\frac{u}{T} \tag{2.23}$$

Integrating this differential equation results in

$$u = C_1 T^4$$

or

$$\frac{4E_b(T)}{c} = C_1 T^4$$

Then

$$E_b(T) = \frac{cC_1}{4} T^4 = \sigma T^4 \tag{2.24}$$

where

$$\sigma = \frac{cC_1}{4}$$

Equation 2.24 is Stephan's result from the comparison of a large amount of experimental data. The constant σ is called the *Stephan-Boltzmann constant*. This constant has been determined accurately from other physical constants to be 1713×10^{-12} Btu per hr-sq ft-°R^4, or 5.6699×10^{-12} watts per sq cm-°K^4 [5]. Physicists are continually refining the accuracy of the physical constants used in evaluating the Stephan-Boltzmann constant; therefore, small changes may occur in future publications. In general, for engineering usage, these values are well within the accuracy of other parameters used.

Wien's Distribution Law

The Stephan-Boltzmann equation developed in Sections 2.4–2.6 presents the relationship between the total emissive power and the temperature of a perfect (black) radiator. Another important relationship that is required is the relationship between the monochromatic emissive power and the two variables, temperature and wavelength, for a black radiator. In the late 19th century, Wilhelm Wien presented the following distribution law.

2.7 Wavelength Shift by a Moving Mirror [4]

An initial step in obtaining Wien's law is to determine the shift in wavelength caused by reflection from a moving mirror. This shift may be determined by considering Figure 2.9, in which is assumed a train of waves propagating along OA incident at the angle ϕ on a moving mirror. For ease of understanding, consider the distance OA to be a single wavelength λ. When the initial point in the wave is reflected along AC, the angle of reflection ϕ' will be slightly different than angle ϕ [3]. Since in reality the velocity of the

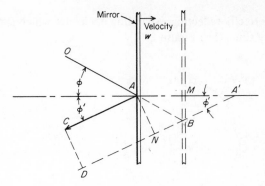

Figure 2.9   Wavelength Shift by a Moving Mirror.

mirror w must be much less than the velocity of propagation c, this angle will be equal to ϕ (negligible error). With this assumption, let the mirror move to position M while the initial wavefront A has moved out to point C. At this time the two significant points in the wave will be a distance $DN + NB + BA$ separated. If the mirror had not been moving, the separation would have been DN; therefore, the change in wavelength due to the mirror's movement is approximately $AB + BN$. This approximation arises because of the angular shift ϕ to ϕ'. Within this approximation

$$\Delta\lambda = AB + BN$$

but

$$AB = A'B \text{ (by construction)} \qquad \Delta\lambda = A'B + BN$$

or

$$\Delta\lambda = AA' \cos\phi$$

but

$$AA' = 2AM \qquad \Delta\lambda = 2AM \cos\phi$$

The distance AM is equal to the velocity of the mirror w times the period of the incident wave λ/c. Thus

$$\Delta\lambda = \frac{2w\lambda \cos\phi}{c} \qquad\qquad (2.25)$$

Equation 2.25 describes the increase in wavelength, on the average, for the wave train incident at polar angle ϕ on a moving mirror. This result can be obtained in a more rigorous manner through electromagnetic theory.

2.8 Derivation of Wien's Displacement Law

Wien's law may be derived in several ways. The following derivation is similar to the work in [4]. For a more rigorous discussion, [3] should be consulted.

Consider a perfectly reflecting expanding enclosure which is an isothermal enclosure at any time. (See Figure 2.10).

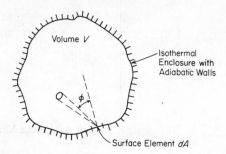

Volume V

Isothermal Enclosure with Adiabatic Walls

ϕ

Surface Element dA

Figure 2.10   Expanding Volume for Derivation of Wien's Law.

The power with wavelength λ to $\lambda + d\lambda$ incident upon the surface element dA in the direction ϕ can be written

$$I_{b\lambda} \cos \phi \, dA \, d\omega \, d\lambda$$

During a time interval dt, the energy incident is

$$I_{b\lambda} \cos \phi \, dA \, d\omega \, d\lambda \, dt$$

For all angles ϕ around the normal, the solid angle $d\omega$ is given by

$$d\omega = \frac{2\pi(r \sin \phi)r \, d\phi}{r^2} = 2\pi \sin \phi \, d\phi$$

Using this solid angle, the energy incident upon dA during a time dt becomes

$$I_{b\lambda} \cos \phi \, dA(2\pi \sin \phi \, d\phi) \, d\lambda \, dt$$

or

$$2E_{b\lambda} \sin \phi \cos \phi \, d\phi \, dA \, d\lambda \, dt \qquad E_{b\lambda} = \pi I_{b\lambda}$$

At any given time, the total energy contained in the isothermal enclosure is

$$u_\lambda V \, d\lambda = \frac{4E_{b\lambda}V \, d\lambda}{c}$$

Then, during a time dt, the fraction of the total energy incident upon dA from the angle ϕ is

$$\frac{2E_{b\lambda} \sin \phi \cos \phi \, d\phi \, dA \, d\lambda \, dt}{(4E_{b\lambda}V \, d\lambda)/c} = \frac{c \sin \phi \cos \phi \, d\phi \, dA \, dt}{2V}$$

Now, if the volume is expanding at a rate such that dA has a velocity w, the average change of wavelength for the fraction involved is

$$\frac{2w\lambda \cos \phi}{c} \times \frac{c \sin \phi \cos \phi \, d\phi \, dA \, dt}{2V} = w\lambda \cos^2 \phi \sin \phi \, d\phi \, d\omega \, dt$$

Since this is the change of wavelength for the energy fraction incident upon dA from the direction ϕ, the change for all ϕ-direction energy is

$$dt \frac{w \, dA}{V} \int_0^{\pi/2} \lambda \cos^2 \phi \sin \phi \, d\phi = \frac{dt \, w \, dA \, \lambda}{3v}$$

Assuming that the entire surface is moving for the enclosure expansion, each elemental area dA will contribute a change of wavelength for an energy fraction of this quantity. The total wavelength change for the volume can be obtained by integration over all elemental areas, or

$$\Delta\lambda = \int_{\text{surface } A} \frac{\lambda \, dt}{3V} w \, dA \tag{2.26}$$

In Equation 2.26, the velocity w is a function of the location of dA. This arbitrary assignment can be removed by considering the change in volume during the time dt as

$$\Delta v = \int_{\text{surface } A} (w \, dt) \, dA$$

Using this result, Equation 2.26 becomes

$$\Delta\lambda = \frac{\lambda \, \Delta V}{3V}$$

or

$$\frac{\Delta\lambda}{\lambda} = \frac{\Delta V}{3V}$$

From

$$\lim_{\Delta\lambda \to 0} \frac{\Delta\lambda}{\lambda} = \frac{d\lambda}{\lambda} \quad \text{and} \quad \lim_{\Delta\lambda \to 0} \frac{\Delta V}{V} = \frac{dV}{V}$$

$$\frac{d\lambda}{\lambda} = \frac{dV}{3V} \quad \text{or} \quad \lambda = C_1 V^{1/3} \tag{2.27}$$

If a change in volume from V_o to V occurs, Equation 2.27 results in

$$\frac{\lambda}{\lambda_o} = \left(\frac{V}{V_o}\right)^{1/3} \tag{2.28}$$

Since our volume was taken arbitrarily, let r represent the characteristic dimension of the volume, such that

$$\left(\frac{r}{r_o}\right)^3 = \frac{V}{V_o}$$

Then

$$\frac{\lambda}{\lambda_o} = \frac{r}{r_o} \qquad (2.29)$$

In the case of an expanding thermodynamic system

$$dQ = dU + dW$$

For this analysis the isothermal enclosure is considered to be adiabatic and, since the changes must be small, reversible. Under these assumptions

$$dU = -dW = -P\,dV$$

or

$$d(uV) = -\frac{1}{3}u\,dV$$

$$u\,dV + V\,du = -\frac{1}{3}u\,dV$$

$$\frac{4}{3}u\,dV = -V\,du$$

$$\frac{4}{3}\frac{dV}{V} = -\frac{du}{u}$$

which integrates to

$$\frac{u}{u_o} = \left(\frac{V_o}{V}\right)^{4/3}$$

Using Equation 2.29, we find that

$$\frac{u}{u_o} = \left(\frac{r_o}{r}\right)^4 \qquad (2.30)$$

From the derivation of Section 2.6 we obtained

$$u(T) = \frac{4E_b(T)}{c}$$

and $E_b(T) = \sigma T^4$. By combining these two expressions, we get

$$\frac{u}{u_o} = \left(\frac{T}{T_o}\right)^4 \qquad (2.31)$$

Substituting Equations 2.29 and 2.30 into Equations 2.31 results in

$$\frac{T}{T_o} = \frac{\lambda_o}{\lambda}$$

or

$$\lambda T = \lambda_o T_o = \text{constant} \tag{2.32}$$

Equation 2.32 expresses a basic fact concerning the character of black system radiation. The isothermal enclosure considered was specified adiabatic. For this reason, the only method available to change the temperature of the walls or the contents is by doing work on the system. Consider the radiant energy within the enclosure in the wavelength interval λ_o to $\lambda_o + d\lambda_o$ when the temperature is T_o. This energy will shift wavelength to an interval λ to $\lambda + d\lambda$ when the temperature changes to T as a result of work done. In the discussion that follows, the relative monochromatic emissive power of this particular energy after the shift in wavelength is determined.

As implied previously, the energy density in a hohlraum for the monochromatic emissive power $E_{b\lambda}$ is given as $u \propto E_{b\lambda}\, d\lambda$. The reason for the $d\lambda$ is that $E_{b\lambda}$ does not represent finite energy for a zero wavelength interval. With this expression, Equation 2.31 becomes

$$\frac{E_{b\lambda}}{E_{b\lambda_o}}\frac{d\lambda}{d\lambda_o} = \left(\frac{T}{T_o}\right)^4 \tag{2.33}$$

Assuming $dT \ll d\lambda$ and $dT_o \ll d\lambda_o$, we get from Equation 2.32

$$\frac{d\lambda}{d\lambda_o} = \frac{T_o}{T}$$

or

$$\frac{E_{b\lambda}}{E_{b\lambda_o}} = \left(\frac{T}{T_o}\right)^5 \tag{2.34}$$

Equations 2.32 and 2.34 may be used to determine $E_{b\lambda}(T)$ if $E_{b\lambda}(T_o)$ is known. That is, the total monochromatic emissive power $E_{b\lambda}(T)$ can be determined from Equation 2.34, and the wavelength location of $E_{b\lambda}(T)$ can be determined from Equation 2.32.

The typical representation of Equations 2.34 and 2.32 is obtained by multiplying both sides of Equation 2.34 by $(\lambda/\lambda_o)^5$.

$$\frac{E_{b\lambda}}{E_{b\lambda_o}}\left(\frac{\lambda}{\lambda_o}\right)^5 = \left(\frac{\lambda T}{\lambda_o T_o}\right)^5$$

or

$$\frac{E_{b\lambda}\lambda^5}{(\lambda T)^5} = \frac{E_{b\lambda_o}\lambda_o^5}{(\lambda_o T_o)^5} \tag{2.35}$$

Equation 2.35 is valid only if λT is chosen equal to $\lambda_o T_o$. That is, the values of the product of λT are not arbitrary in the equation. This can be indicated mathematically by

$$\frac{E_{b\lambda}\lambda^5}{(\lambda T)^5} = f_1(\lambda T)$$

or
$$E_{b\lambda}\lambda^5 = f(\lambda T)$$
where
$$f(\lambda T) = (\lambda T)^5 f_1(\lambda T)$$

This is typically written as
$$E_{b\lambda} = \frac{1}{\lambda^5} f(\lambda T) \tag{2.36}$$

Equation 2.36 will be called Wien's distribution law in this book but is also called Wien's displacement law. The importance of the equation is that any distribution law for $E_{b\lambda}$ of a black surface must be in the form of Equation 2.36.

Exercises

2.1 Calculate the total radiant energy contained in an isothermal enclosure that has a volume of 10 cu ft at temperatures of 10^3, 10^5, and 10^7 °R.

2.2 Determine the specific heat of radiant energy in Btu per ft^3-°R at 10^3, 10^5, and 10^7 °R.

2.3 From the specific heat information of Problem 2.2 determine the increase in internal energy of a 10-cu-ft hohlraum if the temperature is changed from 1000 °R to 2000 °R.

2.4 The force on a perfectly reflecting surface due to the reflection of electromagnetic plane waves is given by

$$F = \frac{4\cos\phi}{c} P$$

where P is the power vector and ϕ is the angle between the surface normal and P. When the surface is not perfectly reflecting, the force must be multiplied by $(1 + \rho)/2$. From this information, determine the force on the earth's surface due to solar energy. Assume that the sun is a black body with temperature 11,000 °R and the earth albedo is 0.4.

2.5 The solution in Problem 2.4 assumes the earth's surface to be a specular reflector. Actually, the energy reflected is more likely to be reflected diffusely. Assuming diffuse reflection, what is the force on the earth [3]?

References

1. BEVANS, J. T., J. T. GIER, and R. V. DUNKLE, "Comparison of Total Emittances with Values Computed from Spectral Measurements," *ASME Transactions*, October 1958, pp. 1405–1416.

2. EDWARDS, D. K., and R. D. RODDICK, "Basic Studies in the Use and Control of Solar Energy," Department of Engineering Report 62–27, University of California at Los Angeles, July 1962.

3. PLANCK, MAX, *The Theory of Heat Radiation*. New York: Dover Publications, 1959.
4. PRESTON, THOMAS, *Theory of Heat*. London: Macmillan & Co., Ltd., 1929.
5. SNYDER, N. W., "A Review of Thermal Radiation Constants," *ASME Transactions*, vol. 76 (1954), p. 537.

CHAPTER 3

Characteristics of Black
and Real Systems

The evaluation of the spectral distribution of thermal energy emitted from a perfect (black) system was a major problem to physicists in the late 19th century. Wien's work as discussed in the last chapter had been completed and showed the direction required for the distribution equation. Excellent experimental work had been completed by Lummer and Pringsheim [9], which could not be reconciled with the theoretical distribution functions of Wien and Rayleigh. With this background of information, Max Planck presented his now famous distribution law, which required the assumption of quantitized energy emission from a dipole oscillator system. The results of Wien and Rayleigh are presented, along with Planck's distribution, for their historical, and occasionally practical, value.

Planck's Distribution Law

3.1 Experimental Evidence

As is frequently the case, experimental evidence preceded theoretical predictions for the distribution of thermal radiation emitted from black systems. Among the many experimental tests which were made, Planck in his text *The Theory of Heat Radiation* [13] cites Rubens and Kurlbaum [15], Paschen [11], and Lummer and Pringsheim [9].

The results of Lummer and Pringsheim were typical of the data obtained. Using a fluorspar prism, they dispersed the radiant energy emitted from a gas-fired black cavity. The spectral distribution for the wavelength range of approximately 1–6 μ of the energy emitted was measurable with their system. For this wavelength range, and a temperature range 723–1646°C, their results were typical of those shown in Figure 3.1. From these measurements, Wien's displacement law, $\lambda T = \lambda_o T_o$, can be verified by using the location of maximum intensity. Furthermore, the distribution curves can be

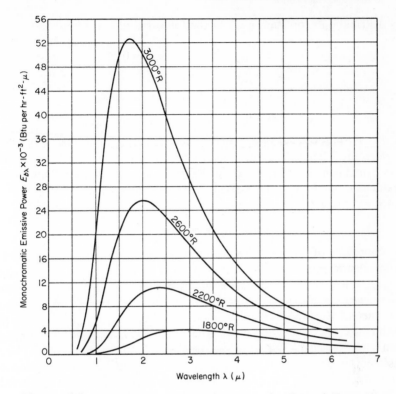

Figure 3.1   Monochromatic Emissive Power for Several Temperatures versus Wavelength.

used to check the distribution function from Wien's derivation. That is, suppose one curve at temperature T_1 has been obtained experimentally. According to Wien's law the values of the second curve can be obtained by shifting each ordinate toward the origin in the ratio T_1/T_2 and increasing its height in the ratio T_2^5/T_1^5. The values of Lummer and Pringsheim were used in this manner to validate Wien's law.

3.2 Wien's Distribution Function

In an attempt to describe the results of the experimentalists, Wien proposed the distribution equation

$$E_{b\lambda} = \frac{c_1}{\lambda^5}\left[\frac{1}{\exp(c_2/\lambda T)}\right] \qquad (3.1)$$

This expression was derived from classical mechanics and accurately represents the experimental results for small values of the λT product. However, any distribution expression must fit the following physical boundary conditions:

$$\begin{array}{llll}
(a) & E_{b\lambda} \to 0 & \text{as} & \lambda \to 0 \\
(b) & E_{b\lambda} \to 0 & \text{as} & \lambda \to \infty \\
(c) & E_{b\lambda} \to \infty & \text{as} & T \to \infty \\
(d) & E_{b\lambda} \to 0 & \text{as} & T \to 0
\end{array}$$

Wien's distribution function matches the boundary conditions a, b, and d but does not fit condition c. For this reason, and because significant departure from experimental result occurs for long wavelengths, the distribution was regarded as incorrect. The typical departure from correct distribution is shown in Figure 3.2.

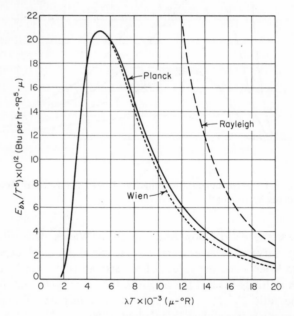

Figure 3.2 Comparison of Planck, Wien, and Rayleigh Distribution Laws.

3.3 Rayleigh's Distribution Function

Lord Rayleigh derived the distribution equation

$$E_{b\lambda} = \frac{c_1}{\lambda^5} \left[\frac{\lambda T}{c_2} \right] \tag{3.2}$$

using the Maxwell-Boltzmann law of equipartition of energy. Equation 3.2 may be examined in terms of the physical boundary conditions listed above.

This examination shows that boundary conditions b, c, and d are satisfied, but that condition a is not satisfied. Rayleigh's equation should, therefore, show a significant departure for small values of the wavelength λ. This departure is shown on the plot in Figure 3.2.

3.4 Planck's Distribution Function

The distribution of thermal radiation emitted by a perfect system of dipole oscillators (or any perfect emitter) as derived by Planck is

$$E_{b\lambda} = \frac{c_1}{\lambda^5}\left[\frac{1}{\exp(c_2/\lambda T) - 1}\right] \tag{3.3}$$

Examination of this distribution using the physical boundary conditions in Section 3.2 indicates that all of the limits are satisfied. Furthermore, the distribution agrees closely with all experimental evidence obtained.

Since the work of Rayleigh and Wien appeared before Planck's distribution and each distribution seemed to agree with theory in limited regions, Planck's equation was examined for similarities in regions of interest. First, Wien's law, which fits experimental data well for small values of λT, appears immediately for small λT. In this case $\exp(c_2/\lambda T) \gg 1$; thus, Planck's distribution is equivalent to Wien's distribution for small λT. Rayleigh's expression for the distribution fits experimental data for large λT products. By expanding $\exp(c_2/\lambda T)$ as

$$\exp\frac{c_2}{\lambda T} = 1 + \frac{c_2}{\lambda T} + \left(\frac{c_2}{\lambda T}\right)^2 \frac{1}{2!} + \left(\frac{c_2}{\lambda T}\right)^3 \frac{1}{3!} + \cdots$$

the value

$$\exp\left(\frac{c_2}{\lambda T}\right) - 1 \approx \frac{c_2}{\lambda T} \qquad \text{for} \qquad \lambda T \gg c_2$$

Thus, Planck's distribution once again degenerates into the previously obtained distribution equation of Rayleigh. Although this was conclusive evidence in favor of Planck's distribution and the quantum hypothesis, it was some years before the scientific community was universally receptive to Planck's work.

Characteristics of Black System Radiators

3.5 Relationships for Wavelength and Frequency

The expression for the distribution of radiant energy emitted from a black system on the basis of wavelength (as given by Equation 3.3) may be used to determine the location of the maximum value of $E_{b\lambda}$. If $E_{b\lambda}(\lambda, T)$ is partially differentiated and the result set equal to zero, the value of $E_{b\lambda_{max}}$ may be obtained.

$$\left(\frac{\partial E_{b\lambda}}{\partial \lambda}\right)_T = \frac{-5c_1}{\lambda^6}\left[\frac{1}{\exp B - 1}\right] + \frac{c_1}{\lambda^6}\left[\frac{B \exp B}{(\exp B - 1)^2}\right]$$

where $B = (c_2/\lambda T)$.
Setting this equal to 0, we get the transcendental equation

$$\frac{B}{5} + \frac{1}{\exp B} - 1 = 0 \tag{3.4}$$

Equation 3.4 has the positive real root $B = 4.9651$; therefore

$$\lambda_{max} T = \frac{c_2}{4.9651} \tag{3.5}$$

For $c_2 = 1.43879 \pm 0.00003$ cm-°K [12]

$$\lambda_{max} T = 5216.04 \ \mu\text{-°R}$$

If the expression for the distribution of radiant energy with frequency as the independent variable is required, the expression of energy equivalence is

$$E_{b\lambda} \ d\lambda = -E_{b_f} \ df \tag{3.6}$$

where the negative sign is required because $d\lambda \propto -df$. Thus

$$E_{bf} = -E_{b\lambda} \frac{d\lambda}{df} = \frac{c_1}{c^4} f^3 \left[\frac{1}{\exp(c_2 f/cT) - 1}\right] \tag{3.7}$$

The maximum of E_{b_f} may be obtained by taking the partial derivative of Equation 3.7 with respect to f and setting the result equal to zero:

$$3e^B - Be^B - 3 = 0 \tag{3.8}$$

where $B = 2.8214$; thus

$$\frac{f_{max}}{T} = \frac{2.8214c}{c_2} = 3.2683 \times 10^{10} \ (1/\text{°R-sec})$$

It is interesting to note that f_{max}/T cannot be obtained from $\lambda_{max} T$ by using $\lambda f = c$. This points out the importance of careful use of the Planck distribution function.

Another basic constant for radiant energy emitted from a black body can be obtained by integrating Equation 3.7 over all frequencies, since this must be equal to the total emissive power given by the Stephan-Boltzmann equation.

$$\sigma T^4 = \int_0^\infty E_{b_f} \ df$$

from which

$$\sigma = \frac{2\pi^5 k^4}{15c^2 h^3} = 0.17134 \times 10^{-8} \text{ Btu per hr-ft}^2\text{-}°R^4$$

where k is Boltzmann's constant and h is Planck's constant. Notice that the Stephan-Boltzmann constant σ is a function of the velocity of propagation in the medium c. The value given for σ is for free space in which $c \approx 3 \times 10^{10}$ cm per sec. Since this value of σ is widely used, the Stephan-Boltzmann equation is sometimes written as

$$E_b = n^2 \sigma T^4 \tag{3.9}$$

where n is the index of refraction. Equation 3.9 expresses the power emitted from a black surface radiating into a medium other than air, or a vacuum. Such an expression is seldom used in heat transfer since conduction or convection energy transfer is usually much larger than radiative transfer—in media other than the usual gases.

3.6 Planck Radiation-Function Tabulation

The values of the Planck distribution function are required in the solution of many practical problems. These values are most conveniently tabulated or plotted as functions of the single independent variable λT.

The expression for $E_{b\lambda}$ given by Equation 3.3 involves the two independent variables λ and T. By dividing each side of the equation by T^5, a function of λT results:

$$\frac{E_{b\lambda}}{T^5} = \frac{c_1}{(\lambda T)^5} \left[\frac{1}{\exp(c_2/\lambda T) - 1} \right] \tag{3.10}$$

Another expression required in solving problems is the value

$$\int_{\lambda_1}^{\lambda_2} E_{b\lambda} \, d\lambda$$

This quantity is most conveniently obtained from the integration of

$$\frac{E_b(0 \to \lambda T)}{\sigma T^4} \equiv \int_0^{\lambda T} \frac{E_{b\lambda}}{\sigma T^5} \, d(\lambda T)$$

The quantity $E_b(0 \to \lambda T)/\sigma T^4$ is the fraction of the total radiant power emitted by a black body at temperature T in the wavelength interval from 0 to λ, where λ is defined from λT. Examination of Equation 3.10 indicates that

$$\int_0^{\lambda T} \frac{E_{b\lambda}}{\sigma T^5} \, d(\lambda T) = \int_0^{\lambda T} \frac{c_1}{\sigma (\lambda T)^5} \left[\frac{1}{\exp(c_2/\lambda T) - 1} \right] d(\lambda T) \tag{3.11}$$

TABLE 3.1
Planck Radiation Functions

$\lambda T[\mu°R]$	$\dfrac{E_{b\lambda} \times 10^5}{\sigma T^5}$	$\dfrac{E_b(0 - \lambda T)}{\sigma T^4}$	$\lambda T[\mu°R]$	$\dfrac{E_{b\lambda} \times 10^5}{\sigma T^5}$	$\dfrac{E_b(0 - \lambda T)}{\sigma T^4}$
1000.0	0.000039	0.0000	10400.0	5.142725	0.7183
1200.0	0.001191	0.0000	10600.0	4.921745	0.7284
1400.0	0.012008	0.0000	10800.0	4.710716	0.7380
1600.0	0.062118	0.0000	11000.0	4.509291	0.7472
1800.0	0.208018	0.0003	11200.0	4.317109	0.7561
2000.0	0.517405	0.0010	11400.0	4.133804	0.7645
2200.0	1.041926	0.0025	11600.0	3.959010	0.7726
2400.0	1.797651	0.0053	11800.0	3.792363	0.7803
2600.0	2.761875	0.0098	12000.0	3.633505	0.7878
2800.0	3.882650	0.0164	12200.0	3.482084	0.7949
3000.0	5.093279	0.0254	12400.0	3.337758	0.8017
3200.0	6.325614	0.0368	12600.0	3.200195	0.8082
3400.0	7.519353	0.0507	12800.0	3.069073	0.8145
3600.0	8.626936	0.0668	13000.0	2.944084	0.8205
3800.0	9.614973	0.0851	13200.0	2.824930	0.8263
4000.0	10.463377	0.1052	13400.0	2.711325	0.8318
4200.0	11.163315	0.1269	13600.0	2.602997	0.8371
4400.0	11.714711	0.1498	13800.0	2.499685	0.8422
4600.0	12.123821	0.1736	14000.0	2.401139	0.8471
4800.0	12.401105	0.1982	14200.0	2.307123	0.8518
5000.0	12.559492	0.2232	14400.0	2.217411	0.8564
5200.0	12.613057	0.2483	14600.0	2.131788	0.8607
5400.0	12.576066	0.2735	14800.0	2.050049	0.8649
5600.0	12.462308	0.2986	15000.0	1.972000	0.8689
5800.0	12.284687	0.3234	16000.0	1.630989	0.8869
6000.0	12.054971	0.3477	17000.0	1.358304	0.9018
6200.0	11.783688	0.3715	18000.0	1.138794	0.9142
6400.0	11.480102	0.3948	19000.0	0.960883	0.9247
6600.0	11.152254	0.4174	20000.0	0.815714	0.9335
6800.0	10.807041	0.4394	21000.0	0.696480	0.9411
7000.0	10.450309	0.4607	22000.0	0.597925	0.9475
7200.0	10.086964	0.4812	23000.0	0.515964	0.9531
7400.0	9.721078	0.5010	24000.0	0.447405	0.9579
7600.0	9.355994	0.5201	25000.0	0.389739	0.9621
7800.0	8.994419	0.5384	26000.0	0.340978	0.9657
8000.0	8.638524	0.5561	27000.0	0.299540	0.9689
8200.0	8.290014	0.5730	28000.0	0.264157	0.9717
8400.0	7.950202	0.5892	29000.0	0.233807	0.9742
8600.0	7.620072	0.6048	30000.0	0.207663	0.9764
8800.0	7.300336	0.6197	40000.0	0.074178	0.9891
9000.0	6.991475	0.6340	50000.0	0.032617	0.9941
9200.0	6.693786	0.6477	60000.0	0.016479	0.9965
9400.0	6.407408	0.6608	70000.0	0.009192	0.9977
9600.0	6.132361	0.6733	80000.0	0.005521	0.9984
9800.0	5.868560	0.6853	90000.0	0.003512	0.9989
10000.0	5.615844	0.6968	100000.0	0.002339	0.9991
10200.0	5.373989	0.7078			

Equation 3.11 can be integrated by expanding the integrand in a series; however, the least laborious procedure is to replace $E_{b\lambda}\, d\lambda$ with $E_{b_f}\, df$ for integration. By a procedure such as this Table 3.1 was obtained. This table was originally presented by R. V. Dunkle [6]; however, the values given here have been re-evaluated using a digital computer.

Real-System Characteristics

From the external point of view, real systems can be classed as specular (mirror-like), partially diffusing, or totally diffusing. In order to eliminate an entire class of systems, this discussion will consider systems that are opaque to thermal radiation. Systems that are transparent or partially transparent are discussed later. With this specialization, opaque systems can be examined in detail without concern for bulk or substrate material thickness.

3.7 Homogeneous Systems

When a system under consideration is homogeneous, the main factors that affect its radiant properties are the optical parameters n and k for the bulk material and the surface condition. If its surface is smooth—that is, any irregularities have dimensions much less than the wavelength of the electromagnetic waves being considered—Fresnel's equations may be used to predict its properties.

In the case of a nonconducting medium, Fresnel's equations as given in Equations 1.30, 1.31, 1.32, and 1.33 can be used to determine the reflectivity of its surface. Since $\rho(\phi)$ or the directional reflectance results from these equations, the hemispherical reflectance must be obtained by integration. (This is discussed in detail later.) The typical variation of $\rho_p(\phi)$, $\rho_s(\phi)$, and $\rho(\phi)$, where

$$\rho(\phi) = \frac{\rho_p}{2} + \frac{\rho_s}{2}$$

is shown in Figure 3.3. For this figure the incident beam is assumed to be in vacuum or air for which the index of refraction is one. The range of values of n for typical materials is given by Figure 3.4.

In the case of a conducting medium in contact with vacuum or air, Fresnel's equations become complex. However, if a complex index of refraction n' is defined as

$$n' = n - ik \tag{3.12}$$

the power reflectivities can be calculated. It is assumed that n and k data are available for the conductor; $\rho(\phi, n, k)$ is given as a function of the incident

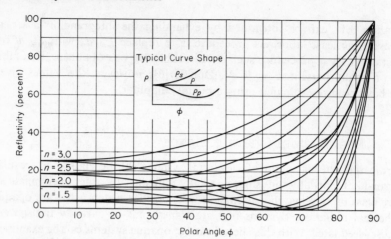

Figure 3.3 **Reflectivity Values from Fresnel's Equations for a Nonconductor.**

angle ϕ for specified n and k by

$$\rho_s = \frac{\sin^2(\phi - N) + M}{\sin^2(\phi + N) + M} \tag{3.13}$$

$$\rho_p = \rho_s \frac{\cos^2(\phi + N) + M}{\cos^2(\phi - N) + M} \tag{3.14}$$

where

$$N \equiv \text{arc cos} \frac{b}{\sqrt{M}}$$

$$M \equiv -\frac{C}{2} + \left(\frac{C^2}{4 + b^2}\right)^{1/2}$$

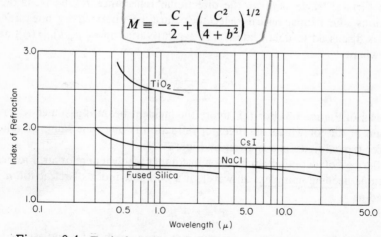

Figure 3.4 **Typical Index of Refraction Data for Dielectric Materials.**

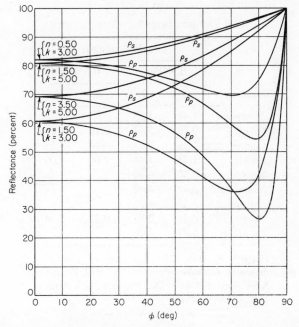

Figure 3.5   Reflectance Values from Fresnel's Relations for Conducting Media (Equations 3.13 and 3.14).

$$C \equiv 1 - \frac{\sin^2 \phi}{n^2 + k^2}$$

$$b \equiv \frac{k \sin \phi}{n^2 + k^2}$$

The complexity of these expressions, along with the fact that the reflectivities have three independent variables, precludes effective graphical representation unless many graphs are used. However, the typical behavior of certain materials is represented in Figure 3.5. A complete compilation of this information is available in [8]. Typical values of n and k for real materials (which vary with wavelength) are given in Table 3.2.

3.8 Specular Emittance

The values of reflectance given by Fresnel's equations are specified as *specular reflectance*. Specular reflectance is the mirror-like reflectance in which each incident ray entering at polar angle ϕ is reflected with reduced intensity at outgoing polar angle ϕ'. Since the surface is specular, $\phi = \phi'$.

TABLE 3.2

Optical Parameters for Conductors†

Material	Wavelength			
	0.5893 μ		0.6943 μ	
	n	k	n	k
Aluminum	1.44	5.23		
Silver	0.18	3.64	0.19	4.29
Copper	1.39	2.63	0.44	3.50
Nickel	1.59	3.41	2.00	4.00
Steel	2.80	4.40		
Magnesium	0.38	4.42		
Chromium	3.59	4.52		
Gold	0.48	2.83	0.27	5.20
Tungsten	3.47	3.26		

† Herbert B. Holl, *The Reflection of Electromagnetic Radiation.* Redstone Arsenal Report RF–TR–63–4. Huntsville, Alabama: U.S. Army Missile Command.

In the general case, two angles are required to located incoming and outgoing rays. These angles are the *polar angle* and the *azimuth angle*; thus, typically, ϕ, θ represent incoming angles, and ϕ', θ' represent outgoing angles. These angles are shown in Figure 3.6, where the reflecting surface is in the xz plane.

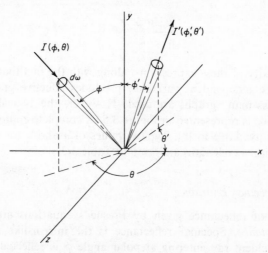

Figure 3.6   Geometry for Surface Reflection.

The emittance for specular surfaces may be obtained from Fresnel's equations. Using the general Kirchhoff-law relationship given in Equations 2.13, emittance is given by

$$\varepsilon(\phi, \theta, T, \lambda) = 1 - \rho(\phi, \theta, T, \lambda) \qquad (3.15)$$

The value of $\rho(\phi, \theta, T, \lambda)$ for unpolarized incident energy as given by the Fresnel equations is $\rho_s/2 + \rho_p/2$. A question may arise as to the independent variables T and λ in Equation 3.15, but this is reconciled by noting that n and k are functions of temperature and wavelength. (It is interesting to note that energy emitted from smooth surfaces is polarized according to Fresnel's equations.)

Emittance as given by Equation 3.15 is a directional emittance. If the value of emittance as calculated from Fresnel's equations is plotted on a polar diagram as a function of the polar angle ϕ, the two typical curves shown in Figure 3.7 result. Real materials display similar characteristics, as shown in Figure 3.8.

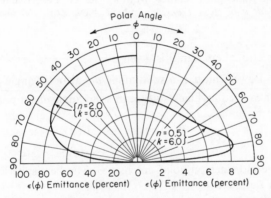

Figure 3.7   Directional Emittance Values from Fresnel's Equations.

The data of Figure 3.8 was obtained for surfaces that were not very rough and, most important, at low temperatures. For low-temperature emission, most of the energy is associated with long wavelengths. Surfaces are smooth or rough, depending upon the ratio of the characteristic dimension of roughness to wavelength. For long wavelengths, many real surfaces may be considered smooth, and Fresnel's equations will be valid. Of course, the necessary data for the index of refraction and absorption coefficient may be difficult to obtain. However, if the normal emittance $\varepsilon(0)$ can be obtained and the type of material identified, Fresnel relationships are useful guides in determining directional characteristics.

If the emittance over all angles, or the hemispherical emittance as defined in Section 1.23, is required, the directional value can be used as follows:

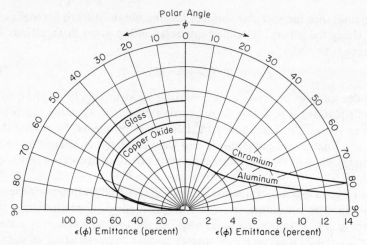

Figure 3.8 Directional Emittance for Conducting and Non-conducting Materials (Adapted from E. R. G. Eckert and R. M. Drake, *Heat and Mass Transfer*, 2nd ed. New York: McGraw-Hill, Inc., 1959).

First, the directional emittance is given by

$$\varepsilon(\phi) = \frac{\text{Power emitted in solid angle } d\omega \text{ at polar angle } \phi}{\text{Power emitted by black surface in solid angle } d\omega \text{ at polar angle } \phi}$$

or

$$\varepsilon(\phi) = \frac{I'(\phi) \cos \phi \, d\omega}{I_b' \cos \phi \, d\omega} = \frac{I'(\phi)}{I_b'} \tag{3.16}$$

where the prime indicates outgoing intensities. The hemispherical emittance is defined from Equation 1.37 as

$$\varepsilon = \frac{\displaystyle\int_{2\pi} I'(\phi) \cos \phi \, d\omega}{\displaystyle\int_{2\pi} I_b \cos \phi \, d\omega} \tag{3.17}$$

Since the directional emittance of a smooth surface does not depend on the azimuth angle, $d\omega = 2\pi \sin \phi \, d\phi$; therefore,

$$\varepsilon = \int_0^{\pi/2} \varepsilon(\phi) \sin 2\phi \, d\phi \tag{3.18}$$

3.9 Surface Roughness

Many real surfaces are not smooth by comparison to wavelength. When a surface is slightly rough, hemispherical emittance or hemispherical reflectance does not change [2]. However, when the roughness is so large that inter-reflections occur, the properties of the surface change. This is caused by several phenomena; the primary one is the multiple absorptions that occur with multiple reflections.

In order to discuss the effects of surface roughness, the bidirectional reflectance must be defined.

$$\rho(\phi, \theta; \phi', \theta'; T, \lambda) = \frac{I'(\phi', \theta', T, \lambda)}{I(\phi, \theta, T_s^*, \lambda)} \tag{3.19}$$

Equation 3.19 is interpreted as the ratio of outgoing intensity at angles ϕ' and θ' to incoming intensity at angles ϕ and θ, as shown in Figure 3.6. The functional description of bidirectional reflectance $\rho(\phi, \theta; \phi', \theta'; T, \lambda)$ indicates incoming angles first, then outgoing angles. In the case of specular reflectance from a surface, incoming and outgoing angles are related. That is, $\phi' = \phi$ and $\theta' = \theta + \pi$. Thus, specular reflectance expressed as a bidirectional reflectance is given by

$$\rho_{\text{specular}}(\phi, \theta, T, \lambda) = \rho(\phi, \theta; \phi, \theta + \pi; T, \lambda)$$

With this nomenclature, the effects of surface roughness as treated by Davies [5], Bennett and Porteus [1], [3], [14], and Birkebak [4] may be examined.

For perfect conductors, Bennett and Porteus extended Davies' work to obtain the following expression:

$$R_s = \exp\left[-16\pi^2 \cos^2 \phi \left(\frac{a}{\lambda}\right)_{\text{opt}}^2\right] \tag{3.21}$$

in which

$$R_s \equiv \frac{\rho_{\text{rough}}(\phi, \theta; \phi, \theta + \pi; T, \lambda)}{\rho_{\text{smooth}}(\phi, \theta; \phi, \theta + \pi; T, \lambda)}$$

and $(a/\lambda)_{\text{opt}}$ is the ratio of the optical roughness a to the wavelength of incoming radiation. The ratio R_s is the ratio of the specular reflectance of the base material when rough, to the specular reflectance of the base material when smooth. For the case of roughened glass coated with aluminium, Equation 3.21 represents experimental data closely, as shown in Figure 3.9.

In using Equation 3.21, the main difficulty is obtaining $(a/\lambda)_{\text{opt}}$. The reason for this is that the optical roughness a is not equivalent to the roughness measured by standard mechanical measuring devices. As shown by Birkebak [4], measured root-mean-square roughness must be multiplied by a factor between 1.40 and 1.76 to obtain optical roughness. This text will use arithmetic average roughness, even though this is still not equal to the optical roughness.

The theoretical expression of Davies (Equation 3.21) is only for reflectance at the specular angle. When the angle of reflectance is some angle other than the specular, the expression requires the explicit specification of all angles. Since one azimuth angle is arbitrary, the typical representation is to take the incoming azimuth angle θ equal to zero. With this understanding, the bidirectional reflectance is given as $\rho(\phi, 0; \phi', \theta'; T, \lambda)$ or simply $\rho(\phi; \phi', \theta'; T, \lambda)$.

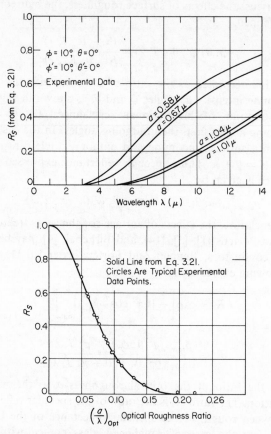

Figure 3.9   Specular Reflectance Values for Aluminum Overcoating on Ground-Glass Samples [4].

Davies' expression, for R in the case where outgoing angles are not the specular angle, for a of the order of λ, and for $a/m < 1$ as given by Birkebak [4], is

$$R = \left(\frac{1}{32}\right)\left(\frac{m}{\pi a}\right)^2 (\cos \phi' + \cos \phi)^2 \times$$

$$\times \exp\left\{-\left(\frac{m^2}{2a^2}\right)\left[\frac{(\sin \phi' \cos \theta' - \sin \phi)^2 + \sin^2 \phi' \sin^2 \theta'}{(\cos \phi' + \cos \phi)^2}\right]\right\} \quad (3.22)$$

where

$$R \equiv \frac{\rho_{\text{rough}}(\phi, 0; \phi', \theta'; T, \lambda)}{\rho_{\text{smooth}}(\phi, 0; \phi, 0; T, \lambda)}$$

$$m = \sqrt{2} \frac{a}{s}$$

and s is the root-mean-square of the slope of the surface profile. Since R has two parameters that depend on surface topography, a and m, the exact evaluation of Equation 3.22 is not generally possible. However, for the experimental work of Birkebak [4], the expression fit satisfactorily to experimental data.

The difficulty of obtaining a general equation is illustrated by examination of Figure 3.10. In this Figure the ratio R' defined as

$$R' \equiv \frac{\rho_{\text{rough}}(\phi, 0; \phi', \theta'; T, \lambda)}{\rho_{\text{rough}}(\phi, 0; \phi; 0; T, \lambda)}$$

is plotted. R' is the bidirectional reflectance in the directions $(\phi, 0; \phi', \theta')$ divided by the bidirectional reflectance in the specular direction. Notice that the denominator is for the rough surface, not the smooth-base material used previously. As indicated on Figure 3.10, R' is plotted for $\phi = 10$ deg as a function of ϕ', with various outgoing azimuth angles θ' shown. For the two shorter wavelengths, $\lambda = 1.5$ μ and $\lambda = 2.0$ μ, a cosine distribution is shown as a dotted line. A perfectly diffusing surface would have R' values along this line.

Although it is not possible with present surface-measurement techniques to predict the values of R, the experimental curves are generally very similar to theoretical expressions [4].

3.10 Goniometric Definitions

Assuming that information such as presented in Figure 3.10 becomes available in the future, the use of the values will depend upon the following defined quantities.

First, the directional reflectance will be obtained from bidirectional reflectance data. Directional reflectance is defined as *the total energy reflected from an incoming beam at some particular direction*. Using the prime symbol for outgoing intensity, we have

$$\rho(\phi, \theta, T, \lambda) \equiv \frac{\int_{2\pi} I'(\phi', \theta', T, \lambda) \cos \phi' \, d\omega'}{I(\phi, \theta, T_s^*, \lambda) \cos \phi \, d\omega} \qquad (3.23)$$

or, from Equation 3.19

$$\rho(\phi, \theta, T, \lambda) = \frac{1}{\cos \phi \, d\omega} \int_{2\pi} \rho(\phi, \theta; \phi', \theta', T, \lambda) \cos \phi' \, d\omega' \qquad (3.24)$$

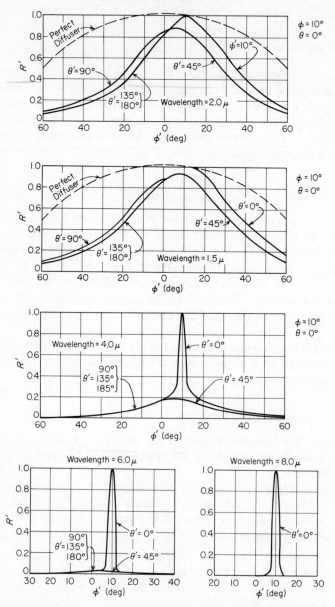

Figure 3.10 Bidirectional Reflectance Ratio for a Ground-Glass Surface with Aluminum Overcoating. (Surface Optical Roughness = 0.67 μ.) [4].

Equation 3.24 points out a basic problem in using the bidirectional reflectance for property representation, in that $\cos \phi d\omega$ must be specified. If the bidirectional reflectance has been measured for $d\omega'$ very small, the information can be used as indicated; however, any such information should be carefully examined before using it in Equation 3.24.

Hemispherical reflectance is another term encountered in the literature. This is defined as *the energy reflected from a surface from incoming energy regardless of direction*. Stated mathematically, it is

$$\rho(T, \lambda) = \frac{\displaystyle\int_{2\pi} I'(\phi', \theta', T, \lambda) \cos \phi' \, d\omega'}{\displaystyle\int_{2\pi} I(\phi, \theta, T_s^*, \lambda) \cos \phi \, d\omega} \tag{3.25}$$

Using Equation 2.23, we get

$$\rho(T, \lambda) = \frac{\displaystyle\int_{2\pi} \rho(\phi, \theta, T, \lambda) I(\phi, \theta, T_s^*, \lambda) \cos \phi \, d\omega}{\displaystyle\int_{2\pi} I(\phi, \theta, T_s^*, \lambda) \cos \phi \, d\omega} \tag{3.26}$$

Thus, the hemispherical reflectance for any type of irradiation $I(\phi, \theta, T_s^*, \lambda)$ may be obtained if the directional reflectances for all incoming angles are known.

A very lucid discussion of this material for the case of visible light is presented by McNicholas [10]. The discussion presented herein has been limited to values which may be calculable for the infrared region.

3.11 Heterogeneous Systems

Systems that consist of two or more optically different materials are considered heterogeneous systems. They may be base materials or substrates with thin films of oxides or grease, or base materials with two different distributed materials, such as paint. Unfortunately, so many different types of heterogeneous systems exist that a general description of them is not possible.

Even more important is the fact that a seemingly single material may have two different characteristics. This occurs when surface composition and structure is different from base composition and structure. The effects of surface chemistry or surface metallurgy are generally impossible to determine in this case because of the difficulty in obtaining a complete description of the material under consideration.

When a base material has well-defined thin films of a known material on the surface, theoretical predictions can be made [6]. Of course, this type of analysis is generally applicable only when the surface is optically smooth. In fact, for well-defined systems, thin films may be used to produce particular applications in solar energy conversion and spacecraft thermal control.

3.12 Real System Property Information

Values for real system properties as measured experimentally are presented in Appendixes 1, 2, and 3 of this text. These values are digested from a review of the literature made by a group of scientists at the Honeywell Research Center [7]. Values presented in this survey of experimental properties should normally be considered as estimates for any given material. This is so because the condition of the system tested usually makes any results unique for each sample. That is, property values for different samples of the same material are different because of unknown or unspecified surface or bulk conditions. Hopefully, experimentalists will in the future specify sample conditions more exactly.

Exercises

3.1   Using Planck's equation, plot $E_{b\lambda}/E_{b\lambda max}$ and $E_{bf}/E_{bf max}$ as a function of λT and f/T respectively. Use the physical constants $c_1 = 2\pi hc^2$ (where $h = 6.6254 \times 10^{-27}$ erg-sec and $c = 3 \times 10^{10}$ cm per sec, and $c_2 = 1.4380$ cm-°K.

3.2   Materials with real index-of-refraction values ranging from $n = 1.0$ to about $n = 3.0$ are common. For this range of values for n, plot the variation of the Stephan-Boltzmann constant σ.

3.3   Show that $3e^B - Be^B - 3 = 0$ results for the location of the maximum value of E_{bf}. (See Equations 3.7 and 3.8.)

3.4   Show that $\dfrac{E_b(0 \to \lambda T)}{\sigma T^4}$ is given by $\displaystyle\int_0^{f/T} \dfrac{E_{bf}}{\sigma T^3}\, d\left(\dfrac{f}{T}\right)$.

3.5   In the case of a nonconductor, Fresnel's equations result in $\rho(\phi)$, as shown in Figure 3.3. An approximation for $1 - \rho(\phi)$, which is sometimes valuable, is

$$[1 - \rho(\phi)] = A(\cos\phi)^m$$

By numerical curve (least square error or similar system), determine the best values of A and m for the $n = 2.0$ curve. (See Equations 1.31–1.33 and ff.)

3.6   In the case of a conducting medium, $\rho(\phi)$ as given by Fresnel's equation may be approximated for polar angles not too near 90 deg by†

$$[1 - \rho(\phi)] = \frac{1}{A}\left(\cos\phi + \frac{1}{\cos\phi}\right)$$

For the case of $n = 0.5$ and $k = 3.0$ as given by Figure 3.5, determine the best value of A.

---

† Max Jakob, *Heat Transfer*, vol. 1 (New York: John Wiley & Sons, Inc., 1950).

3.7 Assuming $[1 - \rho(\phi)] = \varepsilon(\phi)$, and $\varepsilon(\phi)$ expressed by the two approximate equations of Problems 3.5 and 3.6, determine the ratio of $\varepsilon/\varepsilon(0)$, or the ratio of the hemispherical emittance to the normal direction emittance. For a material that is a conductor, values may be compared to similar values in the literature.†

3.8 An early publication‡ in the area of radiation property data examined the reliability of the calculation of total emissivity from monochromatic reflectivity. For the particular sample—stainless steel type 321 with 1000 hours of heat treatment at 705°F—the monochromatic reflectance values given in the table below were obtained. Measured values of the total emittance at four temperatures are also given. By calculation, determine the total emittance at (a) 200°F, (b) 400°F, (c) 600°F, (d) 800°F, and compare with the measured value.

Wavelength (in microns)		Monochromatic Reflectance (in percent)		Measured Values	
				temp (°F)	emittance (%)
1.0	11.0	32	70	200	31
2.0	12.0	47	70		
3.0	13.0	54	70	400	33
4.0	15.0	61	65		
5.0	17.0	65	63	600	31
6.0	19.0	67	62		
7.0	21.0	69	64	800	33
8.0	23.0	70	65		
9.0	25.0	67	62		
10.0		68			

3.9 In Problem 3.8, the assumption required for the evaluation of the total emittance from monochromatic reflectance data is not explicitly defined. Define the assumption by evaluating the total reflectance for the surface described in Problem 3.8, assuming that the monochromatic reflectance data was obtained for a room-temperature sample. Let the source of the irradiation be a gray body at (a) 2500°F, (b) 5000°F, (c) 10,000°F.

3.10 Explain why radiation property data presented in the literature should be monochromatic data or total emittance data rather than reflectance or absorptance data. Notice that literature values are frequently supplied for materials in terms of solar absorptance. Is this a valid presentation, and, if so, what condition should be described?

---

† See, for example, E. R. G. Eckert and R. M. Drake, *Heat and Mass Transfer* (New York: McGraw-Hill, Inc., 1959), p. 380.

‡ J. T. Bevans, J. T. Gier, and R. V. Dunkle, " Comparison of Total Emittances with Values Computed from Spectral Measurements," *ASME Transactions*, October 1958, pp. 1405–1416.

References

1. BENNETT, H. E., "Specular Reflectance of Aluminized Ground Glass and the Height Distribution of Surface Irregularities," *Journal, Optical Society of America*, vol. 53, no. 12 (1963), pp. 1389–1394.

2. ———," The Thermal Radiation of Solids," San Francisco symposium proceedings (March 1964), to be published.

3. ———, and J. O. PORTEUS, "Relation Between Surface Roughness and Specular Reflectance at Normal Incidence," *Journal, Optical Society of America*, vol. 51 (1961), pp. 123–129.

4. BIRKEBAK, R. C., "Monochromatic Directional Distribution of Reflected Thermal Radiation from Roughened Surfaces," Ph.D. Dissertation 64–3830. Ann Arbor, Michigan: University Microfilms, Inc., September 1962.

5. DAVIES, H., "The Reflection of Electromagnetic Waves from a Rough Surface," *Proceedings IEEE*, vol. 101 (1954), pp. 209–213.

6. DUNKLE, R. V., "Thermal Radiation Tables and Applications," *ASME Transactions*, vol. 76 (1954), pp. 549–552.

7. GUBAREFF, G. G., J. E. JANSSEN, and R. H. TORBORG, *Thermal Radiation Properties Survey*, 2nd ed. Minneapolis, Minnesota: Honeywell Research Center, 1960.

8. HOLL, HERBERT B., "The Reflection of Electromagnetic Radiation," Redstone Arsenal Report RF–TR–63–4. Huntsville, Alabama: U.S. Army Missile Command.

9. LUMMER, O., and E. PRINGSHEIM, *Ann. d. Phys.*, vol. 6 (1901), p. 210.

10. MCNICHOLAS, H. J., "Absolute Methods in Reflectometry," *Bureau of Standards Research Journal*, vol. 1 (March 1928), pp. 29–73.

11. PASCHEN, F., *Ann. d. Phys.*, vol. 4 (1901), p. 277.

12. PIVOVONSKY, MARK, and MAX R. NAGEL, *Tables of Blackbody Radiation Functions*. New York: Crowell Collier and Macmillan, Inc., 1961.

13. PLANCK, MAX, *The Theory of Heat Radiation*. New York: Dover Publications, 1959.

14. PORTEUS, J. O., "Relation Between the Height Distribution of a Rough Surface and the Reflectance at Normal Incidence," *Journal, Optical Society of America*, vol. 53, no. 12 (1963), pp. 1394–1402.

15. RUBENS, H., and F. KURLBAUM, *Sitz. Ber. d. Akad. d. Wiss.* zu Berlin vom 25. Okt. (1900), p. 929.

16. VASICEK, A., *Optics of Thin Films*. New York: Interscience Publishers, Inc., 1960.

CHAPTER 4

Energy Exchange Concepts
and Geometric Factors

The purpose of this chapter is to introduce the general concepts of the calculation of energy exchange for system elements. In order to simplify the concepts required, all of the surfaces are considered to be perfectly diffuse emitters and reflectors. This assumption eliminates the requirement of considering any angular-dependent properties; the properties required are hemispherical rather than angular in nature. In general, their emittance, absorptance, and reflectance are required, and these characteristics are described as $\varepsilon(T)$, $\alpha(T, T_s{}^*)$, $\rho(T, T_s{}^*)$, where the functional notation indicates that (1) emittance is hemispherical emittance, as defined by Equation 1.37, (2) absorptance is hemispherical absorptance, as defined by Equation 1.43, and (3) the reflectance is hemispherical reflectance, as defined by Equation 1.44.

In the case where a system consists of several surfaces, for example surfaces 1, 2, 3, . . . n, the notation $\varepsilon_1(T_1)$, $\varepsilon_2(T_2)$, . . . $\varepsilon_n(T_n)$ is used to indicate the surface element involved. Although this notation is not really required for emittance—that is, $\varepsilon(T_1)$ would be complete—it is important for absorptance or reflectance: $\alpha_1(T_1, T_s{}^*)$ for example, or the case where several surfaces of different materials have the same temperature.

Another assumption used in this chapter is that of gray surfaces. A *gray surface* is defined in this text as *a surface for which the monochromatic emittance is constant with respect to wavelength*. Actually, this gray assumption can be relaxed somewhat by noting that monochromatic emittance needs be constant only over the wavelength region of importance for a given problem. For example, if an enclosure has surfaces that range in temperature from room temperature to 3000°R, the radiant energy present will have wavelengths of approximately 1–100 μ. Thus, if the monochromatic emittance is nearly constant in the range 1–100 μ, or, more practically, 1–25 μ, the surface under consideration may be described as gray. A further stipulation is that most gray surfaces are considered to be nondirectional or diffuse in character.

Although this characteristic is used in this chapter, it will not be used in all cases in the following chapters.

When a surface is considered to be black, the surface's monochromatic emittance is identically one. Furthermore, the monochromatic directional emittance is one for all angles. This definition is required when considering directional emittance definitions for the following chapters' work.

Energy Exchange between Surfaces

4.1 Basic Concepts

Frequently, calculation of the gain or loss of surface energy by radiation is done in a manner that obscures the engineering aspects of the analysis. In order to avoid this, surface energy gain or loss will be considered thermo-dynamically.

If we describe a surface element in an enclosure as part of a large system, that portion under consideration is itself a subsystem. Let the curved wall of Figure 4.1 be a subsystem within some large system that is exchanging energy,

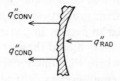

Figure 4.1   Radiation Subsystem.

with other subsystems by the radiation mode on the right side, and by conduction or convection on the left side.

For a steady-state condition, the rate of energy gain by radiation input is equal to the rate of energy loss by conduction and convection. Since we are primarily concerned with energy gain by the radiation mode, we usually indicate this by specifying $q''_{net} = q''_{rad}$. Thus, the primary problem to be described is the evaluation of energy input by radiation, with the implied assumption that this may be calculated separately from any convection or conduction process. Of course, this is not a valid assumption if the medium to the right of the surface element is a medium that itself absorbs or emits

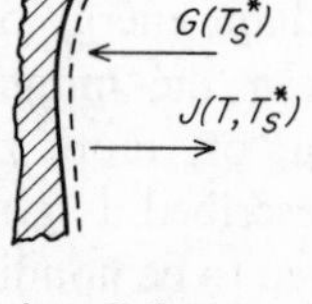

$$G(T_S^*)$$

$$J(T, T_S^*)$$

Figure 4.2   Radiation Subsystem with **Radiant Terms**.

radiant energy. For the case of a participating medium, the energy exchange becomes more complex, and is discussed separately in another chapter.

When the medium through which radiant energy is propagated is non-participating or diathermic, the quantity q''_{net} may be expressed in one of two ways. In Figure 4.2 the same subsystem as shown in Figure 4.1 is repeated with radiant irradiation and radiosity shown diagramatically. If the right-hand surface of the subsystem is considered, the rate of energy gain can be obtained by either of the following two methods. First, consider an observer stationed just outside the surface element at the surface extension shown as a dotted line. In this position the net rate of energy gain is given by

$$q''_{net} = G(T_s^*) - J(T, T_s^*) \tag{4.1}$$

Equation 4.1 results from an energy balance on the imaginary plane which is the surface extension. This plane cannot have any thermal capacity; therefore, it has the rate of energy flow across the plane as described by Equation 4.1.

The second method of describing the rate of energy flow requires the observer to be located just below the surface of the subsystem. At this location energy is being transmitted to the surface by internal emission and into the surface from external irradiation. Again, if the plane of observation is very thin so that it has no thermal capacity, an energy balance can be described by

$$q''_{net} = \alpha(T, T_s^*)G(T_s^*) - E(T) \tag{4.2}$$

Either Equation 4.1 or Equation 4.2 may be used to obtain the net heat transfer for a surface element. In either case, the solution of the radiant problem becomes the evaluation of the irradiation and radiosity for the surfaces in an enclosure.

4.2 Evaluation of Irradiation and Radiosity for Simple Geometries

When a system has simple geometry, such as infinite plates, concentric infinite cylinders, or concentric spheres, the evaluation of the irradiation and radiosity is greatly simplified. As an example, consider the two infinite parallel plates shown in Figure 4.3. For simplicity the two plates are considered to

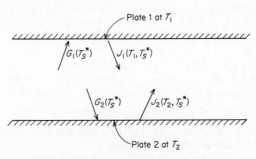

Figure 4.3 Parallel Plate System.

have uniform temperature and uniform emittance over the surface, that is, $T(\text{position})$ for either plate is constant and $\varepsilon(\text{position})$ for either plate is constant. In the most simple case, plates one and two may be considered to be black. For the black-plate system

$$J_1(T_1, T_s^*) = E_{b_1}(T_1) + \rho_1 G_1(T_s^*)$$

but ρ_1 will be zero; thus

$$J_1(T_1) = E_{b_1}(T_1)$$

Similarly

$$J_2(T_2) = E_{b_2}(T_2)$$

Since all of the energy radiated away from either plate is directly incident upon the other plate, the irradiation is related to the radiosity by

$$J_1(T_1) = G_2(T_{s_2}^*) \tag{4.3}$$

and

$$J_2(T_2) = G_1(T_{s_1}^*) \tag{4.4}$$

Using these expressions for irradiation and radiosity, the net heat transfer for each surface is

$$q''_{net_1} = E_{b_2}(T_2) - E_{b_1}(T_1) \qquad \text{and} \qquad q''_{net_2} = E_{b_1}(T_1) - E_{b_2}(T_2)$$

An important concept to note from this discussion is the method used to evaluate the irradiation of a surface from the radiosity of the surrounding surfaces. Also, from Equations 4.3 and 4.4, the previously undefined value of T_s^* is defined for the black system, that is, for the black surfaces discussed, $T_{s_1}^* = T_2$ and $T_{s_2}^* = T_1$. In this particular case the hypothetical equivalent surrounds temperature is explicitly defined. This is not generally the case, as will be seen in the following discussion.

Consider the two plates of Figure 4.3 to be gray, opaque surfaces with given emittances $\varepsilon_1(T_1)$ and $\varepsilon_2(T_2)$. Under this condition the value of the

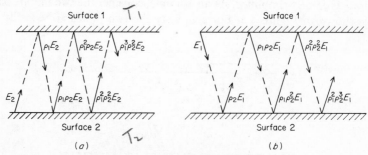

Figure 4.4 Irradiation of Parallel Surfaces (*a*) Irradiation from Surface 2 (*b*) Irradiation from Surface 1.

irradiation of the surfaces is somewhat more complicated. For example, consider the evaluation of the irradiation of surface 1.

In Figure 4.4 the irradiation of surface 1 is divided into two parts: (a) the irradiation from surface 2, and (b) the irradiation from surface 1. Consider the left-hand side of Figure 4.4: the irradiation of surface 1 from surface 2 consists of all the upward-pointing arrows, or

$$E_2 + \rho_1\rho_2 E_2 + \rho_1{}^2\rho_2{}^2 E_2 + \rho_1{}^3\rho_2{}^3 E_2 + \cdots + \rho_1{}^n\rho_2{}^n E_2$$

where the functional notation has been omitted for simplicity, but

$$E_2 = E_2(T_2) \qquad \rho_1 = \rho_1(T_1, T^*_{s_1}) \qquad \rho_2 = \rho_2(T_2, T^*_{s_2})$$

This infinite series can be expressed as

$$\frac{E_2(T_2)}{1 - \rho_1(T_1, T^*_{s_1})\rho_2(T_2, T^*_{s_2})}$$

In a similar manner, the summation of all of the upward-pointing arrows on the right side of Figure 4.4 results in

$$\frac{\rho_2(T_2, T^*_{s_2})E_1(T_1)}{1 - \rho_1(T_1, T^*_{s_1})\rho_2(T_2, T^*_{s_2})}$$

The sum of these two terms is the irradiation of surface 1; thus

$$G_1(T^*_{s_1}) = \frac{E_2(T_2)}{1 - \rho_1(T_1, T^*_{s_1})\rho_2(T_2, T^*_{s_2})} + \frac{\rho_2(T_2, T^*_{s_2})E_1(T_1)}{1 - \rho_1(T_1, T^*_{s_1})\rho_2(T_2, T^*_{s_2})} \tag{4.5}$$

Using Equation 4.2, we find that the net heat exchange for surface 1 is

$$q''_{net_1} = \alpha_1(T_1, T^*_{s_1})G_1(T^*_{s_1}) - E_1(T_1)$$

or

$$q''_{net_1} = \frac{\alpha_1(T_1, T^*_{s_1})E_2(T_2)}{1 - \rho_1(T_1, T^*_{s_1})\rho_2(T_2, T^*_{s_2})} + \frac{\alpha_1(T_1, T^*_{s_1})\rho_2(T_2, T^*_{s_2})E_1(T_1)}{1 - \rho_1(T_1, T^*_{s_1})\rho_2(T_2, T^*_{s_2})} - E_1(T_1) \tag{4.6}$$

One of the basic practical difficulties in the analysis of systems assumed to be gray is the problem of what property values are to be used. This problem is easily illustrated by examination of Equation 4.6. A typical gray assumption would be to let $\alpha(T, T_s{}^*) = \varepsilon(T)$, and, therefore, $\rho(T, T_s{}^*) = 1 - \varepsilon(T)$. With this assumption the absorptance and reflectance terms become

$$\alpha_1(T_1, T^*_{s_1}) = \varepsilon_1(T_1)$$
$$\rho_1(T_1, T^*_{s_1}) = 1 - \varepsilon_1(T_1)$$
$$\rho_2(T_2, T^*_{s_2}) = 1 - \varepsilon_2(T_2)$$

and Equation 4.6 reduces to the simple form

$$q''_{net_1} = \frac{E_{b_2}(T_2) - E_{b_1}(T_1)}{(1/\varepsilon_1(T_1)) + (1/\varepsilon_2(T_2)) - 1} \qquad (4.7)$$

4.3 Gray and Semigray Assumptions

A difficulty arises when the total emittance values for a material are given as a function of temperature. Examination of the data in Appendix 1 will illustrate that this is the typical case. With emittance values that vary with temperature, some approximation must be made as to what value of $\varepsilon(T)$ should be used. Equation 4.7 by itself does not indicate the problem, but the assumption $\alpha_1(T_1, T_{s_1}^*) = \varepsilon_1(T_1)$ does. The absorptance of surface 1, or any surface, depends on the surface temperature T_1 and the equivalent temperature of the incoming energy $T_{s_1}^*$. This was described explicitly in Chapter I by

$$\alpha(T, T_s^*) = \frac{\displaystyle\int_0^\infty \alpha_\lambda(T) G_\lambda(T_s^*)\, d\lambda}{\displaystyle\int_0^\infty G_\lambda(T_s^*)\, d\lambda} \qquad (1.43)$$

Since $G_\lambda(T_s^*)$ may be any kind of function, the typical approach used to obtain $\alpha(T, T_s^*)$ is to assume $G_\lambda(T_s^*) = E_{b\lambda}(T_i)$, where T_i is used to indicate the temperature of the incoming radiation. With this assumption the absorptance of a surface at T for energy incoming at T_i is

$$\alpha(T, T_i) = \frac{\displaystyle\int_0^\infty \alpha_\lambda(T) E_{b\lambda}(T_i)\, d\lambda}{\displaystyle\int_0^\infty E_{b\lambda}(T_i)\, d\lambda} \qquad \alpha_\lambda(T) = \varepsilon_\lambda(T) \qquad (4.8)$$

Comparison of Equation 4.8 and a modified Equation 1.42

$$\varepsilon(T_i) = \frac{\displaystyle\int_0^\infty \varepsilon_\lambda(T_i) E_{b\lambda}(T_i)\, d\lambda}{\displaystyle\int_0^\infty E_{b\lambda}(T_i)\, d\lambda} \qquad (1.42)$$

indicates that

$$\alpha(T, T_i) = \varepsilon(T_i)$$

if $\varepsilon_\lambda(T_i) = \alpha_\lambda(T)$. This approximation is equivalent to $\varepsilon_\lambda(T_i) = \varepsilon_\lambda(T)$ since $\alpha_\lambda(T)$ is exactly equal to $\varepsilon_\lambda(T)$. In general, surfaces do not exhibit a large variation in monochromatic emittance with surface temperature change. (This was examined in the discussion of Section 2.3). For this reason, the approximation $\alpha(T, T_i) = \varepsilon(T_i)$ is not as severe as the approximation $\alpha(T, T_i) = \varepsilon(T)$.

In either case, the values of $\varepsilon_1(T_1)$ and $\varepsilon_2(T_2)$ to be used in Equation 4.7 are questionable. An approximation for use in equation 4.7 introduced by Hottel [6] is to evaluate the emittance of the cooler surface at $T_s^* = \sqrt{T_1 T_2}$ when the surfaces are metals. For example, if surface 1 is hot and surface 2 is cool, Equation 4.7 becomes

$$q''_{net_1} = \frac{E_{b_2} - E_{b_1}}{(1/\varepsilon_1(T_1)) + (1/\varepsilon_2(T_s^*)) - 1}$$

where $T_s^* = \sqrt{T_1 T_2}$. The use of this approximation results in heat transfer values that are more nearly correct than the values obtained from Equation 4.7, but there is still considerable error in some cases.

The results of some comparison calculations as presented in [1] are shown in Table 4.1. In this case the two infinite plates are assumed to be diffuse tungsten.

TABLE 4.1

Ratios of $q''_{gray}/q''_{nongray}$†

Temperature difference: hot and cool surfaces	Temperature of Hotter Surface		
	2000°K	3000°K	4000°K
800°K	0.86	0.90	0.94
1600°K		0.87	0.92
2400°K			0.88
3200°K			0.75

† J. R. Branstetter, "Radiant Heat Transfer between Nongray Parallel Plates of Tungsten," NASA TN D–1088, August 1961.

In order to obtain the heat transfer rates, the energy exchange in finite-width wavelength bands were summed. The results of this calculation are indicated as $q''_{nongray}$, and the values calculated from Equation 4.7 using Hottel's [6] empirical formulation are listed as q''_{gray}. The maximum error indicated in Table 4.1 of about 25 percent occurs for the maximum temperature difference. As may be noted, the error tends to decrease in each case as the temperature difference decreases. This is exactly the behavior expected from the discussion of the approximation used.

The accuracy of calculations can be considerably improved by using Equation 4.6 rather than Equation 4.7. As described in the derivation, the first term to the right of the equality consists of energy originally emitted by surface 2, and the second term consists of energy originally emitted by surface 1. A semigray approximation is described as the assumption that the absorptance of a surface is equal to the emittance of that surface evaluated at the approximate black-body temperature of the incoming radiation. In terms of the properties to be used in Equation 4.6, the semigray assumption requires

$$\alpha_1(T_1, T_2) = \varepsilon_1(T_2)$$
$$\rho_1(T_1, T_2) = 1 - \varepsilon_1(T_2)$$
$$\rho_2(T_2, T_2) = 1 - \varepsilon_2(T_2)$$
$$\alpha_1(T_1, T_1) = \varepsilon_1(T_1)$$
$$\rho_1(T_1, T_1) = 1 - \varepsilon_1(T_1)$$
$$\rho_2(T_2, T_1) = 1 - \varepsilon_2(T_1)$$

Thus

$$q''_{net_1} = \frac{\varepsilon_1(T_2)\varepsilon_2(T_2)E_{b_2}(T_2)}{1 - [1 - \varepsilon_1(T_2)][1 - \varepsilon_2(T_2)]} +$$

$$\frac{\varepsilon_1(T_1)\varepsilon_1(T_1)[1 - \varepsilon_2(T_1)]E_{b_1}(T_1)}{1 - [1 - \varepsilon_1(T_1)][1 - \varepsilon_2(T_1)]} - \varepsilon_1(T_1)E_{b_1}(T_1)$$

which reduces to

$$q''_{net_1} = \frac{E_{b_2}(T_2)}{(1/\varepsilon_1(T_2)) + (1/\varepsilon_2(T_2)) - 1} - \frac{E_{b_1}(T_1)}{(1/\varepsilon_1(T_1)) + (1/\varepsilon_2(T_1)) - 1} \tag{4.9}$$

When Equation 4.9 is used to calculate the heat transfer for a parallel tungsten-plate system, the heat transfer is nearly the same as values obtained using nongray assumptions. A comparison of the results similar to Table 4.1 is presented in Table 4.2. The value indicated as $q''_{semigray}$ is the heat transfer calculated from Equation 4.9.

TABLE 4.2

Ratio of $q''_{semigray}/q''_{nongray}$ for Infinite Parallel Tungsten Plates

Temperature difference: hot and cool surfaces	Temperature of Hotter Surface		
	2000°K	3000°K	4000°K
800°K	1.03	1.01	1.00
1600°K		1.005	1.005
2400°K			1.005
3200°K			1.00

As can be seen, the semigray approximation for the particular case of the tungsten plates is much closer to the nongray solution. The maximum error indicated is approximately 3 percent. Since this error is much less than the error associated with gray analysis, it is worthwhile to consider this type of analysis for more complex systems. This will be considered in Chapter 6.

4.4 Finite-Size Surfaces

In previous sections, the evaluation of the irradiation of a surface was simplified by the fact that all of the energy leaving one surface was incident upon the other surface. When a system consists of surfaces not arranged in this manner, it is necessary to determine the fraction of the energy leaving one surface that is incident upon another surface. This is illustrated by considering two parallel finite-size plates as shown in Figure 4.5.

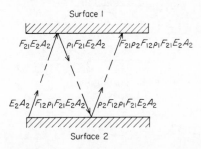

Figure 4.5   Finite-size Plate System.

The irradiation of plate 1 by energy directly from plate 2 consists of $E_2 A_2 F_{A_2 \to A_1}$. In this expression the term $F_{A_2 \to A_1}$ is the fraction directly incident upon surface 1 of the energy leaving surface 2. This term is called the *configuration factor*. As indicated in Figure 4.5, the energy originally emitted by area A_2 is partially reflected by area A_1. This energy is $\rho_1 F_{21} E_2 A_2$, where F_{21} is used as shorter notation for $F_{A_2 \to A_1}$. Of this reflected energy, the fraction F_{12} returns to surface 2 and is partially reflected back to surface 1. By considering terms of this type one after the other, the irradiation of surface 1 by energy from surface 2 becomes

$$A_1 G_{1 \text{ from } 2} = F_{21} E_2 A_2 + \rho_1 \rho_2 F_{12} F_{21}^2 E_2 A_2 + \rho_1{}^2 \rho_2{}^2 F_{12}^2 F_{21}^3 E_2 A_2 + \cdots$$

or

$$A_1 G_{1 \text{ from } 2} = \frac{F_{21} E_2 A_2}{1 - \rho_1 \rho_2 F_{12} F_{21}} \tag{4.10}$$

Comparison of Equation 4.10 with the terms of Equation 4.5 shows that the only new term introduced by finite-size surfaces is the *configuration factor*. Since this is an important consideration, the next section is devoted to an examination of the term and its evaluation.

Configuration Factors

4.5 Definitions

A configuration factor is defined as *the fraction of energy directly incident on one surface, from another surface assumed to be emitting energy diffusely.* Expressions for configuration factors are easily obtained by considering Figure 4.6.

The energy leaving surface-area element dA_1 that is directly incident on dA_2 is

$$I_1 \cos \phi_1 \, dA_1 \, d\omega_{12}$$

(where $d\omega_{12}$ is the solid angle through which dA_1 "sees" dA_2) or

$$d\omega_{12} = \frac{\cos \phi_2 \, dA_2}{r^2}$$

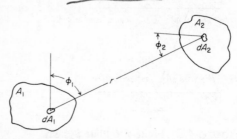

Figure 4.6   Geometry for Configuration-factor Analysis.

From the definition of the configuration factor,

$$F_{dA_1 \to dA_2} = \frac{I_1 \cos \phi_1 \, dA_1 \, d\omega_{12}}{I_1 \pi \, dA_1} = \frac{\cos \phi_1 \, d\omega_{12}}{\pi} \tag{4.11}$$

or

$$F_{dA_1 \to dA_2} = \frac{\cos \phi_1 \cos \phi_2 \, dA_2}{\pi r^2} \tag{4.12}$$

Neither Equation 4.11 nor Equation 4.12 involves any radiation characteristic of the surfaces dA_1 or dA_2; therefore, $F_{dA_1 \to dA_2}$ is a function of geometry only.

When the energy transfer between an infinitesimal area dA_1 and a finite area A_2 is required, the configuration factor will be

$$F_{dA_1 \to A_2} = \frac{\int_{A_2} I_1 \cos \phi_1 \, dA_1 \cos \phi_2 \, dA_2 / r^2}{\pi I_1 \, dA_1}$$

$$F_{dA_1 \to A_2} = \int_{A_2} \frac{\cos \phi_1 \cos \phi_2 \, dA_2}{\pi r^2} \tag{4.13}$$

If the configuration factor for a finite area A_1 to a finite area A_2 is examined, the result is

$$F_{A_1 \to A_2} = \frac{1}{A_1} \int_{A_1} dA_1 \int_{A_2} \frac{\cos \phi_1 \cos \phi_2 \, dA_2}{\pi r^2} \tag{4.14}$$

Certain interrelationships between configuration factors are useful. These relationships may be obtained from Equations 4.12, 4.13, and 4.14. First, the configuration factor $F_{dA_1 \to A_2}$ from a differential area to a finite-size area is

$$F_{dA_1 \to A_2} = \int_{A_2} F_{dA_1 \to dA_2} \tag{4.15}$$

Equation 4.15 indicates the additive nature of configuration factors when the area being irradiated is a subdivided area. That is, the fractions of total energy leaving area element dA_1 and going to small areas on A_2 are simply added to get the fraction going to A_2. This concept of additive fractions for this condition is useful when geometric flux algebra is discussed.

Secondly, the configuration factor from a finite-size area to a finite-size area is

$$F_{A_1 \to A_2} = \frac{1}{A_1} \int_{A_1} (F_{dA_1 \to A_2}) \, dA_1 \tag{4.16}$$

In contrast to the discussion concerning Equation 4.15, Equation 4.16 indicates that when the emitting surface is subdivided, the area-weighted average of the configuration factors from subareas must be used. This may be more easily seen if area A_1 is divided into finite subelements ΔA_i; in this case Equation 4.16 may be approximated by

$$F_{A_1 \to A_2} \simeq \frac{1}{A_1} \sum_i \Delta A_i F_{\Delta A_i \to A_2} \tag{4.17}$$

Once again, this is a useful concept for geometric flux algebra.

Thirdly, and perhaps most important, the reciprocity relationship is obtained from Equation 4.14. Consider Equation 4.14 written as

$$A_1 F_{A_1 \to A_2} = \int_{A_1} \int_{A_2} \frac{\cos \phi_1 \cos \phi_2 \, dA_2 \, dA_1}{\pi r^2} \tag{4.18}$$

By cyclic interchange of the subscripts, Equation 4.18 becomes

$$A_2 F_{A_2 \to A_1} = \int_{A_2} \int_{A_1} \frac{\cos \phi_2 \cos \phi_1 \, dA_1 \, dA_2}{\pi r^2} \tag{4.19}$$

Since the double integrals in Equations 4.18 and 4.19 differ only in the order of integration,

$$A_1 F_{A_1 \to A_2} = A_2 F_{A_2 \to A_1} \tag{4.20}$$

Equation 4.20 expresses the reciprocity that must exist between configuration factors for finite-size areas. By considering Equations 4.12 and 4.13, we may write similar expressions of reciprocity for differential areas, that is

$$dA_1 F_{dA_1 \rightarrow dA_2} = dA_2 F_{dA_2 \rightarrow dA_1}$$

$$dA_1 F_{dA_1 \rightarrow A_2} = A_2 F_{A_2 \rightarrow dA_1}$$

Finally, from the definition of a configuration factor from one surface to a second surface as being the fraction of the total energy leaving the first surface, the following expression must be valid:

$$\sum_{k=1}^{n} F_{A_j \rightarrow A_k} = 1 \qquad \text{for an enclosure only} \tag{4.21}$$

In Equation 4.21 the n surface elements indicated in the summation are considered to completely enclose the jth surface element. Since these n elements enclose the jth surface, the sum of the fractions of the energy leaving A_j must add to the total energy leaving A_j.

4.6 Evaluation of Configuration Factors

The most desirable result from a configuration-factor evaluation is an algebraic expression for the desired quantity. This type of answer occurs after mathematical evaluation of the basic equations. Certain geometries are amenable to this type of evaluation and have been tabulated in [2], [3], [5], and [9]. The basic approach to mathematical integration can be seen from the following example.

In Figure 4.7 the geometric system for a differential area dA_1 and finite

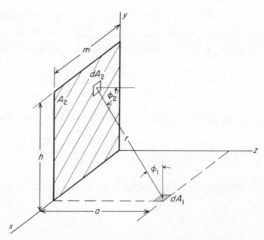

Figure 4.7   Geometry for Mathematical Integration.

area A_2 are shown. From

$$F_{dA_1 \to dA_2} = \frac{\cos \phi_1 \cos \phi_2 \, dA_2}{\pi r^2} \qquad (4.12)$$

and the geometry, this expression becomes

$$F_{dA_1 \to dA_2} = \frac{ay}{\pi[x^2 + y^2 + a^2]^2} \, dx \, dy$$

The desired configuration factor $F_{dA_1 \to A_2}$ can be expressed as

$$F_{dA_1 \to A_2} = \int_{A_2} F_{dA_1 \to dA_2} \qquad (4.15)$$

or

$$F_{dA_1 \to A_2} = \int_0^h \int_0^m \frac{ay}{\pi[x^2 + y^2 + a^2]^2} \, dx \, dy$$

which may be integrated using standard techniques [3] to obtain

$$F_{dA_1 \to A_2} = \frac{1}{2\pi} \left[\tan^{-1} M - \frac{H}{\sqrt{1 + H^2}} \tan^{-1} \frac{M}{\sqrt{1 + H^2}} \right]$$

where $H = h/a$ and $M = m/a$.

The next step in the evaluation of configuration factors by this method is to use Equation 4.16 when a finite-size area A_1 is considered. When finite areas are used, mathematical integration usually results in quite complex algebraic equations. These expressions have been evaluated and tabulated for numerous practical geometries in [3]. Since these results are extremely important in the solution of any practical problem, they have been reproduced in Appendix 4.

Another very simple method of evaluation for certain cases is the *unit-sphere* method. The basic concepts for this method, which is primarily geometric, are illustrated in Figure 4.8. The differential area dA_1 is the base

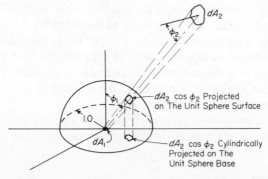

Figure 4.8   Illustration of the Unit Sphere Method.

plane of a hemisphere with unit radius. The differential area dA_2 is located away from dA_1 (in this case outside of the unit sphere, but this is not necessary) and the projections required are shown. First the area dA_2 is conically projected from dA_1 onto the unit-sphere surface. Then this projection is cylindrically projected onto the unit-sphere base.

Consider the conical projection first: This area on the sphere surface is $(dA_2 \cos \phi_2)_{\text{proj}}$, and since the sphere radius is unity, the area represents the solid angle through which dA_1 "sees" dA_2 projected on the line of sight. When this area is cylindrically projected onto the base, the area on the base is equal to the solid angle (represented by the area projection on the sphere) multiplied by the cosine of ϕ_2, which is the polar angle for dA_1. Expressing this mathematically, we get

$$\frac{(dA_2 \cos \phi_2 \cos \phi_1)}{(1)^2} = \text{area on the base}$$

or

$$d\omega_{12} \cos \phi_1 = \text{area on the base}$$

where $d\omega_{12}$ is the solid angle through which dA_1 "sees" dA_2. Since the configuration factor $F_{dA_1 \to dA_2}$ is defined as

$$F_{dA_1 \to dA_2} = \frac{\cos \phi_1 \, d\omega_{12}}{\pi}$$

the configuration factor is represented geometrically by

$$F_{dA_1 \to dA_2} = \frac{\text{projected area on the base}}{\text{area of the base}}$$

This method works equally well for a configuration factor of the type $F_{dA_1 \to A_2}$, or for a differential area to a finite-size area.

4.7 Contour-Integration Method of Evaluating Configuration Factors

The method of mathematical integration presented above involves the evaluation of area integrals, which require double integrations that are frequently quite complex. The complexity of this integration may be reduced by using contour integration. Basically, contour integration involves the use of Stokes' theorem to reduce a double or area integral to a single or line integral. Either of two methods may be used; one is presented in [7] and the other in [8]. For engineering purposes, the method used by Sparrow is somewhat more useful; it is described below.

Since the basic problem is to convert the area integral into a contour or line integral, Stokes' theorem is used. This theorem as stated in [4] may be put in the form

$$\oint_c (P \, dx + Q \, dy + R \, dz)$$

$$= \iint_s \left[\left(\frac{\partial R}{\partial y} - \frac{\partial Q}{\partial z} \right) \cos \alpha + \left(\frac{\partial P}{\partial z} - \frac{\partial R}{\partial x} \right) \cos \beta + \left(\frac{\partial Q}{\partial x} - \frac{\partial P}{\partial y} \right) \cos \gamma \right] dS$$

(4.22)

where P, Q, and R are defined from $\mathbf{V} = P\mathbf{i} + Q\mathbf{j} + R\mathbf{k}$ and are twice continuously differentiable functions. The angles α, β, and γ in Equation 4.22 are used to define the direction cosines of the differential area dS. In terms of the configuration-factor geometry shown in Figure 4.7, dS would be dA_2, and $\cos \alpha$, $\cos \beta$, and $\cos \gamma$ would be the direction cosines of the line normal to dA_2. Following Sparrow's nomenclature, $\cos \alpha$, $\cos \beta$, and $\cos \gamma$ will be called l_2, m_2, and n_2 respectively. Similarly, the direction cosines of the line normal to dA_1 will be called l_1, m_1, and n_1.

From Equation 4.12, the configuration factor $F_{dA_1 \to dA_2}$ is

$$F_{dA_1 \to dA_2} = \frac{\cos \phi_1 \cos \phi_2 \, dA_2}{\pi r^2}$$

(4.12)

Since the connecting line r and the normals to the two surface elements intersect to form the angles ϕ_1 and ϕ_2, the cosines are

$$\cos \phi_1 = l_1 \left(\frac{x_2 - x_1}{r} \right) + m_1 \left(\frac{y_2 - y_1}{r} \right) + n_1 \left(\frac{z_2 - z_1}{r} \right)$$

$$\cos \phi_2 = l_2 \left(\frac{x_1 - x_2}{r} \right) + m_2 \left(\frac{y_1 - y_2}{r} \right) + n_2 \left(\frac{z_1 - z_2}{r} \right)$$

(4.23)

With these expressions for the configuration factors, Equation 4.12 becomes

$$F_{dA_1 \to dA_2} = \frac{[l_1(x_2 - x_1) + m_1(y_2 - y_1) + n_1(z_2 - z_1)]}{\pi r^4} \times [l_2(x_1 - x_2) + m_2(y_1 - y_2) + n_2(z_1 - z_2)] \, dA_2$$

(4.24)

The configuration factor $F_{dA_1 \to A_2}$ is given by Equation 4.15 as

$$F_{dA_1 \to A_2} = \int_{A_2} F_{dA_1 \to dA_2}$$

(4.15)

Using this expression to simplify Equation 4.18, we get

$$F_{dA_1 \to A_2} = \int_{A_2} \{ l_2[(x_1 - x_2)f] + m_2[(y_1 - y_2)f] + n_2[(z_1 - z_2)f] \} \, dA_2$$

(4.25)

in which

$$f = \frac{[l_1(x_2 - x_1) + m_1(y_2 - y_1) + n_1(z_2 - z_1)]}{\pi r^4}$$

Comparison of Equation 4.22 and 4.25, with the realization that l_2, m_2, and

n_2 are $\cos \alpha$, $\cos \beta$, and $\cos \gamma$ respectively, shows that the area integral can be converted to a contour integral if

$$\frac{\partial R}{\partial y} - \frac{\partial Q}{\partial z} = (x_1 - x_2)f$$

$$\frac{\partial P}{\partial z} - \frac{\partial R}{\partial x} = (y_1 - y_2)f$$

$$\frac{\partial Q}{\partial x} - \frac{\partial P}{\partial y} = (z_1 - z_2)f$$

These partial differential equations were solved by Sparrow, resulting in the following functions for P, Q, and R:

$$P = \frac{-m_1(z_2 - z_1) + n_2(y_2 - y_1)}{2\pi r^2}$$

$$Q = \frac{l_1(z_2 - z_1) - n_1(x_2 - x_1)}{2\pi r^2}$$

$$R = \frac{-l_1(y_2 - y_1) + m_1(x_2 - x_1)}{2\pi r^2}$$

With these values of P, Q, and R, the configuration factor becomes

$$F_{dA_1 \to A_2} = \frac{1}{2\pi} \oint_c \left[\frac{-m_1(z_2 - z_1) + n_1(y_2 - y_1)}{r^2} \right] dx_2$$

$$+ \left[\frac{l_1(z_2 - z_1) - n_1(x_2 - x_1)}{r^2} \right] dy_2$$

$$+ \left[\frac{-l_1(y_2 - y_1) + m_1(x_2 - x_1)}{r^2} \right] dz_2 \qquad (4.28)$$

Equation 4.28 represents a considerable simplification in mathematical integration since the contour integral is a single rather than a double integral. In most cases, the elemental area dA_1 can be located such that two of the direction cosines l_1, m_1, or n_1 will be zero. This results in a further simplification. For this reason it is convenient to rewrite Equation 4.28 in the form shown in below:

$$F_{dA_1 \to A_2} = l_1 \oint_c \frac{(z_2 - z_1) \, dy_2 - (y_2 - y_1) \, dz_2}{2\pi r^2}$$

$$+ m_1 \oint_c \frac{(x_2 - x_1) \, dz_2 - (z_2 - z_1) \, dx_2}{2\pi r^2}$$

$$+ n_1 \oint_c \frac{(y_2 - y_1) \, dx_2 - (x_2 - x_1) \, dy_2}{2\pi r^2} \qquad (4.29)$$

As an example of the use of Equation 4.29, consider Figure 4.7, which was used in demonstrating the mathematical integration method. In this case the direction cosines for dA_1 are $l_1 = 0$, $m_1 = 1.0$, and $n_1 = 0$. Equation 4.29 becomes

$$F_{dA_1 \to A_2} = m_1 \oint_c \frac{(x_2 - x_1)\, dz_2 - (z_2 - z_1)\, dx_2}{2\pi r^2}$$

Since dA_2 is the area with variables dx_2 and dz_2, and dA_1 has constant values,

$$F_{dA_1 \to A_2} = \oint_c \frac{(x - m)\, dz - (z - a)\, dx}{2\pi r^2}$$

but $dz = 0$; therefore

$$F_{dA_1 \to A_2} = \oint_c \left(\frac{a - z}{2\pi r^2} \right) dx \qquad (4.30)$$

Equation 4.30 can be divided into four separate integrals to represent the integration around the contour of area A_2; however, since the two sides parallel to the y axis have no variation in x only two integrals are required.

$$F_{dA_1 \to A_2} = \int_m^0 \left(\frac{a - z}{2\pi r^2} \right) dx + \int_0^m \left(\frac{a - z}{2\pi r^2} \right) dx$$

$$\text{side at } y = h \qquad \text{side at } y = 0$$

substituting for r and noting that $z = 0$ along each line, we get

$$F_{dA_1 \to A_2} = \int_m^0 \frac{a}{2\pi[(m - x)^2 + a^2 + h^2]}\, dx + \int_0^m \frac{a}{2\pi[(m - x)^2 + a^2]}\, dx$$

which integrates easily and becomes

$$F_{dA_1 \to A_2} = \frac{a}{2\pi} \left[\frac{1}{a} \tan^{-1}\left(\frac{m}{a} \right) - \frac{1}{\sqrt{a^2 + h^2}} \tan^{-1}\left(\frac{m}{\sqrt{a^2 + h^2}} \right) \right]$$

This is the same solution as obtained by mathematical integration. It should be noted that if the contour is traced in the opposite direction, the numerical value of $F_{dA_1 \to A_2}$ will be negative. Since a negative configuration factor has no meaning, the value should be interpreted as a positive value. The negative result is caused by using an improper direction for a unit vector in Stokes' theorem.

When the configuration factor for a finite area A_1 is required, the contour-integration method may be used for numerous subelements ΔA_1 on the area

A_1. The approximate solution for $F_{A_1 \to A_2}$ is given from Equation 4.16:

$$F_{A_1 \to A_2} \simeq \frac{1}{A_1} \sum_i \Delta A_i F_{\Delta A_i \to A_2}$$

This approximation is a very powerful tool when used in conjunction with the contour-integration method. Many geometries that are practically impossible to evaluate by mathematical integration are easily evaluated by using a digital computer and the above methods.

Flux Algebra

4.8 Basic Concepts

Evaluation of the configuration factors for a system of surfaces that constitutes an enclosure, or a hypothetical enclosure, can be considerably simplified by applying the flux algebra method. This method involves the use of the following two basic equations:

$$\sum_{i=1}^{n} F_{A_j \to A_i} = 1.0 \qquad (4.21)$$

$$A_i F_{ik} = A_k F_{ki} \qquad (4.20)$$

Equations 4.20 and 4.21 were discussed previously. These two equations are the basis for the laws of flux algebra developed below.

The discussion of and application of flux algebra is simplified by the following definition:

$$G_{ik} \equiv A_i F_{ik} \qquad (4.30)$$

With this definition, Equations 4.20 and 4.21 become

$$G_{ik} = G_{ki} \qquad (4.31)$$

$$\sum_{i=1}^{n} G_{ji} = A_j \qquad (4.32)$$

The symbol G_{ik} is called *geometric flux* [3].

4.9 Algebraic Laws

Geometric fluxes follow certain laws, which are derivable by inspection. Using the symbolism $G_{(1)(23)}$ to represent $G_{(A1)(A2+A3)}$, we can express the first law as

$$G_{(1)(23)} = G_{12} + G_{13} \qquad (4.33)$$

This law is easily proved by writing the meaning of each term, that is,

Equation 4.33 expanded is

$$A_1 F_{A_1 \to (A_2 + A_3)} = A_1 F_{A_1 \to A_2} + A_1 F_{A_1 \to A_3}$$

or

$$F_{A_1 \to (A_2 + A_3)} = F_{A_1 \to A_2} + F_{A_1 \to A_3}$$

Since the sum of the fractions of energy leaving area A_1 and going to A_2 and A_3 separately must equal $F_{A_1 \to (A_2 + A_3)}$, the first law is valid.

The second law or statement of flux algebra requires the use of the symbol $G_{(12)(34)}$, which has the meaning $G_{(A_1 + A_2)(A_3 + A_4)}$. This law is written as

$$G_{(12)(34)} = G_{1(34)} + G_{2(34)} \tag{4.34}$$

Expanded from the definition of geometric flux, Equation 4.34 becomes

$$(A_1 + A_2) F_{(A_1 + A_2) \to (A_3 + A_4)} = A_1 F_{A_1 \to (A_3 + A_4)} + A_2 F_{A_2 \to (A_3 + A_4)}$$

Applying the reciprocity relationship gives

$$(A_3 + A_4) F_{(A_3 + A_4) \to (A_1 + A_2)} = (A_3 + A_4) F_{(A_3 + A_4) \to A_1} + (A_3 + A_4) F_{(A_3 + A_4) \to A_2}$$

or

$$G_{(34)(12)} = G_{(34)1} + G_{(34)2}$$

which is a restatement of the first law.

The last law is the final decomposition equation, expressed as

$$G_{(12)(34)} = G_{13} + G_{14} + G_{23} + G_{24} \tag{4.35}$$

This law is proved by taking the decomposition in steps, as follows:

$$G_{(12)(34)} = G_{(12)(3)} + G_{(12)(4)} \qquad \text{by the first law}$$

and

$$G_{(12)(34)} = G_{13} + G_{23} + G_{14} + G_{24} \qquad \text{by the second law}$$

The final expression is, of course, valid and equal to the original statement of the last law.

4.10 An Example of Simple Flux Algebra

The use of flux algebra in evaluating configuration factors is best shown by an example. In Figure 4.9, the configuration factors F_{12} and $F_{1(23)}$ may be determined from the tabulated values in Appendix 4; however, F_{13} is not

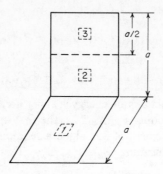

Figure 4.9   Example for Flux Algebra.

tabulated. By using flux algebra, F_{13} can be expressed in terms of known quantities, as follows:

$$G_{1(23)} = G_{12} + G_{13}$$

$$G_{13} = G_{1(23)} - G_{12}$$

$$F_{13} = \frac{A_1 F_{1(23)} - A_1 F_{12}}{A_1} = F_{1(23)} - F_{12}$$

Many untabulated configuration factors may be evaluated in this manner.

4.11 Determining Configuration Factors by Hottel's Crossed-String Method

An interesting and useful example of flux algebra is presented by Hottel [6]. The method of obtaining configuration factors for surface elements that extend infinitely in one direction is as follows: Consider the three-surface enclosure shown on the left-hand side of Figure 4.10. The areas A_1, A_2, and A_3 are assumed to extend indefinitely in the direction normal to the plane of

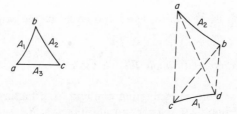

Figure 4.10   The Crossed-string Method.

the paper. By flux algebra,

$$A_1 F_{12} + A_1 F_{13} = A_1$$

$$A_2 F_{21} + A_2 F_{23} = A_2$$

$$A_3 F_{31} + A_3 F_{32} = A_3$$

Solving for $A_1 F_{12}$ gives

$$A_1 F_{12} = \frac{A_1 + A_2 - A_3}{2} \qquad (4.36)$$

Equation 4.36 is then used as follows to obtain the configuration factor between areas A_1 and A_2, shown on the right-hand side of Figure 4.10: Consider the dotted lines $\overline{ac}$ and $\overline{bd}$ to be surfaces that form an enclosure in conjunction with areas A_1 and A_2. Then, from flux algebra,

$$A_1 F_{12} + A_1 F_{1-\overline{ac}} + A_1 F_{1-\overline{bd}} = A_1 \qquad (4.37)$$

If the triangular enclosures $\overline{acd}$ and $\overline{cbd}$ are taken into consideration, the geometric-flux values $A_1 F_{1-\overline{ac}}$ and $A_1 F_{1-\overline{bd}}$ can be written as

$$A_1 F_{1-\overline{ac}} = \frac{A_1 + A_{\overline{ac}} - A_{\overline{ad}}}{2}$$

and

$$A_1 F_{1-\overline{bd}} = \frac{A_1 + A_{\overline{bd}} - A_{\overline{bc}}}{2}$$

Substituting these into Equation 4.37 results in

$$A_1 F_{12} = \frac{(A_{\overline{ad}} + A_{\overline{bc}}) - (A_{\overline{ac}} + A_{\overline{bd}})}{2}$$

or

$$F_{12} = \frac{(A_{\overline{ad}} + A_{\overline{bc}}) - (A_{\overline{ac}} + A_{\overline{bd}})}{2A_1} \qquad (4.38)$$

Since Equation 4.38 is for infinitely long plane areas, the areas are proportional to the lengths shown in the two-dimensional representation. Exchanging areas for lengths in Equation 4.38 results in the crossed-string configuration factor presented by Hottel [6].

$$F_{12} = \frac{(\overline{ad} + \overline{bc}) - (\overline{ac} + \overline{bd})}{2\overline{cd}} \qquad (4.38)$$

Equation 4.38 may be expressed as follows:

$$F_{12} = \frac{(\text{sum of crossed strings}) - (\text{sum of uncrossed strings})}{2 \times \text{length of area 1}}$$

where the string distances are the dotted lines shown in Figure 4.10.

4.12 Special Reciprocity for Flux Algebra

In many cases a special reciprocity relationship for use in flux-algebra solutions for configuration factors is required. This can be illustrated, using Figure 4.11. Two parallel planes are shown, located in the x_1, y_1 and x_2, y_2

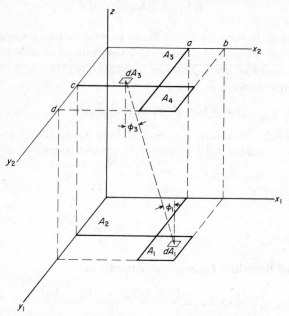

Figure 4.11   Geometry for Special Reciprocity.

planes a distance z apart. The special reciprocity to be demonstrated is $A_1F_{13} = A_2F_{24}$. This reciprocity occurs because of the symmetry with which the various areas are located. In order to prove this, Equation 4.14 is used to express the configuration factors:

$$A_1F_{13} = \int_{A_1} \int_{A_3} \frac{\cos \phi_1 \cos \phi_3}{\pi r^2} \, dA_1 \, dA_3$$

In terms of the coordinate system shown in Figure 4.11, this becomes

$$A_1F_{13} = \frac{1}{\pi} \int_0^c \int_0^a \int_c^d \int_a^b \frac{(x_1 - x_2)^2 + (y_1 - y_2)^2}{[(x_1 - x_2)^2 + (y_1 - y_2)^2 + z^2]^2} \, dx_1 \, dy_1 \, dx_2 \, dy_2$$

$$(4.39)$$

Similarly

$$A_2F_{24} = \frac{1}{\pi} \int_0^c \int_0^a \int_c^d \int_a^b \frac{(x_2 - x_1)^2 + (y_2 - y_1)^2}{[(x_2 - x_1)^2 + (y_2 - y_1)^2 + z^2]^2} \, dx_2 \, dy_2 \, dx_1 \, dy_1$$

(4.40)

Since the integrands of Equations 4.39 and 4.40 are symmetrical in x_1, x_2, and y_1, y_2, and the limits of integration are symmetrical on these variables,

$$A_1F_{13} = A_2F_{24}$$

The special reciprocity relationship is not limited to the particular case shown above. Whenever sets of areas located on planes are arranged such that the limits of integration on the four dimensions are interchangeably equal, reciprocity will be valid.

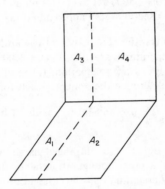

Figure 4.12   Example of Geometry for Special Reciprocity.

An example of the use of this reciprocity is shown in Figure 4.12. Let F_{14} be the value required. Once again tabulated values are available for F_{13}, F_{24}, and $F_{(12)(34)}$; therefore, F_{14} must be expressed in terms of these values. Using flux algebra decomposition, we get

$$G_{(12)(34)} = G_{13} + G_{14} + G_{23} + G_{24}$$

By special reciprocity

$$A_1F_{14} = A_2F_{23} \quad \text{or} \quad G_{14} = G_{23}$$

Thus

$$2G_{14} = G_{(12)(34)} - G_{13} - G_{24}$$

or

$$F_{14} = \frac{A_{12}F_{(12)(34)} - A_1F_{13} - A_2F_{24}}{2A_1}$$

In this example, the special reciprocity relationship for surfaces with different juxtaposition was used. Notice that the limits that would be used in integration are symmetric; therefore, special reciprocity can be used.

Exercises

4.1   Derive an expression for q''_{net} that involves the radiosity J and the total emissive power E. Expand this expression, using the assumption that the absorptance equals the emittance to get q''_{net} as a function of ρ, J, and E_b.

4.2   Assuming that a tungsten surface at 1600°K is irradiated by a black body at 5000°R, that is, $G_\lambda = E_{b\lambda}(5000°R)$, determine $\alpha(1600°K, 5000°R)$ by integration. Compare this value to $\varepsilon(1600°K)$ as given in Appendix 2. Comment on the comparison of $\alpha(1600°K, 5000°R)$ to $\varepsilon(1600°K)$ and $\varepsilon(5000°R)$ as to the most accurate value to be used in a gray approximation.

4.3   Calculate the energy transfer rate between two parallel infinite plates of tungsten if the plate temperatures are 1000°R and 2500°R, using (a) simple gray assumptions, (b) Hottel's approximation, (c) semigray assumptions. Extrapolate Table 4.1 to determine the nongray result for these temperatures.

4.4   Repeat Problem 4.3 (a), (b), and (c) for oxidized brass plates at 200°F and 1000°F.

4.5   Consider the two parallel plates arranged as shown in the accompanying figure. Determine the average configuration factor from the large lower plate to the upper plate by assuming that the configuration factor from each of the four segments indicated is equal to the configuration factor from the differential area in the center of each segment to the smaller upper plate.

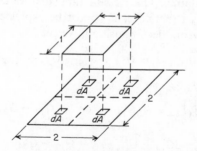

Exercise 4.5

4.6   Using flux algebra, determine the exact configuration factor for the large lower plate to the upper plate in Problem 4.5. Compare this answer to the value obtained by the approximation used in Problem 4.5.

4.7 Using reciprocity relationships, determine the configuration factor between each of the inner walls of a cubic enclosure and a small sphere located in the geometric center of the cube.

4.8 Using the method of contour integration, determine the configuration factor between one of the differential areas and the small upper plate in Problem 4.5. Compare this value with the value given by the exact expression in Appendix 4.

4.9 The semicircular area shown in the accompanying figure is parallel to the x–z plane. Using Sparrow's method of contour integration [8], determine the configuration factor between the differential area dA located at the origin in the x–z plane, and the semicircular area.

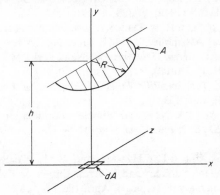

Exercise 4.9

4.10 If both methods of contour integration are considered, the configuration factor from a differential area dA to a semicircular area (as in Problem 4.9) can be obtained for the case when the differential area is tilted through an angle ϕ, where ϕ is the angle between the normal to dA and the y axis. Write $F_{dA \to A}$ as a function of R, h, and ϕ.

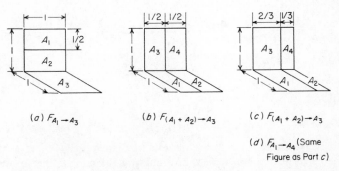

(a) $F_{A_1 \to A_3}$

(b) $F_{(A_1 + A_2) \to A_3}$

(c) $F_{(A_1 + A_2) \to A_3}$

(d) $F_{A_1 \to A_4}$ (Same Figure as Part c)

Exercise 4.11

References

4.11 Using flux algebra methods, determine the configuration factors for the geometries of the accompanying figures.

1. BRANSTETTER, J. R., "Radiant Heat Transfer between Nongray Parallel Plates of Tungsten," NASA TN D–1088, August 1961.
2. BUSCHMAN, A. J., and C. M. PITTMAN, "Configuration Factors for Exchange of Radiant Energy between Axisymmetrical Sections of Cylinders, Cones, and Hemispheres and Their Bases," NASA TN D–944, October 1961.
3. HAMILTON, D. C., and W. R. MORGAN, "Radiant Interchange Configuration Factors," NACA TN 2836, December 1952.
4. HILDEBRAND, F. B., *Advanced Calculus for Engineers*. Englewood Cliffs, N.J.: Prentice-Hall, Inc. (1949), p. 320.
5. LEUENBERGER, H., and R. A. PERSON, "Compilation of Radiation Shape Factors for Cylindrical Assemblies," ASME Paper No. 56–A–144, November 1956.
6. MCADAMS, W. C., *Heat Transmission*. New York: McGraw-Hill, Inc. (1954), chap. 4 (by H. C. Hottel).
7. MOON, PARRY, *The Scientific Basis of Illuminating Engineering*. New York: McGraw-Hill, Inc., 1936.
8. SPARROW, E. M., "A New and Simpler Formulation for Radiative Angle Factors," *ASME Transactions, Journal of Heat Transfer*, vol. 85, series C (1963), p. 81.
9. TRIPP, WILSON, CHING-LAI HWANG, and R. E. CRANK, "Radiation Shape Factors for Plane Surfaces and Spheres, Circles or Cylinders," *Kansas State University Bulletin*, vol. 46, no. 4, April 1962.

CHAPTER 5

Energy Exchange in Gray Enclosures Without Gases

Introduction

The general concepts of energy exchange as introduced in Chapter 4 must be examined in detail, and several practical and theoretical problems of energy exchange must be considered. The methods of energy exchange presented in this chapter will be examined in terms of engineering usefulness and engineering approximations. The integral equations naturally arising in radiation-exchange problems will be examined first. These equations may be solved directly in certain cases, but for the majority of engineering work they must be solved by finite-difference approximations. Finite-difference or numerical schemes for solution will be examined, and recommendations of methods for engineering application will be made.

5.1 Irradiation and Radiosity as Spatial Variables

Irradiation G and radiosity J of surfaces in a normal enclosure are spatial variables. That is, their values are functions of some spatial variable. Since both values are variables, the equation for energy exchange (Equation 4.1 or Equation 4.2) must be handled correctly for finite surface-element areas. For example, the net power input to a surface element with spatial variables x and y would be given from Equation 4.1 as

$$q_{net} = \int_{area} q''_{net} \, dA = \int_x \int_y q''_{net} \, dx \, dy$$

or

$$q_{net} = \int_x \int_y [G(T_s^*) - J(T, T_s^*)] \, dx \, dy \qquad (5.1)$$

From this discussion, it is obvious that both G and J as described in Chapter

95

4 have more independent variables than indicated. That is, Equation 5.1 would imply $G(T_s{}^*, x, y)$ and $J(T, T_s{}^*, x, y)$. Actually there is some duplication of variables, since normally surface temperature is described as $T(x, y)$. Similarly, the surrounds condition as described by the $T_s{}^*$ independent variable is really described by the spatial variables. That is, the enclosure characteristics are the surrounds, and the variables x and y can be used to describe every characteristic.

5.2 Integral Equations of Radiant Transfer

An enclosure as described in a radiant system implies enclosure or space over a surface element. For example, the element on the surface of an enclosure dA located by some spatial coordinates x and y, is shown in Figure 5.1. The

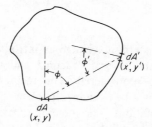

Figure 5.1   Geometry for Intergal Equations.

enclosure for the top of the element dA is anything in view of this top or the half space over the element. Since the entire space is described by one set of spatial variables, the element area dA' located at x', y' is actually described in primed variables only for clarification. With this specification, the irradiation of surface element dA by the entire half space over dA is given by the following expression:

$$G(x, y, T_s{}^*)\, dA = \int_{A'} \frac{I(x', y', T_s{}^*) \cos \phi' \cos \phi\, dA\, dA'}{r^2} \tag{5.2}$$

Equation 5.2 is valid for any characteristic of the intensity $I(x', y', T_s{}^*)$ except for the case when the energy consists of coherent waves. This never occurs in a multiple-source system; since most engineering systems are of this type, it need not be considered. In the case of diffuse emitters and diffuse reflectors, $I(x', y', T_s{}^*)$ can be replaced with $J(x', y', T_s{}^*)/\pi$, and Equation 5.2 becomes

$$G(x, y, T_s{}^*)\, dA = \int_{A'} \frac{J(x', y', T_s{}^*) \cos \phi' \cos \phi\, dA\, dA'}{\pi r^2} \tag{5.3}$$

Since either of the basic energy-exchange equations presented in Chapter 4 may be used to evaluate the net energy-flow rate, Equation 5.3 can be substituted into Equation 4.2, resulting in

$$q''_{net}(x, y) = \alpha(x, y) \int_{A'} \frac{J(x', y', T_s^*) \cos \phi' \cos \phi \, dA'}{\pi r^2} - E(x, y) \quad (5.4)$$

Thus, the net heat flux as a function of x and y can be determined if the function $E(x, y)$ and $J(x', y', T_s^*)$ can be determined. In the usual consideration of a radiant transfer problem solution, it is assumed that $T(x, y)$ and $\varepsilon(x, y)$ are known. This implies that $E(x, y)$ is known, and, of course, since the system is assumed to be gray, $\varepsilon(x, y) = \alpha(x, y)$. Under these conditions the basic quantity that must be determined is $J(x', y', T_s^*)$.

Radiosity is expressed as

$$J(x, y, T_s^*) = \varepsilon(x, y)E_b(x, y) + \rho(x, y)G(x, y, T_s^*)$$

Substituting $G(x, y, T_s^*)$ from Equation 5.3 results in

$$J(x, y, T_s^*) = \varepsilon(x, y)E_b(x, y) + \rho(x, y) \int_{A'} \frac{J(x', y', T_s^*) \cos \phi' \cos \phi \, dA'}{\pi r^2}$$

$$(5.5)$$

This equation is the basic integral equation that must be solved for an enclosure. It is important to note that the solution to the equation is a function of the spatial variables only, that is, the independent variable T_s^* is not actually present in the solution.

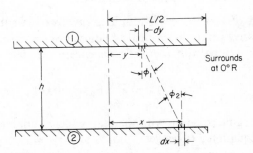

Figure 5.2   Infinite Parallel Plate System.

In certain cases two or more equations of the form of Equation 5.5 arise and must be solved simultaneously. As an example, consider two infinitely long parallel plates as shown in Figure 5.2. Let the temperature along each plate be constant but different values, and the same for the emittance. Then

$$J_1(y) = \varepsilon_1 E_b(T_1) + \rho_1 \int_{A_2} \frac{J_2(x) \cos \phi_2 \cos \phi_1 \, dA_2}{\pi r^2}$$

and

$$J_2(x) = \varepsilon_2 E_b(T_2) + \rho_2 \int_{A_1} \frac{J_1(y) \cos \phi_2 \cos \phi_1 \, dA_1}{\pi r^2}$$

These two equations are solved simultaneously, resulting in the two functions $J_1(y)$ and $J_2(x)$. In an enclosure with many surfaces, many integral equations arise that must be solved simultaneously.

Methods of Solving Integral Equations

The integral equations that naturally occur in radiant transfer problems are of the form

$$u(x) = f(x) + \lambda \int_a^b K(x, t)u(t) \, dt \tag{5.6}$$

This equation is a classical mathematical equation, called a *Fredholm equation of the second kind* [5]. Mathematically, $f(x)$ must be a known real function in the interval of the integration I, where $a \leqslant x \leqslant b$; λ is a constant; and $K(x, t)$, the *kernal*, is a known function. With these conditions satisfied, the Fredholm equation may be solved in several ways. Three methods will be discussed here, not because they are less difficult than other methods but because they appear in heat transfer literature.

5.3 Method of Successive Substitutions

The method of successive substitutions involves the substitution of the function successively into the original equation. For example, let the equation to be solved be written with x as the independent variable:

$$u(x) = f(x) + \lambda \int_a^b K(x, t)u(t) \, dt \tag{5.6}$$

By writing the same equation with the independent variable t and then substituting into equation 5.6, we get

$$u(t) = f(t) + \lambda \int_a^b K(t, t_1)u(t_1) \, dt_1$$

Substituting into Equation 5.6 gives

$$u(x) = f(x) + \lambda \int_a^b K(x, t)f(t) \, dt + \lambda^2 \int_a^b \int_a^b K(x, t)K(t, t_1)u(t_1) \, dt \, dt_1 \tag{5.7}$$

Equation 5.7 is the result after a single substitution. By successively substituting, we get an infinite integral series:

$$u(x) = f(x) + \lambda \int_a^b K(x,t)f(t) \, dt + \lambda^2 \int_a^b \int_a^b K(x,\, t)K(t,\, t_1)f(t_1) \, dt \, dt_1 + \cdots$$

$$+ \lambda^n \left[\int_a^b \right]^n K(x,\, t)K(t,\, t_1) \cdots K(t_{n-2},\, t_{n-1})f(t_{n-1}) \, dt \, dt_1 \cdots dt_{n-1} \quad (5.8)$$

This series will converge to the exact answer if the following criteria is satisfied:

$$|\lambda| < \frac{1}{M(b-a)}$$

where M is the maximum value of the kernal in the rectangle R for which $a \leqslant t \leqslant b$ and $a \leqslant x \leqslant b$ [5].

As an example of the solution of an integral equation by this method, consider the following:

$$u(x) = x + \int_0^x (t - x)u(t) \, dt$$

For this equation, $\lambda = 1$, $M = x$; therefore, the convergence criteria will be satisfied if $x > 1$. Using the infinite series (Equation 5.8), we can write the solution

$$u(x) = x + \int_0^x (t - x)t \, dt + \int_0^x \int_0^x (t - x)(t_1 - t)t_1 \, dt \, dt_1$$

$$+ \int_0^x \int_0^x \int_0^x (t - x)(t_1 - t)(t_2 - t_1)t_2 \, dt \, dt_1 \, dt_2 + \cdots$$

$$u(x) = x - \frac{x^3}{3!} + \frac{x^5}{5!} - \cdots$$

or $u(x) = \sin x$, which can be verified by substitution into the original integral equation.

5.4 Method of Successive Approximations

This method consists of approximating the answer and then improving the approximation. If the initial approximation to the solution of

$$u(x) = f(x) + \lambda \int_a^b K(x,\, t)u(t) \, dt$$

is written as $u^0(x)$, an improved solution [5] is given by

$$u^1(x) = f(x) + \lambda \int_a^b K(x,\, t)u^0(t) \, dt$$

so long as the convergence criteria of Section 5.3 is satisfied. Furthermore,

$$u^n(x) = f(x) + \lambda \int_a^b K(x, t)u^{n-1}(t)\, dt$$

will be the exact solution to the original integral equation.

An example of this type of solution would be to solve

$$u(x) = \frac{5x}{6} + \frac{1}{2} \int_0^1 xtu(t)\, dt$$

In this case, $\lambda = \frac{1}{2}$, $M = 1$, and $b - a = 1$; thus, $|\lambda| < 1/(1 \times 1)$, and therefore the solution is possible by successive approximations. As a first approximation let

$$u^0(x) = \frac{5x}{6}$$

or $f(x)$. In the absence of any other criteria for the first approximation, this is a reasonable choice. Then

$$u^1(x) = \frac{5x}{6} + \frac{1}{2} \int_0^1 (xt)\left(\frac{5t}{6}\right) dt$$

$$u^1(x) = \frac{35}{36} x$$

$$u^2(x) = \frac{5x}{6} \times \frac{1}{2} \int_0^1 xt\left(\frac{35}{36} t\right) dt$$

$$u^2(x) = \frac{215}{216} x$$

$$\vdots \qquad \vdots$$

$$u^n(x) = x$$

Once again the solution can be verified by direct substitution into the original equation.

5.5 Method Using Variational Calculus

The technique of solving Fredholm equations by variational calculus consists of a fitting procedure. Basically, a function $u(x)$ is chosen arbitrarily as the solution of the equation. If the chosen function is a solution, the variational expression I given by Equation 5.9 will be a minimum [3].

$$I = \lambda \int_a^b \int_a^b K(x, t)u(x)u(t)\, dx\, dt - \int_a^b [u(x)]^2\, dx + 2 \int_a^b u(x)f(x)\, dx \quad (5.9)$$

This property can be used to obtain the best solution for a particular problem. A restriction upon the method is that the kernal $K(x, t)$ must be symmetrical, that is, $K(x, t) = K(t, x)$.

As an example of the technique, consider the example problem of the previous section:

$$u(x) = \frac{5x}{6} + \frac{1}{2} \int_0^1 xtu(t) \, dt$$

Let us assume that the solution is given by

$$u(x) = c_1 + c_2 x$$

The variational expression becomes

$$I = \frac{1}{2} \int_0^1 \int_0^1 (xt)(c_1 + c_2 x)(c_1 + c_2 t) \, dx \, dt - \int_0^1 [c_1 + c_2 x]^2 \, dx$$
$$+ 2 \int_2^1 (c_1 + c_2 x) \frac{5x}{6} \, dx$$

or, after integration

$$I = -\frac{7}{8} c_1{}^2 - \frac{5}{6} c_1 c_2 - \frac{5}{18} c_2{}^2 + \frac{5}{6} c_1 + \frac{5}{9} c_2$$

The value of I will be a minimum when the chosen function is a solution. Thus, if

$$\frac{\partial I}{\partial c_1} = 0 \quad \text{and} \quad \frac{\partial I}{\partial c_2} = 0$$

are used to evaluate c_1 and c_2, the best solution possible with the chosen function will result.

Carrying out the partial derivatives and solving for c_1 and c_2, we get $c_1 = 0$, $c_2 = 1$, which makes the chosen function $u(x) = c_1 + c_2 x$, and the exact solution $u(x) = x$. This is a particularly simple problem, and as such, the method results in an exact solution. This should not be expected as a rule.

5.6 *Heat Transfer Example*

An excellent example of the solution of an integral equation resulting from a heat transfer problem is presented by Sparrow [8]. In this paper the problem examined is the energy flux between two parallel plates, as shown in Figure 5.2. In this case, Sparrow let both the upper and lower plates have the same temperature and emittance. This results in equal reflectance values, so that none of the properties need be subscripted in the integral equations. Furthermore, the radiosity function $J_1(x)$ is the same as the radiosity function $J_2(y)$.

The two equations for the system described are

$$J_1(x) = \varepsilon E_b(T_1) + \frac{\rho}{dx} \int_{-L/2}^{L/2} J_2(y)\, dy F_{dy \to dx}$$

$$J_2(y) = \varepsilon E_b(T_2) + \frac{\rho}{dy} \int_{-L/2}^{L/2} J_1(x)\, dx F_{dx \to dy}$$

Using reciprocity for $dy\, F_{dy \to dx}$ and $dx_{dx \to dy}$, the equations become

$$J_1(x) = \varepsilon E_b(T_1) + \rho \int_{-L/2}^{L/2} J_2(y) F_{dx \to dy}$$

$$J_2(y) = \varepsilon E_b(T_1) + \rho \int_{-L/2}^{L/2} J_1(x) F_{dy \to dx}$$

The configuration factor between two infinitely long strips, represented by dx and dy, is given as $(d \sin \phi)/2$ by Jakob [4]. With this expression for the configuration factors, the two integral equations become

$$J(x) = \varepsilon E_b(T) + \rho \int_{-L/2}^{L/2} \left\{ \frac{h^2}{2[(x-y)^2 + h^2]^{3/2}} \right\} J(y)\, dy \qquad (5.10)$$

$$J(y) = \varepsilon E_b(T) + \rho \int_{-L/2}^{L/2} \left\{ \frac{h^2}{2[(x-y)^2 + h^2]^{3/2}} \right\} J(x)\, dx \qquad (5.11)$$

In Equations 5.10 and 5.11, the subscripts on the radiosity and total emissivity terms have been omitted, since the independent variables x and y are sufficient to describe these quantities. Sparrow reduced these two equations to dimensionless variables by defining

$$X = \frac{x}{L} \qquad \beta(X) = \frac{J(x)}{\varepsilon E_b(T)}$$

$$Y = \frac{y}{L} \qquad \beta(Y) = \frac{J(y)}{\varepsilon E_b(T)}$$

$$\gamma = \frac{h}{L}$$

which results in

$$\beta(X) = 1 + \frac{\rho \gamma^2}{2} \int_{-1/2}^{1/2} \frac{\beta(Y)}{[(X-Y)^2 + \gamma^2]^{3/2}}\, dY \qquad (5.12)$$

and

$$\beta(Y) = 1 + \frac{\rho \gamma^2}{2} \int_{-1/2}^{1/2} \frac{\beta(X)}{[(Y-X)^2 + \gamma^2]^{3/2}}\, dX \qquad (5.13)$$

Equations 5.12 and 5.13 are actually the same equation, since $\beta(X) = \beta(Y)$

TABLE 5.1†
Comparison of $\beta(X)$ from Various Computations

		(a) $\gamma = 1$, $\rho = 0.9$				
X	0	0.1	0.2	0.3	0.4	0.5
Quadratic	1.642	1.627	1.620	1.592	1.554	1.504
Exact	1.644	1.638	1.620	1.590	1.552	1.508

		(b) $\gamma = 0.5$, $\rho = 0.9$				
X	0	0.1	0.2	0.3	0.4	0.5
Quadratic	2.479	2.455	2.384	2.266	2.100	1.887
Quartic	2.486	2.460	2.382	2.258	2.096	1.905
Exact	2.485	2.459	2.383	2.259	2.095	1.908

		(c) $\gamma = 0.1$, $\rho = 0.9$				
X	0	0.1	0.2	0.3	0.4	0.5
Quadratic	7.39	7.22	6.73	5.90	4.74	3.25
Quartic	7.21	7.10	6.76	6.07	4.88	2.95
Exact	7.22	7.11	6.75	6.07	4.90	2.97

Numerical Values of C_n and D_n

(a) Values of C_1 and C_2 for quadratic equation (5.14)

	$\gamma = 1$		$\gamma = 0.5$		$\gamma = 0.1$	
ε	C_1	$-C_2$	C_1	$-C_2$	C_1	$-C_2$
0.1	1.642	0.5549	2.479	2.367	7.388	16.54
0.3	1.441	0.3801	1.890	1.403	3.192	4.726
0.5	1.282	0.2423	1.518	0.8045	1.992	1.832
0.7	1.153	0.1315	1.262	0.4013	1.433	0.6996
0.9	1.047	0.03998	1.075	0.1139	1.113	0.1624

(b) Values of D_1, D_2, and D_3 for quartic equation (5.15)

	$\gamma = 0.5$			$\gamma = 0.1$		
ε	D_1	$-D_2$	D_3	D_1	$-D_2$	$-D_3$
0.1	2.486	2.644	1.284	7.205	10.06	27.81
0.3	1.893	1.548	0.6726	3.095	1.128	15.92
0.5	1.519	0.8754	0.3306	1.942	−0.06314	8.564
0.7	1.263	0.4322	0.1440	1.411	−0.1774	4.024
0.9	1.076	0.1210	0.03261	1.107	−0.06997	1.079

† E. M. Sparrow, "Application of Variational Methods to Radiation Heat Transfer Calculations," *ASME Transactions, Journal of Heat Transfer*, vol. 82, series C (1960), pp. 375–380.

for the problem described. Either equation is a Fredholm equation, and since the kernals are symmetrical, either may be solved by the variational technique.

Sparrow did this assuming two power series solutions. These are

$$\beta(X) = C_1 + C_2 X^2 \tag{5.14}$$

$$\beta(X) = D_1 + D_2 X^2 + D_3 X^4 \tag{5.15}$$

Both equations are even functions as dictated by the geometry of the problem. The results obtained by Sparrow appear in Table 5.1, in which $\beta(X)$ values obtained by Equation 5.14 are called *quadratic*, values from Equation 5.15 *quartic*, and values obtained by digital computer *exact*.

Once the solution for $J(x)$ or the dimensionless $\beta(X)$ is obtained, the local heat flux is calculated from $q''(x) = G(x) - J(x)$ by substituting

$$G(x) = \frac{J(x) - E(x)}{\rho}$$

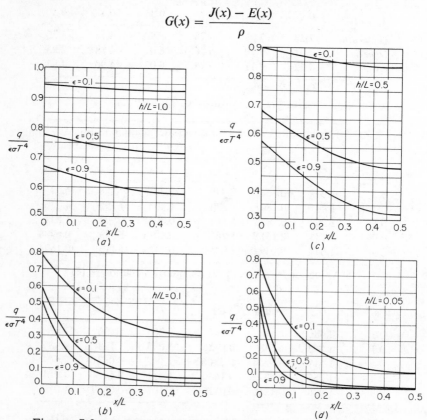

Figure 5.3 Local Heat-transfer Results for a Parallel Plate System (a) Spacing Ratio $h/L = 1.0$ (b) Spacing Ratio $h/L = 0.1$ (c) Spacing Ratio $h/L = 0.5$ (d) Spacing Ratio $h/L = 0.05$.

This results in

$$q''(x) = \frac{\alpha J(x) - E(x)}{\rho}$$

or, if both sides are divided by $E(x)$, in

$$\frac{q''(x)}{E(x)} = \frac{q''(x)}{\varepsilon \sigma T^4} = \frac{1}{\rho} [\alpha \beta(X) - 1] \tag{5.16}$$

The total heat flux to the surface or the dimensionless heat flux is given by

$$\frac{Q/L}{\varepsilon \sigma T^4} = \frac{1}{L} \int_{-L/2}^{L/2} \frac{q''(x)}{\varepsilon \sigma T^4} dx = \int_{-1/2}^{1/2} \frac{1}{\rho} [\alpha \beta(X) - 1] \, dx \tag{5.17}$$

Values obtained from Equation 5.16 are plotted in Figure 5.3, which is presented in [9]. Values of the total heat flux or total heat transfer as calculated from Equation 5.17 appear in Table 5.2. Values calculated from

$$\frac{Q/L}{\sigma T^4} = \frac{\varepsilon(1 - F)}{1 - \rho F} \tag{5.18}$$

where F is the configuration factor between the plates, are also tabulated. This equation assumes constant radiosity across the plate surfaces and is a simplified approach to the calculation since it is not necessary to solve an integral equation to obtain this value. It is interesting and important to notice

TABLE 5.2†
Heat Transfer Results, $(Q/L)/\sigma T^4$

h/L	$\varepsilon = 0.1$		$\varepsilon = 0.5$		$\varepsilon = 0.9$	
	(5.17)	(5.18)	5.17	5.18	5.17	5.18
1.0	0.09338	0.09340	0.3629	0.3694	0.5500	0.5500
0.5	0.08576	0.08607	0.2747	0.2764	0.3658	0.3664
0.1	0.0442	0.05122	0.07964	0.08677	0.09269	0.09402
0.05	0.0252	0.03388	0.04128	0.04649	0.04751	0.04848

† E. M. Sparrow, "Application of Variational Methods to Radiation Heat Transfer Calculations," *ASME Transactions, Journal of Heat Transfer*, vol. 82, series C (1960), pp. 375–380.

that in most cases, the heat transfer results are practically the same for the two methods. Of course, this implies that the simplified method should be used whenever possible. This point will be discussed further later and will be examined in detail in some problems.

Finite-Difference Approximations for Integral Equations

The integral equations presented in the previous section are usually very difficult to solve even for the most simple geometric systems. For this reason, most engineering solutions are accomplished by finite-difference approximations for integral equations. Basically, the finite-difference approach consists of considering the radiosity constant over some finite-size subarea. This type of approximation can be made to closely approach the solution for the integral equations by using many subarea elements.

5.7 Integral Equations Leading to the Network Concept

If an enclosure consists of n diffuse surface elements, each of which has different temperatures and emittances, the integral equation for the net heat transfer at the jth surface element is

$$q_{\text{net}_j} = \left\{ \sum_{k=1}^{n} \int_{A_k} J_k F_{dA_k \to A_j} \, dA_k \right\} - \int_{A_j} J_j \, dA_j \qquad (5.19)$$

where J_k represents the function J (area of the kth element).

In order to determine the net heat transfer from Equation 5.19, we must determine the radiosity functions J_j from the following n integral equations:

$$J_j = E_j + \rho_j \left\{ \frac{1}{A_j} \sum_{k=1}^{n} \int_{A_k} J_k F_{dA_k \to A_j} \, dA_k \right\} \qquad j = 1, 2, 3, \dots n \quad (5.20)$$

Obviously, such a system is difficult to solve analytically except in simple cases. Generally, the finite difference assumption that J_k is constant over some area element ΔA_k, or simply A_k is used. With this assumption, Equation 5.20 becomes

$$J_j = E_j + \rho_j \sum_{k=1}^{n} J_k F_{A_j \to A_k} \qquad j = 1, 2, 3, \dots n \qquad (5.21)$$

Similarly, Equation 5.19 becomes

$$q_{\text{net}_j} = \left\{ \sum_{k=1}^{n} J_k F_{A_k \to A_j} A_k \right\} - J_j A_j \qquad (5.22)$$

Using the symbolism $F_{kj} = F_{A_k \to A_j}$ and noting that

$$\sum_{k=1}^{n} F_{jk} = 1.0$$

we can write Equation 5.22 as

$$q_{\text{net}_j} = \sum_{k=1}^{n} (J_k - J_j) F_{jk} A_j \qquad (5.23)$$

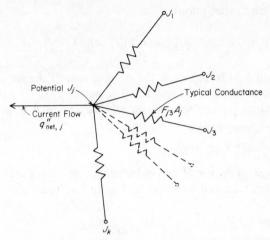

Figure 5.4   Network Representation of a Radiant System.

Equation 5.23 can be interpreted as an electrical network [7]. In this network, the potential differences are represented by $(J_k - J_j)$, the conductances by $F_{jk}A_j$, and the current flow by q_{net_j}. This is illustrated in Figure 5.4.

This network is not complete until the network arm for the current flow is developed. From $q'' = \alpha G - E$

$$q_{net_j} = \alpha_j G_j A_j - E_j A_j \qquad \text{but} \qquad J_j = E_j + \rho_j G_j$$

therefore

$$q_{net_j} = \frac{1}{\rho_j}(\alpha_j J_j A_j - E_j A_j)$$

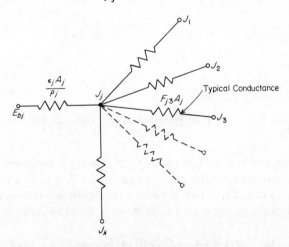

Figure 5.5   Complete Network Representation of a Radiant System.

or, if $\varepsilon_j = \alpha_j$ (gray assumption),

$$q_{net_j} = \frac{\varepsilon_j A_j}{\rho_j}(J_j - E_{b_j}) \tag{5.24}$$

Using Equation 5.24 to represent the missing arm of the network of Figure 5.4, we get the network of Figure 5.5. The networks of Figures 5.4 and 5.5 are handy analogs for radiant transfer and may be used as memory aids.

5.8 Network Examples

As an example of the use of networks for radiant-energy exchange, consider two finite plates arranged as shown in Figure 5.6. These plates are arranged

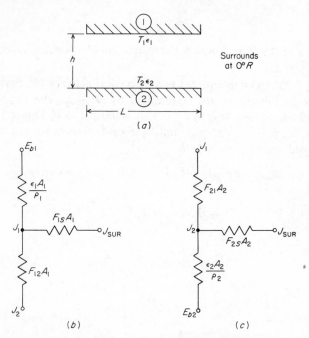

Figure 5.6 (a) Finite Plate System (b) Network for J_1 (c) Network for J_2.

in the same manner as the plates in the integral equation solution. The individual networks for the two radiosity nodes J_1 and J_2 are also shown in Figure 5.6. From these two networks the following two equations result, if the sum of the currents to a node point is equal to zero:

$$(E_{b_1} - J_1)\frac{\varepsilon_1 A_1}{\rho_1} + (J_2 - J_1)A_1 F_{12} + (J_s - J_1)A_1 F_{1s} = 0$$

and

$$(E_{b_2} - J_2)\frac{\varepsilon_2 A_2}{\rho_2} + (J_1 - J_2)A_2 F_{21} + (J_s - J_2)A_2 F_{2s} = 0$$

Since T_1, T_2, ε_1, ε_2, and the values of the configuration factors are known, the two equations above have the three radiosities J_1, J_2, and J_s as unknowns. However, by assumption, the surrounds are at $0°R$; thus, $J_s = 0$. Therefore, the two equations have only the two unknowns J_1 and J_2, which can be evaluated in terms of the remaining parameters. When J_1 and J_2 are known, the net heat transfer from the plates q_{net_1} or q_{net_2} are evaluated as the current flow through the $\varepsilon A/\rho$ resistors. That is

$$q_{net_1} = (J_1 - E_{b_1})\frac{\varepsilon_1 A_1}{\rho_1}$$

and

$$q_{net_2} = (J_2 - E_{b_2})\frac{\varepsilon_2 A_2}{\rho_2}$$

A numerical example will point out some very important facts about the nomenclature used in radiant heat transfer. In the system of Figure 5.6, let $h = L = 1.0$, $T_1 = 1000°R$, $T_2 = 1200°R$, $\varepsilon_1 = 0.3$, $\varepsilon_2 = 0.6$. With these dimensions the configuration factor between plates 1 and 2 can be calculated by using the crossed-string method, resulting in $F_{12} = F_{21} = 0.414$ and $F_{1s} = F_{2s} = 0.586$. Assuming $A_1 = A_2 = 1.0$, we have a complete network with conductance values, as shown in Figure 5.7. In the solution of this network the values of J_1 and J_2 were calculated as 1189 and 2326 respectively.

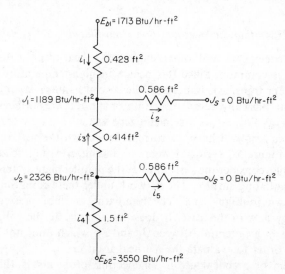

Figure 5.7   Numerical Network Example.

The currents shown on the resistors can be calculated from the potentials and conductance values as

$$i_1 = (1713 \times 1189)\,(0.428) = 225 \text{ Btu per hr}$$

$$i_2 = (1189 - 0)\,(0.586) = 696 \text{ Btu per hr}$$

$$i_3 = (2326 - 1189)\,(0.414) = 470 \text{ Btu per hr}$$

$$i_4 = (3550 - 2326)\,(1.5) = 1836 \text{ Btu per hr}$$

The individual currents may be interpreted as follows: First, i_1 and i_4 are the negatives of q_{net_1} and q_{net_2} respectively. That is, each surface must be supplied with this energy rate in order to maintain the temperature indicated. The energy flow i_3 is energy from surface 2 but does not represent any measureable energy. In some cases, this energy might be specified as the net energy flow between surfaces 1 and 2, written as $q_{1 \rightleftharpoons 2}$ or $q_{2 \rightleftharpoons 1}$. (This technique was widely used before the network system of analysis was introduced.) Notice that the net gain or loss of a surface is given by the sum of the net flow between surfaces, that is,

$$q_{net_2} = q_{1 \rightleftharpoons 2} + q_{sur \rightleftharpoons 2}$$

and

$$q_{net_1} = q_{2 \rightleftharpoons 1} + q_{sur \rightleftharpoons 1}$$

In these two expressions, q_{net} is positive if a surface is gaining energy. Frequently, the opposite sign convention is used, resulting in reversed subscripts. Since many different notations are used in radiant transfer analysis, care must be exercised to determine the physical meaning of the terminology.

5.9 Reradiating Surfaces and Radiation Shields

In furnace enclosures and other engineering heat-transfer devices, the insulated wall is common. Since this occurs in high-temperature apparatus for which radiant transfer is important, the special name *reradiating surfaces* is used for them. Basically, reradiating walls or surfaces are surfaces for which the radiant energy flow q_{net} is assigned a zero value. In a network, a surface for which q_{net} is zero will have no current flow down the first resistor. For example, if in Figure 5.7 surface 1 were reradiating, i_1 would be zero.

As an example, consider the surrounds of the parallel plate system of Figure 5.6 to be a reradiating surface. The network under these conditions could be drawn as shown in Figure 5.8. The reradiating surface presents another path for energy flow in this case. It does not complicate the solution, since the node floats at a potential between J_1 and J_2, which does not have to be determined in order to evaluate the net heat transfer.

Another item of practical use in engineering problems is the *radiation shield*, usually a very thin metallic shield interposed between two surfaces

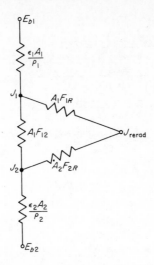

Figure 5.8   Network for a System with a Reradiating Surface.

to reduce the radiant transfer. Since the shield is very thin, it may be considered to be an isothermal system. Isothermal shields are analyzed (using the network method) as follows:

Consider two infinite parallel plates with temperatures T_1 and T_2 and emittances ε_1 and ε_2 respectively. The network for transfer between these two plates would be represented as in Figure 5.9. Since all of the energy that leaves surface 1 is incident upon surface 2, $F_{12} = 1.0$. If unit areas are used, the energy transfer between the two plates when the shield is not present is

$$q_{\mathrm{net}_1} = \frac{(E_{b_2} - E_{b_1})}{(\rho_2/\varepsilon_2) + (\rho_1/\varepsilon_1) + 1} \tag{5.25}$$

If the shield is inserted, it is

$$q_{\mathrm{net}_1} = \frac{(E_{b_2} - E_{b_1})}{(\rho_1/\varepsilon_1) + 1 + (\rho_{s_1}/\varepsilon_{s_1}) + (\rho_{s_2}/\varepsilon_{s_2}) + 1 + (\rho_2/\varepsilon_2)} \tag{5.26}$$

Notice that, if the surfaces are black and the shield is black on both sides, the net energy flow is reduced by one half. Under the usual conditions of highly reflective shield surfaces, the energy flow is reduced very much more than one half.

5.10 The Iteration Technique for Solving Radiation Equations

The usual engineering radiation-heat-transfer problem is reduced to a finite number of constant radiosity surfaces. After the system and system

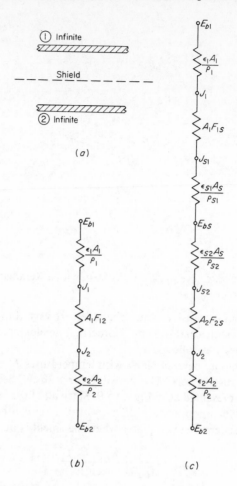

Figure 5.9 Networks for (a) a Parallel Plate System (b) without a Shield (c) with a Shield.

properties are specified, a large number of equations must be solved simultaneously. Since the accuracy of the finite-difference approach to system solution is improved with increased subdivision, there is a tendency to use many surfaces, which results in many equations to be solved. A technique convenient for hand calculation or digital computer solution is the *iteration technique* of reference [1].

This method involves the use of Equation 5.21, rewritten as follows:

$$J_j = \left[\frac{\varepsilon_j}{1 - \rho_j F_{jj}}\right] E_{b_j} + \left[\frac{\rho_j}{1 - \varepsilon_j F_{jj}}\right] \sum_{\substack{k=1 \\ k \neq j}}^{n} J_k F_{jk} \qquad (5.27)$$

Equation 5.27 is used for either a source or sink surface element, but for reradiating surfaces Equation 5.27 is rewritten. Note that for a reradiating surface, $q_{net} = 0$; thus, Equation 5.27 becomes

$$J_j = \left[\frac{1}{1 - F_{jj}} \right] \sum_{\substack{k=1 \\ k \neq j}}^{n} J_k F_{jk} \qquad (5.28)$$

Equations 5.27 and 5.28 are used to iterate the values of the radiosity for each surface. The nature of the equation system is such that they will converge to the exact solution, and usually the convergence is rapid. An example of this method is as follows:

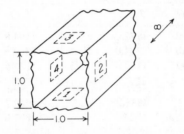

Figure 5.10   System Geometry for Example.

In Figure 5.10 an infinite square duct is shown. Let the system be described as a four-surface system, that is, let each of the sides of the duct be considered to have constant radiosity. In order to illustrate the method, the following information will be assumed for the example:

$$T_1 = 1000°R \qquad \varepsilon_1 = 0.6 \qquad E_{b_1} = 1713 \text{ Btu per hr-ft}^2$$

$$T_2 = 1200°R \qquad \varepsilon_2 = 0.7 \qquad E_{b_2} = 3552 \text{ Btu per hr-ft}^2$$

$$T_3 = 1400°R \qquad \varepsilon_3 = 0.8 \qquad E_{b_3} = 6581 \text{ Btu per hr-ft}^2$$

$$\varepsilon_4 = 0.3$$

Surface 4 insulated or reradiating

The procedure is to assume the value of the radiosity for each node and then improve the value by iteration, as shown in Table 5.3. Notice how rapidly the values of the radiosity converge. Actually, the values of trials 3 and 4 are very nearly the same; three iterations would be sufficient to obtain the radiosities in this example.

The heat transfer per node can be calculated from the tabulation by using

$$q''_{net_j} = \left[\sum_{\substack{k=1 \\ k \neq j}}^{n} J_k F_{jk} \right] - J_j$$

if none of the nodes "see" themselves, that is, $F_{jj} = 0$. For the example this is true; thus

$$q''_{\text{net}_1} = 4809.3 - 2951.5 = 1857.8 \text{ Btu per hr ft}^2$$

TABLE 5.3

Example Iteration Table

Node pair j–k	F_{jk}	Trial 1		Trial 2		Trial 3	
		J_k	J_kF_{jk}	J_k	J_kF_{jk}	J_k	J_kF_{jk}
1–2	0.293	4000	1172.0	3770.7	1104.8	3788.4	1110.0
1–3	0.414	6000	2484.0	5965.2	2469.6	5975.5	2473.8
1–4	0.293	4000	1172.0	4175.9	1223.5	4182.7	1225.5
	ΣJ_kF_jk		4828.0		4797.9		4809.3
	$\rho_1\Sigma J_jk$		1931.2		1919.2		1923.7
	ε_1E_{b1}		1027.8		1027.8		1027.8
	J_1		2959.0		2947.0		2951.5
2–1	0.293	2959	867.0	2947.0	863.5	2951.5	864.8
2–3	0.293	6000	1758.0	5965.2	1747.8	5975.5	1750.8
2–4	0.414	4000	1656.0	4175.9	1728.8	4182.7	1731.6
	ΣJ_kF_{jk}		4281.0		4340.1		4347.0
	$\rho_2\Sigma J_kF_{jk}$		1284.3		1302.0		1304.1
	ε_2E_{b2}		2486.4		2486.4		2486.4
	J_2		3770.7		3788.4		3790.5
3–1	0.414	2959.0	1225.0	2947.0	1220.0	2951.5	1221.9
3–2	0.293	3770.7	1104.8	3788.4	1110.0	3790.5	1110.6
3–4	0.293	4000.0	1172.0	4175.9	1223.5	4182.7	1225.5
	ΣJ_kF_{jk}		3501.8		3553.5		3558.0
	$\rho_3 \Sigma J_kF_{jk}$		700.4		710.7		711.6
	ε_3E_{b3}		5264.8		5264.8		5264.8
	J_3		5965.2		5975.5		5976.4
4–1	0.293	2959.0	867.0	2947.0	863.5	2951.5	864.8
4–2	0.414	3770.7	1561.1	3788.4	1568.4	3790.5	1569.3
4–3	0.293	5965.2	1747.8	5975.5	1750.8	5976.4	1751.1
	ΣJ_kF_{jk}		4175.9		4182.7		4185.2

$$q''_{net_2} = 4347.0 - 3790.5 = 556.5 \text{ Btu per hr ft}^2$$

$$q''_{net_3} = 3558.0 - 5976.4 = -2418.4 \text{ Btu per hr ft}^2$$

$$q''_{net_4} = 0 \text{ (reradiating)}$$

Since the system is symmetrical, that is, $A_1 = A_2 = A_3$, the sum of the heat fluxes add to zero if the solution is correct.

In some cases, it may be convenient to determine the temperature of the reradiating surface. This may be done by using $q''_{net} = \alpha_4 G_4 - \varepsilon_4 E_{b4}$. In the gray assumption case, this yields $E_{b4} = G_4$, regardless of the surface emittance. For the example, G_4 is given by the sum

$$\sum_{\substack{k=1 \\ k \neq j}}^{n} J_k F_{jk}$$

since $F_{44} = 0$. The surface temperature is

$$E_{b4} = \sigma T_4^4 = 4185.2 \text{ Btu per hr ft}^2$$

$$T_4 = 1250^\circ \text{R}$$

Computational Techniques for Radiant Systems

The computational technique described in Section 5.10 is not always the most convenient method. In certain cases, the techniques introduced by Hottel in [6] or by Gebhart [2] are useful. These two methods, plus a few comments on application of the network method, will be discussed in this section.

5.11 Hottel's Method

For the method described by Hottel in [6], the terminology $q_{1 \to 2}$ and $q_{1 \rightleftarrows 2}$ are required. The symbol $q_{1 \to 2}$ means the total energy flow in Btu per hour from surface element 1 that is absorbed by surface element 2. The symbol $q_{1 \rightleftarrows 2}$, defined from $q_{1 \rightleftarrows 2} = q_{2 \to 1} - q_{1 \to 2}$, is the total energy exchange between surfaces 1 and 2. The relationship between q_{net_1} and the term $q_{1 \rightleftarrows k}$ is given by

$$q_{net_1} = \sum_{k=1}^{n} q_{k \rightleftarrows 1}$$

in an n surface enclosure. Recalling that q_{net_1} is the heat transfer from the surface, we can see that $q_{1 \rightleftarrows 2}$ values are computational, not actual, energy terms. From these energy quantities, another definition is introduced:

$$q_{1 \to 2} = \mathscr{F}_{12} A_1 E_{b_1} \tag{5.29}$$

where $\mathscr{F}_{12}$ is the fraction of the energy emitted by surface 1 (if it is assumed to be a black surface) absorbed by surface 2. The quantity $\mathscr{F}_{12}$ depends on the geometric arrangement of all the surfaces that make up the enclosure and on the total emittance of all the surfaces (gray surfaces, $\varepsilon = \alpha$, are assumed to be present).

The basic method depends on determining or proving the following three statements:

(a) Determination of $\mathscr{F}_{jk}$

(b) $A_k \mathscr{F}_{kj} = A_j \mathscr{F}_{jk}$

(c) $\sum_{k=1}^{n} \mathscr{F}_{jk} = \varepsilon_j$

The determination of $\mathscr{F}_{jk}$ is carried out as follows: First, consider an enclosure with n surfaces, each of which has a known temperature T_n and a known emittance ε_n. If reradiating sufaces occur in the enclosure, the emittance may be assumed to be zero, and the temperature does not have to be known. As a calculation operation, assume that all the surfaces in the enclosure have a temperature of zero absolute except surface 1 (assuming $\mathscr{F}_{1k}$ is to be evaluated). With this assumption, any energy received by a surface is energy emitted by surface 1. Furthermore, the energy absorbed (q_{net_k} or $q_{1 \to k}$) can be evaluated from

$$q_{\text{net}_k} = q_{1 \to k} = (G_k - J_k)A_k \tag{5.30}$$

Since the kth surface is assumed to have a temperature of zero absolute

$$\rho_k G_k = J_k \tag{5.31}$$

Notice that Equation 5.31 is valid only if the surface does not emit any energy. For convenience in this procedure, Hottel defined the *radiosity* of the surface as *the energy leaving a surface as a result of the energy emitted by surface 1.* This definition is not the same as our previous definition. For any surface other than surface 1, the radiosity is the same as our previous definition; however, for surface 1, the total outgoing energy is $(E_1 + J_1)$. Examination shows that Hottel's special radiosity really includes only the energy reflecting around in the enclosure due to the original emission from surface 1. With this definition

$$\rho_1 G_1 = J_1 \tag{5.32}$$

The irradiation G of a surface is given by

$$G_k A_k = (E_1 + J_1) F_{11}A_1 + J_2 F_{21}A_2 + \cdots + J_n F_{n1}A_n \tag{5.33}$$

Now the following equations can be written for the n surfaces:

$$\rho_1[(E_1 + J_1) F_{11}A_1 + J_2F_{21}A_2 + \cdots + J_nF_{n1}A_n] = A_1J_1$$

$$\rho_2[(E_1 + J_1) F_{12}A_1 + J_2F_{22}A_2 + \cdots + J_nF_{n2}A_n] = A_2J_2$$

$$\vdots \qquad \vdots \qquad \vdots \qquad \vdots \qquad \vdots$$

$$\rho_n[(E_1 + J_1) F_{1n}A_1 + J_2F_{2n}A_2 + \cdots + J_nF_{nn}A_{nn}] = A_nJ_n \qquad (5.34)$$

Equations 5.34 can be put into a more convenient form by using $F_{jk}A_j = G_{jk}$ and writing an augmented matrix:

$$
\begin{array}{ccccc|c}
J_1 & J_2 & J_3 \cdots J_n & & & \text{constant} \\
\end{array}
$$

$$
\left|
\begin{array}{cccc}
G_{11} - (A_1/\rho_1) & G_{21} & G_{31} & G_{n1} \\
G_{12} & G_{22} - (A_2/\rho_2) & G_{32} & G_{n2} \\
G_{13} & G_{23} & . & . \\
. & . & . & . \\
. & . & . & . \\
G_{1n} & G_{2n} & G_{3n} \, G_{nn} - (A_n/\rho_n)
\end{array}
\right|
\left|
\begin{array}{c}
-G_{11}\varepsilon_1 E_{b_1} \\
-G_{12}\varepsilon_1 E_{b_1} \\
. \\
. \\
. \\
-G_{1n}\varepsilon_1 E_{b_1}
\end{array}
\right|
\qquad (5.35)
$$

The n equations represented by Equation 5.35 can be solved by using the coefficient determinate D and the determinate $_1D_n$, where

$$
D =
\begin{vmatrix}
G_{11} - (A_1/\rho_1) & & G_{21}\cdots\cdots\cdots & G_{n1} \\
G_{12} & & G_{22} - (A_2/\rho_2) & \cdots\cdots & G_{2n} \\
\vdots & & \vdots & & \vdots \\
G_{1n} & & G_{2n} & & G_{nn} - (A_n/\rho_n)
\end{vmatrix}
\qquad (5.36)
$$

$_1D_n$ is the coefficient determinate, and the nth column is replaced by the constant column given in Equation 5.35. Then $J_n = {}_1D_n/D$, or, as Hottel writes it, $_1J_n = {}_1D_n/D$, where the subscript before J_n indicates that J_n is from energy originally emitted by source 1.

Now, using Equations 5.30 and 5.31, we get

$$q_{1 \to k} = (J_k/\rho_k - J_k)A_k$$

or

$$q_{1 \to k} = \frac{\alpha_k A_k J_k}{\rho_k} \qquad (5.37)$$

using Hottel's notation. Therefore

$$q_{1 \to k} = \frac{\alpha_k}{\rho_k} A_k \frac{_1D_k}{D} \qquad (5.38)$$

or

$$\mathscr{F}_{1k}A_1 E_{b1} = \frac{\alpha_k A_k}{\rho_k} \frac{_1D_k}{D}$$

$$\mathscr{F}_{1k}A_1 = \frac{\alpha_k A_k}{\rho_k E_{b1}} \frac{_1D_k}{D} \qquad (5.39)$$

When the determinate $_1D_k$ is written, it will be noted that the constant or k column has $\varepsilon_1 E_{b1}$ in every element. This may be factored out of the determinate. If the symbol $_1D_k'$ is used for the determinate with this term removed, $_1D_k = \varepsilon_1 E_{b_11} D_k'$, and Equation 5.39 becomes

$$\mathscr{F}_{1k} = \frac{\alpha_k \varepsilon_1 A_k}{\rho_k A_1} \frac{_1D_k'}{D} \tag{5.40}$$

Equation 5.40 is in the form used by Hottel, which has the advantage of not depending upon the temperature of surface 1.

In the calculation of the determinate of the form $_jD_k'$, simplification occurs, which can be seen from the following: Let the determinate $_1D_3'$ be evaluated.

$$_1D_3' = \begin{vmatrix} G_{11} - \dfrac{A_1}{\rho_1} & G_{21} & G_{11} \\[2mm] G_{12} & G_{22} - \dfrac{A_2}{\rho_3} & G_{12} \\[2mm] G_{13} & G_{23} & G_{13} \end{vmatrix} = \begin{vmatrix} -\dfrac{A_1}{\rho_1} & G_{21} & G_{11} \\[2mm] 0 & G_{22} - \dfrac{A_2}{\rho_2} & G_{12} \\[2mm] 0 & G_{23} & G_{13} \end{vmatrix}$$

$$= \frac{-A_1}{\rho_1} \begin{vmatrix} G_{22} - \dfrac{A_2}{\rho_2} & G_{12} \\[2mm] G_{23} & G_{13} \end{vmatrix}$$

This is typical of any determinate; thus, an n^2 determinate becomes an $(n-1)^2$ determinate. Furthermore, if the determinate $_3D_1'$ is written, it will be

$$_3D_1' = -\frac{A_3}{\rho_3} \begin{vmatrix} G_{31} & G_{21} \\[2mm] G_{32} & G_{22} - \dfrac{A_2}{\rho_2} \end{vmatrix}$$

which shows that $(\rho_3 \, _3D_1')/A_3 = (\rho_1 \, _1D_3')/A_1$. Although this does not prove the following, the skew symmetry of $_jD_k'$ determinates will always give $(\rho_j \, _jD_k')/A_j = (\rho_k \, _kD_j')/A_k$. Using this expression in conjunction with Equation 5.40 results in

$$\mathscr{F}_{jk} A_j \alpha_j \varepsilon_k = \mathscr{F}_{kj} A_k \alpha_k \varepsilon_j \tag{5.41}$$

Since the assumption $\varepsilon = \alpha$ is the normal gray surface assumption, Equation 5.41 reduces to

$$\boxed{\mathscr{F}_{jk} A_j = \mathscr{F}_{kj} A_k} \tag{5.42}$$

The final requirement of Hottel's method is to show that

$$\sum_{k=1}^{n} \mathscr{F}_{jk} = \varepsilon_j$$

This may be proved by considering the meaning of $q_{j \to k}$. As defined, this is the energy leaving surface j that is absorbed by surface k. If we sum all of these energy flows

$$\sum_{k=1}^{n} q_{j \to k}$$

for all of the surfaces in the enclosure, the summation must equal all of the energy emitted by surface element j.

$$\sum_{k=1}^{n} q_{j \to k} = \varepsilon_j E_{b_j} A_j \qquad (5.42)$$

With Equation 5.29, this becomes

$$\sum_{k=1}^{n} \mathscr{F}_{jk} = \varepsilon_j \qquad (5.43)$$

5.12 Example of Hottel's Method

As an example of the use of Hottel's method, consider the system of the example described in Section 5.10. This four-surface system has the following properties:

Surface	Area	Emittance	Temperature	Characteristic
1	1.0	0.6	1000°R	Source
2	1.0	0.7	1200°R	Source
3	1.0	0.8	1400°R	Source
4	1.0	0.3	?	Reradiating

Configuration Factors

$F_{11} = 0$	$F_{21} = 0.293$	$F_{31} = 0.293$	$F_{41} = 0.414$
$F_{12} = 0.293$	$F_{22} = 0$	$F_{32} = 0.414$	$F_{42} = 0.293$
$F_{13} = 0.293$	$F_{23} = 0.414$	$F_{33} = 0$	$F_{43} = 0.293$
$F_{14} = 0.414$	$F_{24} = 0.293$	$F_{34} = 0.293$	$F_{44} = 0$

From this information the determinate D is found to be

$$D = \begin{vmatrix} -2.5 & 0.293 & 0.293 & 0.414 \\ 0.293 & -3.33 & 0.414 & 0.293 \\ 0.293 & 0.414 & -5.00 & 0.293 \\ 0.414 & 0.293 & 0.293 & -1.43 \end{vmatrix} = -52.52$$

and the determinate $_1 D_2'$ is found to be

$$_1 D_2' = \begin{vmatrix} -2.5 & 0 & 0.293 & 0.414 \\ 0.293 & 0.293 & 0.414 & 0.293 \\ 0.293 & 0.293 & -5.00 & 0.293 \\ 0.414 & 0.414 & 0.293 & -1.43 \end{vmatrix} = -7.31$$

Then, with Equation 5.40, the $\mathscr{F}$ value is

$$\mathscr{F}_{12} = \frac{\alpha_2 \varepsilon_1 A_2}{\rho_2 A_1} \frac{{}_1 D_2{}'}{D} = \frac{(0.7)(0.6)(1.0)}{(0.3)(1.0)} \frac{-7.31}{-52.52} = 0.0195$$

In the same manner $\mathscr{F}_{13}$ and $\mathscr{F}_{14}$ are calculated as $\mathscr{F}_{13} = 0.2715$, $\mathscr{F}_{14} = 0.0726$. Then $\mathscr{F}_{11}$ is calculated from Equation 5.43 as $\mathscr{F}_{11} = \varepsilon_1 - \mathscr{F}_{12} - \mathscr{F}_{13} - \mathscr{F}_{14} = 0.0614$. By reciprocity, $\mathscr{F}_{12}A_1 = \mathscr{F}_{21}A_2$; thus, $\mathscr{F}_{21} = 0.1945$, $\mathscr{F}_{31} = 0.2715$, and $\mathscr{F}_{41} = 0.0726$. Continuing this process, all of the $\mathscr{F}$ factors are determined, resulting in the following values:

$\mathscr{F}_{11} = 0.0614$	$\mathscr{F}_{21} = 0.1945$	$\mathscr{F}_{31} = 0.2715$	$\mathscr{F}_{41} = 0.0727$
$\mathscr{F}_{12} = 0.1945$	$\mathscr{F}_{22} = 0.1157$	$\mathscr{F}_{32} = 0.2792$	$\mathscr{F}_{42} = 0.1106$
$\mathscr{F}_{13} = 0.2715$	$\mathscr{F}_{23} = 0.2792$	$\mathscr{F}_{33} = 0.1450$	$\mathscr{F}_{34} = 0.1043$
$\mathscr{F}_{14} = 0.0726$	$\mathscr{F}_{24} = 0.1106$	$\mathscr{F}_{34} = 0.1043$	$\mathscr{F}_{44} = 0.0124$
$\varepsilon_1 = 0.6000$	$\varepsilon_2 = 0.7000$	$\varepsilon_3 = 0.8000$	$\varepsilon_4 = 0.3000$

After the $\mathscr{F}$ values have been obtained, the net heat transfer for each source or sink surface is calculated as follows:

$$q_{net_1} = q_{2\rightleftharpoons1} + q_{3\rightleftharpoons1} + q_{4\rightleftharpoons1}$$

However, since $q_{4\rightleftharpoons1}$ is not zero, the temperature of the reradiating surface must be calculated first:

$$q_{net_4} = 0 = q_{1\rightleftharpoons4} + q_{2\rightleftharpoons4} + q_{3\rightleftharpoons4} + q_{4\rightleftharpoons4}$$

$$0 = \mathscr{F}_{14}A_4(E_{b_4} - E_{b_1}) + \mathscr{F}_{24}A_4(E_{b_4} - E_{b_2}) \\ + \mathscr{F}_{34}A_4(E_{b_4} - E_{b_3}) + \mathscr{F}_{44}A_4(E_{b_4} - E_{b_4})$$

$$0 = \varepsilon_4 E_{b_4} - \mathscr{F}_{14}E_{b_1} - \mathscr{F}_{24}E_{b_2} - \mathscr{F}_{34}E_{b_3} - \mathscr{F}_{44}E_{b_4}$$

$$E_{b_4} = \frac{\mathscr{F}_{14}E_{b_1} + \mathscr{F}_{24}E_{b_2} + \mathscr{F}_{34}E_{b_3}}{\varepsilon_4 - \mathscr{F}_{44}} = 4180 \text{ Btu per hr-ft}^2$$

Thus, $T_4 = 1250°R$. Then

$$q_{net_1} = \mathscr{F}_{12}A_1(E_{b_2} - E_{b_1}) + \mathscr{F}_{13}A_1(E_{b_3} - E_{b_1}) \\ + \mathscr{F}_{14}A_1(E_{b_4} - E_{b_1}) = 1859 \text{ Btu per hr}$$

$$q_{net_2} = 557 \text{ Btu per hr}$$

$$q_{net_3} = -2416 \text{ Btu per hr}$$

In this solution, the emittance of the reradiating surface is used as 0.3, the value given. The solution is somewhat easier if the emittance of the reradiating surface is taken as zero. This will result in $\mathscr{F}_{41}$, $\mathscr{F}_{42}$, $\mathscr{F}_{43}$, and $\mathscr{F}_{44}$ values of zero. With these four values known, the number of calculations is reduced; however, the temperature of the reradiating surface cannot be obtained.

If $\varepsilon_4 = 0$ is used, the following values are obtained for the $\mathscr{F}$ values:

$$\mathscr{F}_{11} = 0.0797 \quad \mathscr{F}_{21} = 0.2224 \quad \mathscr{F}_{31} = 0.2979$$

$$\mathscr{F}_{12} = 0.2224 \quad \mathscr{F}_{22} = 0.1583 \quad \mathscr{F}_{32} = 0.3193$$

$$\mathscr{F}_{13} = 0.2979 \quad \mathscr{F}_{23} = 0.3193 \quad \mathscr{F}_{33} = 0.1828$$

$$\mathscr{F}_{14} = 0.0000 \quad \mathscr{F}_{24} = 0.0000 \quad \mathscr{F}_{34} = 0.0000$$

Then the values of q_{net_1}, q_{net_2}, and q_{net_3} are calculated without calculating the temperature of the reradiating surface:

$$q_{net_1} = 1859 \text{ Btu per hr}$$

$$q_{net_2} = 557 \text{ Btu per hr}$$

$$q_{net_3} = -2416 \text{ Btu per hr}$$

Notice that the net heat transfer obtained in both of these methods is essentially the same as the values obtained for the same system using the network scheme. In general, the method used here does not offer any advantage over the network method when the surface temperatures are known. In the case where the surface temperatures are unknown, for example, a transient numerical analysis of a complete system, the $\mathscr{F}$ method is preferable.

5.13 Gebhart's Method

In 1957, Gebhart [2] introduced another method for the solution of gray enclosure problems, somewhat similar to Hottel's method discussed in the last section. Assumptions required for this method are the same as for the previous methods; that is, surfaces are gray, diffuse, and uniformly irradiated.

First define B_{ij} as the fraction of the total energy emitted by surface i that is absorbed by surface j. This includes energy from i that is directly incident on j, plus any energy that reaches j by multiple reflections within the enclosure. The easiest way to express B_{ij} is to consider an enclosure such as that shown in Figure 5.11.

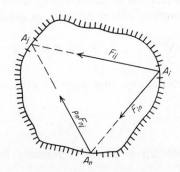

Figure 5.11   Enclosure to Illustrate Gebhart's Method.

The enclosure is divided into n surface elements, as indicated. Arrow F_{ij} indicates the fraction of the total energy emitted by the i surface that is directly incident on the jth surface. The energy from the ith surface, which is directly incident on the nth surface, is indicated as F_{in}; of this energy, ρ_n will be reflected. Since by assumption the energy from the nth surface is diffusely reflected, the fraction absorbed by the jth surface is B_{nj}, even though this energy was not emitted by the nth surface. That is, the fraction absorbed does not depend on the energy originating from the nth surface. Using these facts, the following set of equations can be written:

$$B_{1j} = \varepsilon_j F_{1j} = \rho_1 F_{11} B_{1j} + \rho_2 F_{12} B_{2j} + \cdots + \rho_n F_{1n} B_{nj}$$

$$B_{2j} = \varepsilon_j F_{2j} + \rho_1 F_{21} B_{1j} + \rho_2 F_{22} B_{2j} + \cdots + \rho_n F_{2n} B_{nj}$$

$$\vdots$$

$$B_{nj} = \varepsilon_j F_{nj} + \rho_1 F_{n1} B_{1j} + \rho_2 F_{n2} B_{2j} + \cdots + \rho_n F_{nn} B_{nj} \qquad (5.44)$$

These equations can be written in an augmented matrix as in Hottel's method, resulting in

$$
\begin{array}{ccccc}
B_{1j} & B_{2j} & B_{3j} & B_{nj} & \text{constant}
\end{array}
$$

$$
\left|
\begin{array}{cccc}
\rho_1 F_{11} - 1 & \rho_2 F_{12} & \rho_3 F_{13} & \rho_n F_{1n} \\
\rho_1 F_{21} & \rho_2 F_{22} - 1 & \rho_3 F_{23} & \rho_n F_{2n} \\
\vdots & \vdots & \vdots & \\
\rho_1 F_{n1} & \rho_2 F_{n2} & \rho_3 F_{n3} & \rho_n F_{nn} - 1
\end{array}
\right\|
\left.
\begin{array}{c}
-\varepsilon_j F_{ij} \\
-\varepsilon_j F_{2j} \\
\vdots \\
-\varepsilon_j F_{nj}
\end{array}
\right| \qquad (5.45)
$$

If we define D as the coefficient determinate, and $_k D_j$ as the determinate D, with the kth column replaced by the constant column,

$$B_{kj} = \frac{_k D_j}{D} \qquad (5.46)$$

In order of reduce the number of calculations required to solve a problem, we must have the following relations: Since B_{ij} is defined as a fraction,

$$\sum_{j=1}^{n} B_{ij} = 1 \qquad i = 1, 2, 3, \ldots n \qquad (5.47)$$

Another convenient relationship that may be proved by considering the above definitions is

$$B_{ij} \varepsilon_i A_i = B_{ji} \varepsilon_j A_j \qquad (5.48)$$

This reciprocity relationship is proved rigorously in Gebhart's original paper [2].

Once the n^2 values of B_{kj} have been determined, the net energy gain or loss by a surface may be obtained by

$$q_{net_j} = (\text{energy absorbed}) - (\text{energy emitted})$$

Or, in terms of the absorption factors

$$q_{net_j} = \sum_{k=1}^{n} B_{kj}\varepsilon_k A_k E_{b_k} - \varepsilon_j A_j E_{b_j} \tag{5.49}$$

Using the reciprocity relationship (Equation 5.48), Equation 5.49 can be written as

$$q_{net_j} = \varepsilon_j A_j \left[\left(\sum_{k=1}^{n} B_{jk} E_{bk} \right) - E_{b_j} \right] \tag{5.50}$$

In general, B_{jj} is not zero even when a surface cannot "see" itself. For this reason, and to call attention to this, we can write Equation 5.50 as

$$q_{net_j} = \varepsilon_j A_j \left[\sum_{\substack{i=1 \\ i \neq j}}^{n} B_{jk} E_{b_i} - (1 - B_{jj}) E_{b_j} \right] \tag{5.51}$$

5.14 Example of Gebhart's Method

A cubic furnace (Figure 5.12) has a floor heated to 1500°F and a door heated to 800°F; the other walls and the top are very well insulated. Assume that each face of the cube is 1 sq ft in area, that the emittances of the floor

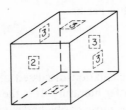

Figure 5.12   Geometry for Example of Gebhart's Method.

and top are 0.7, and that the three sides and the top are a single surface (area 3). Since area 3 is well insulated, this surface is reradiating. For purposes of calculation the emittance of this reradiating surface is assumed to be zero. Calculate the heat transfer from the floor to the door.

The required configuration factors are

$$F_{11} = 0 \qquad F_{21} = 0.2 \quad F_{31} = 0.2$$
$$F_{12} = 0.2 \quad F_{22} = 0 \qquad F_{23} = 0.2$$
$$F_{13} = 0.8 \quad F_{23} = 0.8 \quad F_{33} = 0.6$$

Using Gebhart's method, we have

$$D = \begin{vmatrix} -1 & 0.06 & 0.8 \\ 0.06 & -1 & 0.8 \\ 0.06 & 0.06 & -0.4 \end{vmatrix} = -0.297$$

$$_1D_2 = \begin{vmatrix} -0.14 & 0.06 & 0.8 \\ 0 & -1 & 0.8 \\ -0.14 & 0.06 & -0.4 \end{vmatrix} = -0.1677$$

Then

$$B_{12} = \frac{-0.1677}{-0.297} = 0.565$$

The energy loss by surface 1 is given by

$$q_{net_1} = \varepsilon_1 A_1[(1 - B_{11})E_{b1} - B_{12}E_{b2} - B_{13}E_{b3}]$$

Since surface 3 is a reradiating surface, the constant column has zero in each position. This makes $_1D_3$ identically zero and B_{13} zero.

By Equation 5.47, $B_{11} + B_{12} = 1$; since B_{13} is zero, $1 - B_{11} = B_{12}$. Then

$$q_{net_1} = \varepsilon_1 A_1 B_{12}[E_{b1} - E_{b2}]$$

$$= (0.7)(1)(0.565)(0.1714)\left[\left(\frac{1960}{100}\right)^4 - \left(\frac{1260}{100}\right)^4\right]$$

$$q_{net_1} = 8310 \text{ Btu per hr}$$

5.15 Conclusion

The three methods of calculation discussed above are all considered in various places in heat transfer literature. It is the opinion of the author that the network method is the most easily understood and most economical method of calculation. It should be noted that the network method can be used to calculate the $\mathscr{F}$ factors defined in Hottel's method. This is discussed in the next chapter.

When an engineering heat-transfer problem arises, the usual procedure is to calculate the energy exchange without considering radiant transfer, and then check the magnitude of the radiant transfer. In this case, the network method is the least time-consuming. When radiant transfer is known to be important, the $\mathscr{F}$ method is convenient. In this case, the radiant energy exchange can be considered parallel to the convection transfer by assigning unknown temperatures to the radiant nodes. Thus, in some cases the $\mathscr{F}$ method is preferable; however, it may be more convenient to evaluate $\mathscr{F}$ values from the basic network method.

Exercises

5.1 Determine $u(x)$ for the following integral equation using the method of successive substitutions:

$$u(x) = 2x - 1 + \int u(t)\,dt$$

5.2 In the Fredholm equation of the second kind let $f(x) = x^2$, $K(x, t) = 1.0$, $\lambda = \frac{1}{4}$, and the interval be $0 \leq t \leq 2$. Determine $u(x)$ by the method of (a) successive substitutions, (b) successive approximations, and (c) variation.

5.3 A cubic enclosure has two opposing walls which act as a source-sink combination. These two walls have temperatures and emittances of 340°F, 0.2 and 640°F, 0.8 respectively. (a) Consider the other four walls to be reradiating, that is, $q''_{net} = 0$, and determine the net energy flux from the source-sink walls. (b) Consider the other four walls as black walls with a temperature of 0°R and determine the net energy flux from the source-sink walls. (c) Comment on the energy flux between two parallel opposed walls in any real system if the walls have the temperatures and emittances given.

5.4 Assuming that the radiosity function for the Sparrow's heat transfer example (see Figure 5.2) is given as $\beta(X) = 1.642 - 0.5549X^2$, evaluate and plot $q''(X)/\varepsilon\sigma T^4$ when the plate reflectance is 0.9 and $\gamma = 1.0$. Compare the total energy transfer from the upper plate determined from the curve to the total energy transfer from the upper plate assuming the radiosity is constant.

5.5 Take the parallel-plate system of Problem 5.4, and divide the upper and lower plate into four equal segments, that is, two on each side of the center line of the plate. Calculate the heat transfer from the upper plate, assuming that the radiosity is constant along each of the four segments. In this case consider the plate reflectance value given as 0.9, and let $\gamma = 0.5$. Compare the total energy transfer obtained in this problem to the energy transfer calculated by using Sparrow's values for a quadradic equation and a quartic equation. (*Hint:* In this problem no more than three nodes must be considered in the network.)

5.6 Consider two infinite parallel black plates that are separated by one, two, or three infinite thin black shields. Considering the temperature of the black plates to be 100°F and 1000°F, calculate the energy transfer per square foot between the two surfaces, considering first one, then two, and then three infinite black shields.

5.7 In Problem 5.6, the infinite plates and the shields are considered to be black. Work the same example again, assuming in this case that each of the surfaces of the plate or the shields have an emittance of 0.6.

5.8 In Figure 5.10 (an infinite square duct), let the dimensions of the duct be changed such that one side is equal to twice the length of the adjacent side. For this geometry, repeat the calculations of Section 5.10 and determine from this the net heat transfer of each surface. In this case, let surface 1 be one of the short surfaces in the rectangular duct; that is, surface 1, a short surface, has a temperature of 1000°R and an emittance of 0.6. Surface 2, the adjacent long side of the rectangular duct, has a temperature of 1200°R and an emittance of

0.7. Surface 3, the second short side of the rectangular duct, has a temperature of 1400°R and an emittance of 0.8. Surface 4, the second long side of the rectangular duct, has an emittance of 0.3 and is a reradiating surface.

5.9   Repeat Problem 5.8 and use the method described by Hottel. In the solution, list all of the $\mathscr{F}$ values, that is, $\mathscr{F}$ values from each surface to every other surface, and list the net heat transfer for each surface as obtained from the $\mathscr{F}$ method.

References

1. BEVANS, J. T., and R. V. DUNKLE, "Radiant Interchange within an Enclosure," *ASME Transactions, Journal of Heat Transfer*, vol. 82, (February 1960), p. 1.
2. GEBHART, B., "Unified Treatment for Thermal Radiation Transfer Processes— Gray, Diffuse Radiators and Absorbers," ASME Paper 57–A–34 (1957).
3. HILDEBRAND, F. B., *Methods of Applied Mathematics*. Englewood Cliffs, N.J.: Prentice-Hall, Inc., 1952.
4. JAKOB, MAX, *Heat Transfer*, vol. 2. New York: John Wiley & Sons, Inc., 1957.
5. LOVITT, W. V., *Linear Integral Equations*. New York: McGraw-Hill, Inc., 1924.
6. MCADAMS, W. H., *Heat Transmission*. New York: McGraw-Hill, Inc. (1954), chap. 4 (by H. C. HOTTEL).
7. OPPENHEIM, A. K., "Radiation Analysis by the Network Method," *ASME Transactions*, vol. 78 (1956), p. 725.
8. SPARROW, E. M., "Application of Variational Methods to Radiation Heat Transfer Calculations," *ASME Transactions, Journal of Heat Transfer*, vol. 82, series C (1960), pp. 375–380. *See also* E. M. SPARROW and A. HAJI-SHEIKH, "A Generalized Variational Method for Calculating Radiant Interchange Between Surfaces," ASME Paper 64–HT–11 (1964).
9. ——, J. L. GREGG, J. V. SZEL, and P. MANOS, "Analysis, Results, and Interpretation for Radiation Between Some Simply-Arranged Gray Surfaces," *ASME Transactions, Journal of Heat Transfer*, vol. 83, series C (1961), p. 207.

CHAPTER 6

Nongray or Nondiffuse
System Analysis

The techniques introduced in Chapter 5 were all based on the gray assumption and on the diffuse surface assumption. These assumptions may lead to considerable error with a system which has surfaces that are nongray or nondiffuse. The purpose of this chapter is to present some of the methods of analysis that may be used to improve the accuracy of heat transfer calculations.

Nongray Systems

6.1 Nongray Materials

Literature concerning material properties normally shows grayness or nongrayness in terms of monochromatic reflectance or monochromatic emittance values. If engineering materials are examined, it is found that most of them exhibit considerable variation in their monochromatic properties with changes in wavelength. A typical monochromatic reflectance curve for a metal with the usual oxidation layer is shown in Figure 6.1. A typical nonconductor is shown on the same coordinates. These curves show nongrayness in the amount of monochromatic reflectance change. The curve for true gray surface would show constant monochromatic reflectance with changes in wavelength.

Real surfaces may be considered gray under less severe criteria. These criteria are most easily described in terms of Figure 6.2. In Figure 6.2 the total emittance of inconel X is shown. In the approximate range 150–1000°F, the emittance is constant. If this surface were in an enclosure with temperatures in the range 150–1000°F, the gray assumption would give excellent answers. However, if the enclosure temperatures were between 1000°F and 1600°F, the material would be very nongray. Thus, the convenient criteria for nongray analysis is the total-emittance-versus-temperature curve.

127

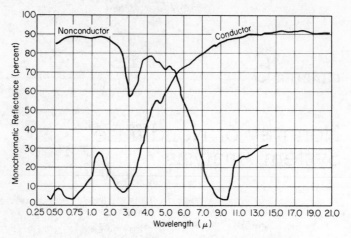

Figure 6.1 Typical Data for Materials.

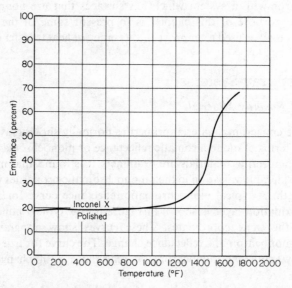

Figure 6.2 Total Emittance of Inconel X (Gubareff, Janssen, Torborg, *Thermal Radiation Properties Survey*).

6.2 Nongray Approximations

In expressing the equations for nongray analysis, the assumptions will be that the surfaces are uniformly irradiated, have uniform temperature, and are diffuse emitters and reflectors. With these assumptions, the radiosity of a node in an n surface enclosure can be written as

$$\int_0^\infty J_{\lambda j}\, d\lambda = \int_0^\infty \varepsilon_{\lambda j} E_{b\lambda j}\, d\lambda + \int_0^\infty \rho_{\lambda j} G_{\lambda j}\, d\lambda \qquad (6.1)$$

where $J_{\lambda j}$ is the monochromatic radiosity of the jth surface element

$E_{b\lambda j}$ is the monochromatic black body emissive power evaluated at the temperature of the jth surface

$G_{\lambda j}$ is the monochromatic irradiation of the jth surface element

$\varepsilon_{\lambda j}$ is the monochromatic hemispherical emittance of the jth surface element

$\rho_{\lambda j}$ is the monochromatic hemispherical reflectance of the jth surface element.

In order to complete Equation 6.1, we must express the monochromatic irradiation as

$$G_{\lambda j} = \sum_{k=1}^n J_{\lambda k} F_{jk}$$

Thus

$$\int_0^\infty J_{\lambda j}\, d\lambda = \int_0^\infty \varepsilon_{\lambda j} E_{b\lambda j}\, d\lambda + \int_0^\infty \rho_{\lambda j} \sum_{k=1}^n J_{\lambda k} F_{jk}\, d\lambda \qquad (6.2)$$

Equation 6.2 represents n integral equations that would have to be solved if the necessary property information were available. Since this is not a practical technique, *band approximation* [1] may be used. This approximation is basically very simple in that it involves the approximation of the integral terms by i bands of finite width $\Delta\lambda_i$. That is, the integral equation (6.2) is changed to the finite difference equation (6.3).

$$\sum_i J_{\Delta\lambda_i j}\Delta\lambda_i = \sum_i \varepsilon_{\Delta\lambda_i j} E_{b\Delta\lambda_i j}\Delta\lambda_i + \sum_i \rho_{\Delta\lambda_i j}\left[\sum_{k=1}^n J_{\Delta\lambda_i k} F_{jk}\right]\Delta\lambda_i \qquad (6.3)$$

In Equation 6.3, the monochromatic values have been replaced by the average values over the wavelength band. Term-by-term, the definitions are

$$J_{\Delta\lambda_i}\Delta\lambda_i = \int_{\Delta\lambda_i} J_\lambda\, d\lambda \qquad (6.4)$$

$$\varepsilon_{\Delta\lambda_i} E_{b\Delta\lambda_i}\Delta\lambda_i = \int_{\Delta\lambda_i} \varepsilon_\lambda E_{b\lambda}\, d\lambda \qquad (6.5)$$

$$\rho_{\Delta\lambda_i} G_{\Delta\lambda_i}\Delta\lambda_i = \int_{\Delta\lambda_i} \rho_\lambda G_\lambda\, d\lambda \qquad (6.6)$$

Since we normally consider the energy transfer in various wavelength bands to be independent, the nongray solution becomes the solution of i gray problems. In each of these bands the values to be used in Equations 6.5 and 6.6 must be specified. Since monochromatic data is presumed to be available, the evaluation of the terms in Equation 6.5 is possible; however, Equations 6.4 or 6.6 cannot be evaluated until all of the band radiosities are known. Since the band radiosities are unknowns in the equations, Equation 6.6 must be approximated.

The only way in which Equation 6.6 may be approximated is to choose $\Delta\lambda$ such that ρ_λ may be considered constant over the band. If this is done, the unknown variation of G_λ does not represent an error. Since few materials will allow this choice without an excessive number of bands, a typical approximation is

$$\rho_{\Delta\lambda}G_{\Delta\lambda}\Delta\lambda \simeq \left[\frac{\int_{\Delta\lambda}\rho_\lambda \, d\lambda}{\Delta\lambda}\right]\int_{\Delta\lambda}G_\lambda \, d\lambda \tag{6.7}$$

The approximation of Equation 6.7 implies that Equation 6.5 may be similarly approximated with no further error. That is

$$\varepsilon_{\Delta\lambda}E_{b\Delta\lambda}\Delta\lambda \simeq \left[\frac{\int_{\Delta\lambda}\varepsilon_\lambda \, d\lambda}{\Delta\lambda}\right]\int_{\Delta\lambda}E_{b\Delta\lambda} \, d\lambda \tag{6.8}$$

The two approximations given in Equations 6.7 and 6.8 reduce the nongray problem to a practical solution.

6.3 The Two-Band Approach

In some applications, energy exchange is the result of two radically different source temperatures. As a typical example, spacecraft are subject to radiation from the sun and radiation from terrestial temperature objects. In these cases the nongray solution may be satisfactorily approximated by only two bands. That is, Equation 6.1 may be expressed as

$$\int_0^{\lambda_a}J_{\lambda j} \, d\lambda + \int_{\lambda_a}^\infty J_{\lambda j} \, d\lambda = \int_0^{\lambda_a}\varepsilon_{\lambda j}E_{b\lambda j} \, d\lambda + \int_{\lambda_a}^\infty \varepsilon_{\lambda j}E_{b\lambda j} \, d\lambda$$

$$+ \int_0^{\lambda_a}\rho_{\lambda j}G_{\lambda j} \, d\lambda + \int_{\lambda_a}^\infty \rho_{\lambda j}G_{\lambda j} \, d\lambda$$

Then, since the two bands are considered independent, Equation 6.1 may be expressed as the sum of the two equations:

$$\int_0^{\lambda_a}J_{\lambda j} \, d\lambda = \int_0^{\lambda_a}\varepsilon_{\lambda j}E_{b\lambda j} \, d\lambda + \int_0^{\lambda_a}\rho_{\lambda j}G_{\lambda j} \, d\lambda \tag{6.9}$$

$$\int_{\lambda_a}^\infty J_{\lambda j} \, d\lambda = \int_{\lambda_a}^\infty \varepsilon_{\lambda j}E_{b\lambda j} \, d\lambda + \int_{\lambda_a}^\infty \rho_{\lambda j}G_{\lambda j} \, d\lambda \tag{6.10}$$

Using the approximations of Equations 6.7 and 6.8, we get

$$\int_0^{\lambda_a} J_{\lambda j}\, d\lambda = \left[\frac{\int_0^{\lambda_a} \varepsilon_{\lambda j}\, d\lambda}{\int_0^{\lambda_a} d\lambda}\right] \int_0^{\lambda_a} E_{b\lambda}\, d\lambda + \left[\frac{\int_0^{\lambda_a} \rho_{\lambda j}\, d\lambda}{\int_0^{\lambda_a} d\lambda}\right] \int_0^{\lambda_a} G_{\lambda j}\, d\lambda \quad (6.11)$$

$$\int_{\lambda_a}^{\infty} J_{\lambda j}\, d\lambda = \left[\frac{\int_{\lambda_a}^{\infty} \varepsilon_{\lambda j}\, d\lambda}{\int_{\lambda_a}^{\infty} d\lambda}\right] \int_{\lambda_a}^{\infty} E_{b\lambda}\, d\lambda + \left[\frac{\int_{\lambda_a}^{\infty} \rho_{\lambda j}\, d\lambda}{\int_{\lambda_a}^{\infty} d\lambda}\right] \int_{\lambda_a}^{\infty} G_{\lambda j}\, d\lambda \quad (6.12)$$

The bracketed terms of these equations can be approximated by using the normally reported solar absorptance and terrestial emittance, if λ_a is carefully chosen. For example, if $\lambda_a = 4\ \mu$ is chosen, about 99 percent of the solar energy will be in the $0-4-\mu$ wavelength range, and 99 percent of the terrestial energy will be in the $4-\infty-\mu$ wavelength range. Using the symbols α_s and ε_t for solar absorptance and terrestial emittance, Equations 6.11 and 6.12 become

$$\int_0^4 J_{\lambda j}\, d\lambda \simeq \alpha_s \int_0^4 E_{b\lambda}(540°\text{R})\, d\lambda + (1 - \alpha_s) \int_0^4 G_{\lambda j}\, d\lambda \quad (6.13)$$

$$\int_4^{\infty} J_{\lambda j}\, d\lambda \simeq \varepsilon_t \int_4^{\infty} E_{b\lambda}(540°\text{R})\, d\lambda + (1 - \varepsilon_t) \int_4^{\infty} G_{\lambda j}\, d\lambda \quad (6.14)$$

In Equation 6.13

$$\int_0^4 E_{b\lambda}(540°\text{R})\, d\lambda \simeq 0.35 \text{ Btu per hr-ft}^2$$

and

$$\int_0^4 G_{\lambda j}\, d\lambda \simeq 440 \text{ Btu per hr-ft}^2$$

(solar irradiation at the earth's distance from the sun). Because of this, Equation 6.13 may be written as

$$J_{(0-4\mu)j}\Delta\lambda \simeq (1 - \alpha_s)G_{(0-4\mu)j}\Delta\lambda \quad (6.15)$$

Similarly, Equation 6.14 is approximated by

$$J_{(4-\infty\mu)j}\Delta\lambda \simeq \varepsilon_t E_{b j}(540°\text{R}) + (1 - \varepsilon_t)G_{(4-\infty\mu)j}\,\Delta\lambda \quad (6.16)$$

In Equation 6.16, $E_{b j}(540°\text{R})$ is representative of the value $E_{b j}(T_j)$; that is, the magnitude of T_j is approximately 540°R. With these temperatures, $E_{b j}(T_j)$ is approximately 145 Btu per hr-ft^2, and the solar irradiation in these wavelengths is less than 5 Btu per hr-ft^2. The approximation assumes that no solar energy is present, which results in an error about 4 percent in the irradiation term. This is usually an acceptable margin of error.

6.4 Multiband Approximation

In cases where temperatures are such that a nongray analysis is required, a multiband approximation is necessary. The multiband approximation is described by Equation 6.3; however, several practical difficulties exist. Perhaps the major difficulty lies in the paucity of monochromatic data available. Typical monochromatic data as given in Appendixes 1–3 is not available for a large variety of materials. The largest collection known to the author is in reference [4], and even this is not as extensive as other types of property information. Furthermore, monochromatic data is limited in wavelength range by experimental factors. The typical monochromatic data curve is for a wavelength range of about 0.3–15 μ, although some selected data is available beyond this range.

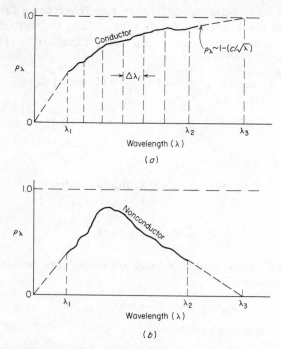

Figure 6.3 Typical Monochromatic Reflectance Data for (a) Conductors (b) Nonconductors.

Assuming that data is available, we find that the typical curve is something like the representations of Figure 6.3 for conductors or nonconductors. When the wavelength bands are chosen, two special regions naturally occur as bands. These two are in the wavelength range $0-\lambda_1$ and $\lambda_2-\infty$, as shown.

Under this condition the multiband equations consist of three types of representations for the following integrated equations:

$$\int_0^{\lambda_1} J_{\lambda j}\, d\lambda = \varepsilon_{(0-\lambda_1)j} \int_0^{\lambda_1} E_{b\lambda j}\, d\lambda + \rho_{(0-\lambda_1)j} \sum_{k=1}^n F_{jk} \int_0^{\lambda_1} J_{\lambda k}\, d\lambda \qquad (6.20)$$

$$J_{\Delta\lambda_i j}\Delta\lambda_i = \varepsilon_{\Delta\lambda_i j} E_{b\Delta\lambda_i j}\Delta\lambda_i + \rho_{\Delta\lambda_i k} \sum_{k=1}^n J_{\Delta\lambda_i k} F_{jk}\Delta\lambda_i \qquad (6.21)$$

$$\int_{\lambda_2}^{\infty} J_{\lambda j}\, \lambda d = \varepsilon_{(\lambda_2-\infty)j} \int_{\lambda_2}^{\infty} E_{b\lambda j}\, d\lambda + \rho_{(\lambda_2-\infty)j} \sum_{k=1}^n F_{jk} \int_{\lambda_2}^{\infty} J_{\lambda k}\, d\lambda \qquad (6.22)$$

The terms of Equation 6.21 are typical center-band terms. Each term is evaluated as previously described. In Equation 6.20, some approximation for the emittance to be used over the wavelength range $0-\lambda_1$ must be made. As indicated diagramatically in Figure 6.3, a linear extrapolation of the reflectance to zero is satisfactory. That is

$$\rho_{(0-\lambda_1)} \simeq \frac{\rho_{\lambda_1}}{2}$$

and

$$\varepsilon_{(0-\lambda_1)} \simeq 1 - \frac{\rho_{\lambda_1}}{2}$$

Neither of these approximations are very good, but they are better than assuming $\rho_{(0-\lambda_1)} = \rho_{\lambda_1}$, since monochromatic reflectance always tends to get smaller at very short wavelengths.

In Equation 6.22, two separate approximations are required. First, the approximate magnitude of λ_3 must be determined. For typical engineering work a value of 100 μ can be used. However, for cryogenic applications a value of 200 or 300 μ may be more reasonable. In either case, the value chosen should be such that very little of the energy emitted from the cooler surfaces occurs beyond λ_3. After choosing λ_3, the appropriate approximations are

$$\left.\begin{aligned} \rho_{(\lambda_2-\lambda_3)} &\simeq \frac{\rho_{\lambda_2}}{2} \\[2mm] \varepsilon_{(\lambda_2-\lambda_3)} &\simeq 1 - \frac{\rho_{\lambda_2}}{2} \end{aligned}\right\} \quad \text{for nonconductors}$$

and

$$\left.\begin{aligned} \rho_{(\lambda_2-\lambda_3)} &\simeq 1 - \frac{2(1-\rho_{\lambda_2})}{1+\sqrt{\lambda_3/\lambda_2}} \\[2mm] \varepsilon_{(\lambda_2-\lambda_3)} &\simeq 1 - \rho_{(\lambda_2-\lambda_3)} \end{aligned}\right\} \quad \text{for conductors}$$

The approximation for conductors is made by using the Hagen-Ruben expression for monochromatic reflectance at long wavelengths [6]. This expression is not exact, but it is an appropriate and simple expression for this case.

If more than three bands are required for a multinode system, the most practical approach to solution is to use a digital computer. In the computation, terms of the type

$$\int_{\lambda_1}^{\lambda_2} E_{b\lambda j}(T_j)\, d\lambda$$

must be determined. An economical method of doing this is to evaluate

$$\int_0^{\lambda} E_{b\lambda j}(T_j)\, d\lambda$$

from the following expressions [8]:

$$\frac{\int_0^{\lambda} E_{b\lambda}(T)\, d\lambda}{\sigma T^4} = \frac{15}{\pi^4} \sum_{m=1} \frac{e^{-mv}}{m^4} (((mv + 3)mv + 6)mv + 6) \quad (6.23)$$

where v is the dimensionless quantity $v = C_2/\lambda T$. Equation 6.23 converges for all values of v; however, the convergence is slow for small values of v. For this reason, the following expression is more convenient for small v:

$$\frac{\int_0^{\lambda} E_{b\lambda}(T)\, d\lambda}{\sigma T^4} = 1 - \frac{15}{\pi^4} v^3 \left(\frac{1}{3} - \frac{v}{8} + \frac{v^2}{60} - \frac{v^4}{5040} + \frac{v^6}{272160} - \frac{v^8}{13305600} \cdots \right) \quad (6.24)$$

Equation 6.24 converges for $|v| < 2\pi$. As a practical suggestion, note that Equation 6.23 converges quite well for $v \geq 2.0$, and that Equation 6.24 gives very good results for $v < 2.0$. For this reason, the value $v = 2.0$ is suggested for a limit on the two ranges. With these two expressions for the evaluation of band energy, nongray problem solution by computer, using the iterative technique of Section 5.10, is extremely rapid.

A program written in Fortran for nongray problems is included in Appendix 5. This program divides the bands on the basis of wave numbers rather than wavelength, but it is programmed as indicated above. Since many difficulties can arise in using a program written by another person, it is recommended that each reader write his own program.

6.5 Nongray Example

An example of a nongray problem that illustrates the number of bands required for a particular system is as follows: A fuel tank for a jet aircraft is exposed to high temperatures on the top surface. This surface has a relatively constant temperature, 300°F. The side walls and fuel in the tank are at the same temperature, 80°F. The tank size is 1.5 × 4 × 8 ft, and the material

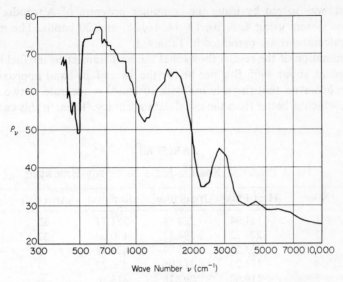

P_ν

Wave Number ν (cm^{-1})

Figure 6.4   Monochromatic Reflectance for Titanium.

is titanium, with monochromatic reflectance as shown in Figure 6.4. Fuel emittance is assumed to be 0.9, and the fuel is assumed to be opaque to radiant energy. If the tank is half full of fuel, what is the radiant flux to the fuel, considering the fuel vapor diathermic?

A sketch of the half-filled fuel tank with surface identification numbers is shown in Figure 6.5. Since the material of this tank has a very erratic monochromatic reflectance, and since the temperatures are not vastly different, a nongray analysis is required. The number of bands required to approximate the monochromatic reflectance is generally unknown. For this reason, the

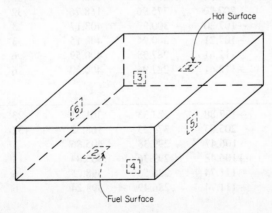

Figure 6.5   Illustration for Nongray Example Analysis.

problem was solved by using the computer program of Appendix 5 for a six-node system using 4, 8, 10, 12, 14, 16, 18, and 20 bands. The results of these calculations are presented in Table 6.1.

Examination of the results shows that the heat transfer to the fuel becomes constant at about 4405 Btu per hr for the 18 and 20 band approximation. Notice, however, that the solution with 10 bands is accurate to two decimal places, which is better than the usual data accuracy. Thus, in this case, 10 or

TABLE 6.1

Heat Transfer Results for a Nongray Example

Bands	Nodes	Heat Flux	Irradiation	Radiosity	Area (ft²)	$q'' \times A$
	1	−151.94	229.81	381.74	32	−4862.08
	2	223.72	394.33	170.60	32	7159.04
	3	−113.23	313.09	426.32	3	− 339.69
4	4	−113.25	313.05	426.29	3	− 339.75
	5	−119.60	299.26	418.86	6	− 717.60
	6	−119.61	299.24	418.85	6	− 717.66
						182.26
	1	−143.92	226.16	370.08	32	−4605.44
	2	213.15	382.58	169.43	32	6820.80
	3	−109.66	305.37	415.03	3	− 328.98
8	4	−109.67	305.34	415.02	3	− 329.01
	5	−115.37	292.06	407.43	6	− 692.22
	6	−115.38	292.05	407.42	6	− 692.28
						172.87
	1	−139.51	224.09	363.60	32	−4464.32
	2	207.20	375.96	168.76	32	6630.40
	3	−107.20	300.97	408.17	3	− 321.60
10	4	−107.21	300.94	408.15	3	− 321.63
	5	−112.61	287.98	400.59	6	− 675.66
	6	−112.61	287.96	400.50	6	− 675.66
						171.53
	1	−137.88	223.33	361.21	23	−4412.16
	2	205.03	373.55	168.52	32	6560.96
	3	−106.47	299.38	405.86	3	− 319.41
12	4	−106.48	299.36	405.84	3	− 319.44
	5	−111.74	286.50	398.25	6	− 670.44
	6	−111.74	286.49	398.24	6	− 670.44
						169.07

TABLE 6.1 *Continued*

Bands	Nodes	Heat Flux	Irradiation	Radiosity	Area (ft²)	$q'' \times A$
	1	−138.30	223.48	361.79	32	−4425.60
	2	205.53	374.11	168.58	32	6576.96
	3	−106.55	299.74	406.29	3	− 319.65
14	4	−106.56	299.71	406.27	3	− 319.68
	5	−111.87	286.84	398.71	6	− 671.22
	6	−111.88	286.83	398.70	6	− 671.28
						169.53
	1	−138.50	223.56	362.06	32	−4432.00
	2	205.76	374.37	168.60	32	6584.32
	3	−106.60	299.90	406.51	3	− 319.80
16	4	−106.61	299.88	406.49	3	− 319.83
	5	−111.94	287.00	398.94	6	− 671.64
	6	−111.94	386.99	398.93	6	− 671.64
						169.41
	1	−137.67	223.15	360.83	32	−4405.44
	2	204.62	373.10	168.48	32	6547.84
	3	−106.07	299.05	405.12	3	− 318.21
18	4	−106.08	299.02	405.10	3	− 318.24
	5	−111.35	286.21	397.57	6	− 668.10
	6	−111.35	286.20	397.56	6	− 668.10
						169.75
	1	−137.66	223.15	360.81	32	−4405.12
	2	204.60	373.08	168.48	32	6547.20
	3	−106.06	299.04	405.10	3	− 318.18
20	4	−106.07	299.01	405.08	3	− 318.21
	5	−111.35	286.20	397.55	6	− 668.10
	6	−111.35	286.19	397.54	6	− 668.10
						169.49

even fewer bands could be used and still result in satisfactory engineering accuracy.

Semigray Analysis

6.6 Parallel Infinite Plate Systems

In Section 4.3, the concepts of a semigray system analysis were introduced, using parallel infinite plate system with only two surfaces. For the two-plate system, energy originating from each of the plates was determined separately.

The irradiation of plate 1 as expressed in Equation 4.5 consists of energy originally emitted by surface 1 and surface 2 separately:

$$G_1(T_{s_1}^*) = \frac{E_2(T_2)}{1 - \rho_1(T_1, T_{s_1}^*)\rho_2(T_2, T_{s_2}^*)} + \frac{\rho_2(T_2, T_{s_2}^*)E_1(T_1)}{1 - \rho_1(T_1, T_{s_1}^*)\rho_2(T_2, T_{s_2}^*)} \qquad (4.5)$$

The question we typically must pose is "What shall be used for a term such as $\rho_1(T_1, T_{s_1}^*)$, which occurs as the first term on the right-hand side of Equation 4.5?" In the semigray cases this term is approximated by $\rho_1(T_1, T_{s_1}^*) \simeq 1 - \varepsilon_1(T_2)$.

The reasoning for this approximation is that the first term on the right, the term with $E_2(T_2)$ in the numerator, is an expression for the irradiation of surface 1 by energy that originates at surface 2. Since this energy has monochromatic characteristics more nearly approximated by a black body at the temperature of surface 2, than by a black body at the temperature of surface 1, the reflectance should be evaluated from the emittance evaluated at T_2. These facts are explained in more detail in Chapter 4.

This semigray approximation is not exact for two reasons: one, the energy incident upon surface 1 is not from a black body at temperature T_2, and two, the monochromatic reflectance is a function of the surface temperature. As pointed out in Chapter 4, both of these errors are small compared to the error introduced by evaluating properties at the wrong temperature for the incident energy.

6.7 Multiple-Surface Systems

The ray-tracing method used in Chapter 4 to determine the irradiation of a surface is not practical when several surfaces are involved. When a system has several sources and sinks, the semigray analysis technique is most convenient, using Hottel's method described in Chapter 5. Briefly, this method consists of the determination of hypothetical energy-flow terms of the form $q_{j\to k}$, where $q_{j\to k}$ represents the energy absorbed by surface k that originates at surface j. This allows us to separate the energy absorbed by the surfaces by energy source. Of course, if this is possible, semigray assumptions may be used. It should be noted that the concepts of Hottel's method are used in semigray analysis, but that the technique is modified in one respect; that is, $\mathscr{F}_{jk}A_j \neq \mathscr{F}_{kj}A_k$ when semigray assumptions are used. This will be discussed further later.

The least difficult method of obtaining the necessary $\mathscr{F}$ factors for the analysis of semigray systems is to use the network concept. Consider the three-node network shown in Figure 6.6. With the three battery potentials given as E_{b1}, E_{b2}, and E_{b3}, net current flow through the system represents net heat transfer rates. Using the principal of superposition, we can determine the net current flow or net heat transfer in any leg of the network by summing the

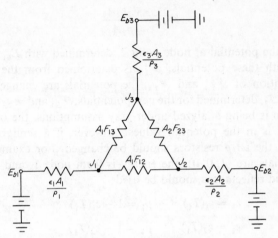

Figure 6.6   Three-node System.

currents when the battery potentials are $(E_{b1}, 0, 0)$, $(0, E_{b2}, 0)$, and $(0, 0, E_{b3})$. The current determined in each of these cases represents heat transfer from each of the source nodes separately. This technique can be extended by using the battery potentials $(1, 0, 0)$, $(0, 1, 0)$, and $(0, 0, 1)$ to obtain $\mathscr{F}$ factors directly from the network. For example, in Figure 6.7 the network with potentials $(1, 0, 0)$ is shown. With this network, J_2 and J_3 may be determined. Then the energy flow from J_2 through the $\varepsilon_2 A_2/\rho_2$ resistor represents energy flow from

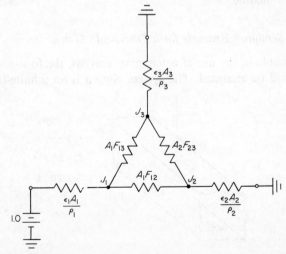

Figure 6.7   Three-node System for $\mathscr{F}_{12}$ and $\mathscr{F}_{13}$ Evaluation.

surface 1 to surface 2, or $q_{1\to2}$. By definition, $q_{1\to2} = \mathscr{F}_{12}A_1E_{b1}$, or with the potential used,

$$\mathscr{F}_{12} = \frac{J_2\varepsilon_2A_2}{\rho_2A_1} \tag{6.23}$$

where J_2 is the potential at node point 2, determined with $E_{b1} = 1$, $E_{b2} = 0$, $E_{b3} = 0$. With these potentials, $\mathscr{F}_{13}$ is determined from the potential J_3. After evaluation of $\mathscr{F}_{12}$ and $\mathscr{F}_{13}$, the potentials are changed to $(0, 1, 0)$. From J_1 and J_3, determined for the new potentials, $\mathscr{F}_{21}$ and $\mathscr{F}_{23}$ are evaluated. If the system is being analyzed under gray assumptions, the only change in the network is in the potential values; however, if a semigray analysis is being made, the $\varepsilon A/\rho$ resistors should be changed. For example, when the node potentials are $(1, 0, 0)$, the energy is from node 1, and the following emittance and reflectances should be used:

$$\varepsilon_1 = \varepsilon_1(T_1) \qquad \rho_1 = 1 - \varepsilon_1(T_1)$$

$$\varepsilon_2 = \varepsilon_2(T_1) \qquad \rho_2 = 1 - \varepsilon_2(T_1)$$

$$\varepsilon_3 = \varepsilon_3(T_1) \qquad \rho_3 = 1 - \varepsilon_3(T_1)$$

That is, all emittance and reflectance values should be evaluated from the emittance values at the specified temperature of node 1. Similarly, when the potentials are $(0,1,0)$, emittance and reflectance values are evaluated at the temperature of node 2. When this technique is used, $\mathscr{F}_{12}A_1 \neq \mathscr{F}_{21}A_2$, as in Hottel's method. However

$$\varepsilon_i = \sum_{j=1}^{n} \mathscr{F}_{ij}$$

as in Hottel's method.

6.8 Semigray Example for a Four-Node System

As an example of the use of a semigray analysis, the four-node system of Figure 6.8 will be analyzed. The system chosen is an infinite-length square

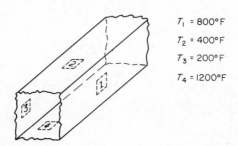

T_1 = 800°F
T_2 = 400°F
T_3 = 200°F
T_4 = 1200°F

Figure 6.8   System for Semigray Example Analysis.

duct with each wall at a different temperature and made of different material. This example is a rather severe test of the accuracy possible in semigray analysis since three of the walls are very nongray in their characteristics. The wall materials and their characteristics are listed in Table 6.2. The properties of each of these materials were taken from [5].

TABLE 6.2

Wall Number	Material	Emittance at Various Temperatures			
		200°F	400°F	800°F	1200°F
1	Titanium C-110, oxidized	0.27	0.32	0.44	0.54
2	321 Stainless Steel	0.33	0.34	0.36	0.39
3	Black paint on Stainless Steel	0.71	0.72	0.74	0.76
4	Titanium C-110, no oxide	0.17	0.19	0.23	0.27

By assigning the node potentials $(1, 0, 0, 0)$, $(0, 1, 0, 0)$, $(0, 0, 1, 0)$, and $(0, 0, 0, 1)$ respectively, the following $\mathscr{F}$ values were obtained:

$$\mathscr{F}_{11} = 0.0598 \qquad \mathscr{F}_{21} = 0.0683$$

$$\mathscr{F}_{12} = 0.0909 \qquad \mathscr{F}_{22} = 0.0491$$

$$\mathscr{F}_{13} = 0.2336 \qquad \mathscr{F}_{23} = 0.1765$$

$$\mathscr{F}_{14} = 0.0557 \qquad \mathscr{F}_{24} = 0.0461$$

$$\overline{\varepsilon_1(T_1) = 0.4400} \qquad \overline{\varepsilon_2(T_2) = 0.3400}$$

$$\mathscr{F}_{31} = 0.1552 \qquad \mathscr{F}_{41} = 0.0744$$

$$\mathscr{F}_{32} = 0.1791 \qquad \mathscr{F}_{42} = 0.0632$$

$$\mathscr{F}_{33} = 0.2880 \qquad \mathscr{F}_{43} = 0.1135$$

$$\mathscr{F}_{34} = 0.0877 \qquad \mathscr{F}_{44} = 0.0189$$

$$\overline{\varepsilon_3(T_3) = 0.7100} \qquad \overline{\varepsilon_4(T_4) = 0.2700}$$

The total emissive powers of the four surfaces are

$$E_{b1} = 0.1713(12.6)^4 = 4317.57 \text{ Btu per hr-ft}^2$$

$$E_{b2} = 0.1713(8.6)^4 = 937.02 \text{ Btu per hr-ft}^2$$

$$E_{b3} = 0.1713(6.6)^4 = 325.04 \text{ Btu per hr-ft}^2$$

$$E_{b4} = 0.1713(16.6)^4 = 13007.38 \text{ Btu per hr-ft}^2$$

From the general expression

$$q''_{net_j} = \left(\sum_{k=1}^{n} \mathscr{F}_{kj} E_{bk} \right) - \varepsilon_j E_{bj}$$

we get

$$q''_{net_1} = (0.0598)(4317.57) + (0.0683)(937.02) + (0.1552)(937.02)$$

$$+ (0.0744)(13007.38) - (0.44)(4317.57)$$

$$= -559.35 \text{ Btu per hr-ft}^2$$

Similarly

$$q''_{net_2} = 1000.08 \text{ Btu per hr-ft}^2$$

$$q''_{net_3} = 2513.14 \text{ Btu per hr-ft}^2$$

$$q''_{net_4} = -2953.95 \text{ Btu per hr-ft}^2$$

This problem was also worked out using nongray assumptions with 12 bands. The results of the nongray solution were

$$q''_{net_1} = -518.6 \text{ Btu per hr-ft}^2$$

$$q''_{net_2} = 1062 \text{ Btu per hr-ft}^2$$

$$q''_{net_3} = 2497 \text{ Btu per hr-ft}^2$$

$$q''_{net_4} = -3038 \text{ Btu per hr-ft}^2$$

Each of these values is within 6 percent of the values obtained with semigray assumptions except q''_{net_1}. The error in the value of q''_{net_1} is 40 Btu per hr-ft^2, which is small, considering the magnitude of the largest heat transfer rate. Since the data for most engineering problems is not very accurate, the semigray solution will probably yield satisfactory results for most engineering applications.

Analysis of Specular-Reflectance Diffuse-Emittance Systems

6.9 Justification of Specular-Reflectance Diffuse-Emittance Surfaces

As discussed in Chapter 3, in the section on real-system characteristics, many real surfaces will reflect energy in a manner, that is not diffuse. The tendency for a surface to reflect in a specular or mirror-like manner is dependent upon the relative roughness of the surface. In describing roughness, the wavelength of incident radiation is the physical property that must be used for comparison, that is, a surface may be optically rough or optically smooth depending upon the wavelengths of incident energy. Many surfaces that appear rough to the eye may actually be smooth for long-wavelength radiation [3].

Since many engineering applications involve relatively smooth metal surfaces and energy transfer in the longer wavelengths, it is appropriate to consider some surfaces to be specular reflectors.

A perfectly smooth surface is a specular reflector and may reflect energy in accordance with the Fresnel equations. Since these equations also give directional emittance, the surface will emit according to the Fresnel relationships. Both conductors and nonconductors have directional emittance values (see Figure 3.7) that may be approximated by a diffuse emittance. For this reason even a very smooth surface is nearly a diffuse emitter, although it is a purely specular reflector.

6.10 Specular-Reflector Diffuse-Emitter Concepts

When a surface is specular, the energy from a surface element that reflects off the specular surface appears to come from the image of the source element [3, 7]. This is illustrated in Figure 6.9, in which area A_2 is a specular surface

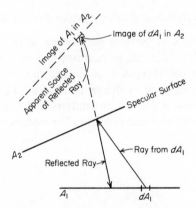

Figure 6.9 Specular Reflection.

normal to the paper and A_1 is a diffuse emitter normal to the surface. In the illustration, a particular ray from dA_1, which reflects specularly off surface A_2, is shown. The ray that returns to A_1 from A_2 appears to have come from the image of dA_1 as "seen through" area A_2. In definitive analysis for energy exchange, the irradiation of surface A_1 by dA_1 through the one reflection requires the evaluation of a configuration factor [3]. If the image of dA_1 can be seen by all parts of A_1, and if the energy emitted by dA_1 is diffuse, A_1 is irradiated by this energy multiplied by ρ_2 as though it came from the location of the image of dA_1. That is, the irradiation of A_1 by dA_1 is

$$G_{A_1 \text{ from } dA_1} = E_{dA_1}\rho_2 F_{dA_1 \text{ image}\to A_1} \qquad (6.24)$$

In Equation 6.24 it is assumed that the energy leaving dA_1 is only the total emissive power E_{dA_1}; more generally this should be the total radiosity J_{dA_1}, but this will be considered later.

In some configurations of specular-surface diffuse-surface geometry, the entire surface A_1 may not be able to "see" dA_1. This is illustrated in Figure 6.10. In this case, under the previous assumptions, the irradiation of A_1 from dA_1 is

$$G_{dA_1 \text{ image} \to A_1} = E_{dA_1} \rho_2 F_{dA_1 \text{ image} \to A_1 \text{ partial}} \qquad (6.25)$$

The partial-view factor of Equation 6.25 may be given a different symbol if it occurs in a system:

$$F_{dA_1 \to A_1 \text{ partial}} \equiv F^*_{dA_1 \to A_1}$$

These two basic concepts are all that are required to analyze specular-reflector diffuse-emitter systems. The technique of analysis using the method of images for enclosures is considered next.

6.11 Specular-Reflector Diffuse-Emitter System Analysis

Several different types of systems may occur when specular surfaces are considered [9]. The least difficult to examine is a system in which only one surface is a specular reflector. A four-surface infinite duct with only one surface as a specular reflector is shown in Figure 6.11. As indicated in the figure, surfaces 1, 2, and 4 are diffuse emitters and reflectors, and surface 3 is the diffuse emitter and specular reflector. The images of the diffuse surfaces

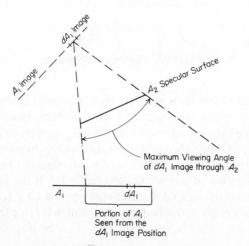

Figure 6.10　Partial View Factor.

are shown dotted and noted as 1(3), 2(3), and 4(3), where the parenthetical notation indicates which surface the image is " seen through."

Using our normal notation, we can express the irradiations of the diffuse-diffuse surfaces as

$$G_1 A_1 = J_2 A_2 F_{21} + J_4 A_4 F_{41} + J_2 A_2 \rho_3 F_{2(3),1} + J_1 A_1 \rho_3 F_{1(3),1}$$
$$+ J_4 A_4 \rho_3 F_{4(3),1} + E_3 A_3 F_{31} \qquad (6.26)$$

$$G_2 A_2 = J_1 A_1 F_{12} + J_4 A_4 F_{42} + J_1 A_1 \rho_3 F_{1(3),2} + J_4 A_4 \rho_3 F_{4(3),2} + E_3 A_3 F_{32} \qquad (6.27)$$

$$G_4 A_4 = J_1 A_1 F_{14} + J_2 A_2 F_{24} + J_1 A_1 \rho_4 F_{1(3),4} + J_2 A_2 \rho_3 F_{2(3),4} + E_3 A_3 F_{34} \qquad (6.28)$$

In Equations 6.26, 6.27, and 6.28, the only terms that require any discussion are the terms multiplied by $E_3 A_3$. In these terms, total emissive power is used rather than radiosity because the energy reflected away from surface 3 has already been accounted for in terms of the type $J_1 A_1 \rho_3 F_{2(3),1}$; that is, in each equation the total energy from surface 3 to the other surfaces is the sum of several terms.

Using the relationship $J_i = E_i + \rho_i G_i$ and reciprocity, we can write Equations 6.26, 6.27, and 6.28 as

$$J_1 = E_1 + \rho_1 [J_2 (F_{12} + \rho_3 F_{1,2(3)}) + J_4 (F_{14} + \rho_3 F_{1,4(3)})$$
$$+ J_1 \rho_3 F_{1,1(3)} + E_3 F_{13}] \qquad (6.29)$$

$$J_2 = E_2 + \rho_2 [J_1 (F_{21} + \rho_3 F_{2,1(3)}) + J_4 (F_{24} + \rho_3 F_{2,4(3)}) + E_3 F_{23}] \qquad (6.30)$$

$$J_4 = E_4 + \rho_4 [J_1 (F_{41} + \rho_3 F_{4,1(3)}) + J_2 (F_{42} + \rho_3 F_{4,2(3)} + E_3 F_{43}] \qquad (6.31)$$

Then, if T_1, T_2, T_3, T_4 and the property data are known, solving these three equations simultaneously will result in the radiosities J_1, J_2, J_4. Once these radiosities are known, the heat transfer rate for the four surfaces can be

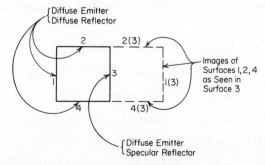

Figure 6.11   Enclosure with One Specular Surface.

evaluated from

$$q''_{net_1} = G_1 - J_1$$
$$q''_{net_2} = G_2 - J_2$$
$$q''_{net_4} = G_4 - J_4$$

where the irradiations are determined from Equations 6.26, 6.27, and 6.28. The heat transfer from the specular surface can be evaluated from

$$q''_{net_3} = \alpha_3 G_3 - E_3$$

where

$$G_3 = J_1 F_{31} + J_2 F_{32} + J_4 F_{34}$$

It is interesting to note that the number of equations that must be solved simultaneously for a system with a specular-diffuse surface is reduced by one.

When more than one specular-diffuse surface is present in an enclosure, multiple images may appear. This is illustrated for the four-surface infinite-duct system in Figure 6.12. In this case the two opposed walls, 1 and 3, are

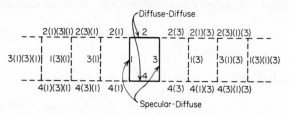

Figure 6.12   Specular-Diffuse Enclosure with Two Specular Surfaces.

specular reflectors and diffuse emitters. The images of the enclosure are repeated over and over again on each side when this occurs. In the figure, the notation 4(1) (3) (1) means the image of 4 as seen in 1 as seen in 3 as seen in 1. This can be written more compactly as $4(1^2,3)$ which indicates the image of 4 with two reflections off surface 1 and one reflection off surface 3. With this nomenclature [9], the irradiations of the two diffuse-diffuse surfaces are given by

$$
\begin{aligned}
G_2 = {}& J_4[F_{24} + \rho_1 F_{2,4(1)} + \rho_3 F_{2,4(3)} + \rho_1 \rho_3 F_{2,4(1,3)} \\
& + \rho_3 \rho_1 F_{2,4(3,1)} + \rho_1{}^2 \rho_3 F_{2,4(1^2,3)} + \rho_3{}^2 \rho_1 F_{2,4(3^2,1)} \\
& + \rho_1{}^2 \rho_3{}^2 F_{2,4(1^2,3^2)} + \rho_3{}^2 \rho_1{}^2 F_{2,4(3^2,1^2)} + \cdots] \\
& + E_1[F_{21} + \rho_3 F_{2,1(3)} + \rho_3 \rho_1 F_{2,1(3,1)} + \rho_3{}^2 \rho_1 F_{2,1(3^2,1)} \\
& + \rho_3{}^2 \rho_1{}^2 F_{2,1(3^2,1^2)} \cdots] \\
& + E_3[F_{23} + \rho_1 F_{2,3(1)} + \rho_1 \rho_3 F_{2,3(1,3)} + \rho_1{}^2 \rho_3 F_{2,3(1^2,3)} \\
& + \rho_1{}^2 \rho_3{}^2 F_{2,3(1^2,3^2)} \cdots]
\end{aligned}
\tag{6.32}
$$

$$G_4 = J_2[F_{42} + \rho_1 F_{4,2(1)} + \rho_3 F_{4,2(3)} + \rho_1 \rho_3 F_{4,2(1,3)}$$
$$+ \rho_3 \rho_1 F_{4,2(3,1)} + \rho_1^2 \rho_3 F_{4,2(1^2,3)} + \rho_3^2 \rho_1 F_{4,2(3^2,1)}$$
$$+ \rho_1^2 \rho_3^2 F_{4,2(1^2,3^2)} + \rho_1^2 \rho_3^2 F_{4,2(3^2,1^2)} \cdots]$$
$$+ E_1[F_{41} + \rho_3 F_{4,1(3)} + \rho_3 \rho_1 F_{4,1(3,1)} + \rho_3^2 \rho_1 F_{4,1(3^2,1)}$$
$$+ \rho_3^2 \rho_1^2 F_{2,1(3^2,1^2)} \cdots]$$
$$+ E_3[F_{43} + \rho_1 F_{4,3(1)} + \rho_1 \rho_3 F_{4,3(1,3)} + \rho_1^2 \rho_3 F_{4,3(1^2,3)}$$
$$+ \rho_1^2 \rho_3^2 F_{4,3(1^2,3^2)} \cdots] \tag{6.33}$$

In this case, if T_1, T_2, T_3, T_4 and the property information are know, only two equations must be solved simultaneously. The technique used to obtain the ret heat transfer rates is the same as in the previous system.

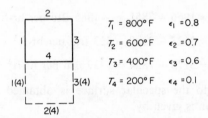

Figure 6.13   Specular-Diffuse Example.

6.12 Example of Specular-Diffuse Analysis

As a simple example of a specular-diffuse system, consider the infinite square duct shown in Figure 6.13. Considering all of the surfaces gray, let surfaces 1, 2, and 3 be diffuse reflectors and diffuse emitters, and let surface 4 be a specular reflector and diffuse emitter. The expressions for the irradiation of each of the diffuse-diffuse surfaces are

$$G_1 = J_2[F_{12} + \rho_4 F_{1,2(4)}] + J_3[F_{13} + \rho_4 F_{1,3(4)}] + E_4 F_{14}$$
$$G_2 = J_1[F_{21} + \rho_4 F_{2,1(4)}] + J_2 \rho_4 F_{2,2(4)}$$
$$+ J_3[F_{23} + \rho_4 F_{2,3(4)}] + E_4 F_{24}$$
$$G_3 = J_1[F_{31} + \rho_4 F_{3,1(4)}] + J_2[F_{32} + \rho_4 F_{3,2(4)}] + E_4 F_{34}$$

or

$$G_1 = J_2[0.293 + 0.9(0.09)] + J_3[0.414 + 0.9(0.203)] + 0.293E_4$$
$$G_2 = J_1[0.293 + 0.9(0.09)] + (0.9)(0.09)J_2$$
$$+ J_3[0.293 + 0.9(0.09)] + 0.414E_4$$
$$G_3 = J_1[0.414 + 0.9(0.203)] + J_2[0.293 + 0.9(0.09)] + 0.293E_4$$

Substituting these expressions for irradiation into the equations for radiosity gives

$$J_1 - E_1 = \rho_1 G_1, \qquad J_2 - E_2 = \rho_2 G_2, \qquad J_3 - E_3 = \rho_3 G_3$$

$$J_1 - 0.0748J_2 - 0.1195J_3 = 3460$$

$$-0.1120J_1 + 0.937J_2 - 0.1120J_3 = 1519$$

$$-0.2396J_1 - 0.1495J_2 + J_3 = 567$$

Solving for radiosity and irradiation values gives

$$J_1 = 1834 \text{ Btu per hr-ft}^2 \qquad G_1 = 1966 \text{ Btu per hr-ft}^2$$

$$J_2 = 2300 \text{ Btu per hr-ft}^2 \qquad G_2 = 2623 \text{ Btu per hr-ft}^2$$

$$J_3 = 3851 \text{ Btu per hr-ft}^2 \qquad G_3 = 3173 \text{ Btu per hr-ft}^2$$

Then

$$q_1'' = 1966 - 3851 = -1885 \text{ Btu per hr-ft}^2$$

$$q_2'' = 2623 - 2300 = 323 \text{ Btu per hr-ft}^2$$

$$q_2'' = 3173 - 1834 = 1339 \text{ Btu per hr-ft}^2$$

The heat transfer to the specular surface is obtained from $q'' = \alpha G - E$, where the irradiation is given by

$$G_4 = F_{41}J_1 + F_{42}J_2 + F_{43}J_3$$

or

$$G_4 = 0.293(1834) + 0.414(2300) + 0.293(3851) = 2618 \text{ Btu per hr-ft}^2$$

Thus

$$q_4'' = 0.1(2618) - 32.5 = 229 \text{ Btu per hr-ft}^2$$

So that the difference in heat transfer rates caused by the specular-diffuse assumption for surface 4 could be shown, the same system was analyzed but assuming surface 4 to be a diffuse-diffuse surface. The result of this calculation is

$$q_{1_D}'' = -1782 \text{ Btu per hr-ft}^2$$

$$q_{2_D}'' = 300 \text{ Btu per hr-ft}^2$$

$$q_{3_D}'' = 1224 \text{ Btu per hr-ft}^2$$

$$q_{4_D}'' = 228 \text{ Btu per hr-ft}^2$$

A comparison of the two sets of heat transfer rates shows that a maximum difference of about 10 percent occurs if the system is analyzed as a diffuse-diffuse system. This difference is typical, although some extreme systems may have a difference up to 30 percent [9]. Since typical real surfaces are neither perfectly specular nor perfectly diffuse reflectors, two analyses such as the above give a range of values that should bracket the real transfer rates.

6.13 Combination of Specular-Diffuse and Diffuse-Diffuse Analysis

In some cases, the results of a specular-diffuse and a diffuse-diffuse analysis may give such different heat transfer rates that a combination of the two methods is desirable. This technique, which is suggested as a possibility in [2], requires a greater amount of information than is normally available. Basically, two reflectance values must be known for the surface under consideration: (1) the directional reflectance (which is assumed to be constant over all angle variations) and (2) the specular reflectance.

When a real surface is examined, it is normally neither specular nor diffuse. Thus, if a narrow beam of energy is directed onto the surface at incident angles ϕ and θ, the beam spreads upon reflection, but the spread is usually around the specular outgoing directions ϕ' and $(\theta + \pi)$. The magnitude of all the collected outgoing energy (regardless of direction) compared to the incoming energy is the directional reflectance. The collected energy coming out in a narrow beam at the specular angle is the specular reflectance.

The possibility then exists of considering the directional reflectance $\rho(\phi, \theta)$ to be made up of a specular reflectance $\rho_s(\phi, \theta)$ and a diffuse reflectance $\rho_D(\phi, \theta)$. Since this is an arbitrary procedure, a first approximation is to define $\rho_D(\phi, \theta) = \rho(\phi, \theta) - \rho_s(\phi, \theta)$. Because reflectance values are actually assumed to be independent of angle, the specification of the angles ϕ and θ is not necessary.

If reflectance data of this type are available, a combination of the two methods is possible. The technique is illustrated by considering the example of Section 6.12. With the reflectance of surface 4 specified as ρ_s for the specular portion and ρ_D for the diffuse portion, the irradiation of the surfaces are

$$G_1 = J_2[F_{12} + \rho_{4_s}F_{2,3(4)}] + J_3[F_{13} + \rho_{4_s}F_{1,3(4)}] + J_4\rho_{4_D}F_{14} + E_4F_{14}$$

$$G_2 = J_1[F_{21} + \rho_{4_s}F_{2,1(4)}] + \rho_{4_s}F_{2,2(4)}J_2 + J_3[F_{23} + \rho_{4_s}F_{2,3(4)}] +$$
$$+ J_4\rho_{4_D}F_{24} + E_4F_{24}$$

$$G_3 = J_1[F_{31} + \rho_{4_s}F_{3,1(4)}] + J_2[F_{32} + \rho_{4_s}F_{3,2(4)}] + J_4\rho_{4_D}F_{34} + E_4F_{34}$$

$$G_4 = F_{41}J_1 + F_{42}J_2 + F_{43}J_3$$

Using these values of irradiation in the following equations, we can evaluate the irradiation and radiosity of each surface and, therefore, the heat transfer rate:

$$J_1 = E_1 + \rho_1 G_1$$
$$J_2 = E_2 + \rho_2 G_2$$

$$J_3 = E_3 + \rho_3 G_3$$
$$J_4 = E_4 + (\rho_{4_s} + \rho_{4_D})G_4$$

This technique is not any more difficult to use than the specular-diffuse or diffuse-diffuse methods mentioned previously. The only difficulty is the lack of sufficient data for reasonable estimates of reflectance values. Such information may be available in the future, making this type of analysis possible. The ideal situation would be to have monochromatic specular and directional reflectance data, so that nongray analysis of specular-diffuse, diffuse-diffuse systems could be made. This would undoubtedly result in values for heat transfer satisfactory for engineering analysis.

Parametric Study of Radiant Systems

6.14 Relationship of Radiation to Conduction and Convection Modes of Transfer

The previous discussions of methods of calculating heat transfer rates by radiation are based on the assumption that the temperatures of the radiating surfaces are known *a priori*. This is not always the case in heat transfer problems. Frequently, radiant transfer occurs within a system such that the transfer of energy by conduction is bounded by radiant and convective transfer. When this is the case, the surface temperatures for the radiating elements may be changing, or at the very least, they may be unknowns in the steady-state transfer equations.

A technique that has been used frequently in the analysis of entire heat transfer systems is the numerical or nodular method. Basically, this method consists of lumping relatively large volumes in a system into a single node and then using a lumped parameter transfer system for analysis. In this technique, the resistance to energy flow from node to node must be known in order to determine the temperatures at the nodes. Of the radiant analysis techniques discussed, only one lends itself to the lumped parameter analysis of an entire system. This is the $\mathscr{F}$ technique.

6.15 Use of $\mathscr{F}$ in a Lumped Parameter Network

As an example of the use of $\mathscr{F}$ values in a lumped parameter network, consider Figure 6.14. A Large segment of a solid material is shown, with a square open duct running through the material. For convenience, consider the duct to be evacuated such that the only transfer from wall to wall through the duct is by radiation. Of each of the conduction nodes adjacent to the square duct, energy transfers into three sides by conduction and into the fourth side by radiation.

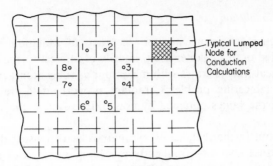

Figure 6.14   Conduction-Radiation Lumped Parameter Study.

An energy balance for a node by the lumped parameter method (for example node 3) would be

$$q_{\text{cond, above}} + q_{\text{cond, below}} + q_{\text{cond, right}} + q_{\text{rad, left}} + q_{\text{stor}} = 0$$

The conduction terms are generally represented by first-power temperature-difference potentials:

$$q_{\text{cond}} = \frac{(T_{\text{above}} - T_3)}{R_{\text{cond, above to 3}}}$$

In order to maintain the same type of expression for the radiant energy input, we express q_{rad} as

$$q_{\text{rad}} = \frac{(T_1 - T_3)}{R_{\text{rad } 1 \to 3}} + \frac{(T_2 - T_3)}{R_{\text{rad } 2 \to 3}} + \cdots + \frac{(T_8 - T_3)}{R_{\text{rad } 8 \to 3}}$$

The radiant resistors are obtained from the basic expression by

$$q_{1 \to 3} = \frac{(T_1 - T_3)}{R_{\text{rad } 1 \to 3}} = \mathscr{F}_{13} A_1 (E_{b_1} - E_{b_3})$$

Thus, if the $\mathscr{F}$ factors can be obtained by any of the techniques mentioned, the radiant resistors for the nodes can be determined. Notice that the $\mathscr{F}$ values have to be evaluated only once, unless very large changes in surface temperature result in significant changes in radiant properties.

Even though the $\mathscr{F}$ values must be evaluated only once, the radiation resistors change with each change of node temperature. If this is a transient heat-transfer problem, each advance in time requires a new calculation for the values of the radiant resistors. Although this introduces a considerable complication when compared to the conduction nodes, the complication is easily handled by a digital computer.

Furthermore, the use of $\mathscr{F}$ factors is obviously much less complicated than calculating the heat transfer by radiation in each time node from a radiation network or some other scheme.

6.16 Conclusion

The techniques for improving the accuracy of radiation heat transfer calculation listed in this chapter are primarily of interest to the analyst who must predict heat transfer rates with maximum possible accuracy. In the vast majority of engineering problems, radiant property data are so scarce or unreliable that the values obtained by gray-diffuse system analysis are satisfactory.

As pointed out in the text, semigray analysis—either using diffuse-diffuse or specular-diffuse analysis—frequently relieves the analyst of the necessity of making a tedious nongray analysis. It is recommended that nongray analysis, when undertaken, involve the use of a digital computer, except when very few bands are required.

The accuracy possible with the most complex analysis procedure, that is, a specular-diffuse, diffuse-diffuse mixture with nongray assumptions, is generally much better than the data available for the analysis. Under these conditions it is to be expected that such analysis will not be common until more and better data are available.

Exercises

6.1   (a) Examine the monochromatic emittance curve for zinc at 70°F in Appendix 1. Assuming that the monochromatic emittance is constant from 9 μ to longer wavelengths, specify the highest temperature at which zinc could be considered to be a gray surface. (b) Examine the monochromatic reflectance and monochromatic emittance curves for the materials in Appendix 1 and comment on the general use of gray assumptions at high or low temperatures.

6.2   Calculate the net energy exchange between two infinite parallel plates using the two-band approach, where the central wavelength λ_a, as described in Section 6.3, is 3 μ. Consider the two plates to be zinc, with temperatures of 100°F and 700°F respectively. Use the monochromatic emittance data from Appendix 1 to obtain the values of the emittance and absorptance required in the two-band approximation.

6.3   Calculate the equilibrium temperature of a zinc plate in space, assuming the solar irradiation to be 442 Btu per hr-ft² with a spectral distribution equivalent to a 10,000°R black body. This calculation may be carried out as a two-band approximation.

6.4   Calculate the energy exchange from a 1-ft diameter sphere of pure chromium suspended centrally in a cubic enclosure, which has an enclosure surface of vanadium. The sphere has a temperature of 100°F and the vanadium surface enclosure has a temperature of 800°F. Use diffuse monochromatic multiband approximations. In this case it would be worthwhile using the long-wavelength monochromatic reflectance approximation of Hagen-Ruben.

6.5   Calculate the net energy exchange between two infinite parallel opposed plates if one of the plates is 301 stainless steel at 1550°F and the other plate is oxidized iron at 500°F. Use the semigray approximation method described in Section 6.7.

6.6 Repeat the example given in Section 6.8. Consider the wall materials to be oxidized iron, cobalt alloy N-155 polished, monel k-5700 polished, and platinum. (Note that this problem will require considerable time.)

6.7 (a) Calculate the net energy exchange in an infinite square duct (see figure) where one surface is assumed to be specularly reflecting and diffusely emitting and the other surfaces are assumed to be diffuse emitters and reflectors. Use the following tabulated temperatures and properties for the surfaces:

Surface	Character	Temperature	Reflectance	Emittance
1	specular-diffuse	100°F	0.8	0.2
2	diffuse-diffuse	1000°F	0.2	0.8
3	diffuse-diffuse	200°F	0.6	0.4
4	diffuse-diffuse	200°F	0.4	0.6

(b) Repeat the calculations, assuming that surface 1 is a diffuse emitter and reflector.

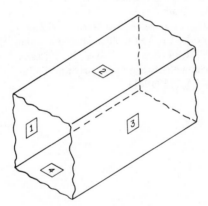

Exercise 6.7   Infinite Square Duct.

6.8 Repeat Problem 6.7, assuming the following properties for the duct surfaces:

Surface	Character	Temperature	Reflectance	Emittance
1	specular-diffuse	100°F	0.8	0.2
2	diffuse-diffuse	1000°F	0.2	0.8
3	diffuse-diffuse	200°F	0.6	0.4
4	specular-diffuse	200°F	0.4	0.6

6.9 Repeat Problem 6.7 again, assuming in this case that surface 1 is neither a perfectly specular nor perfectly diffuse reflector. Let the reflectance be divided such that $\rho_s = 0.5$ and $\rho_D = 0.3$, and determine the net energy exchange for each surface. (Refer to Section 6.13.)

References

1. BEVANS, J. T., and R. V. DUNKLE, "Radiant Interchange within an Enclosure," *ASME Transactions, Journal of Heat Transfer*, vol. 82 (February 1960).
2. BIRKEBAK, R. C., E. M. SPARROW, E. R. G. ECKERT, and J. W. RAMSEY, "Effect of Surface Roughness on the Total Hemispherical and Specular Reflectance of Metallic Surfaces," ASME Paper 63-HT-6 (1963).
3. ECKERT, E. R. G., and E. M. SPARROW, "Radiative Heat Exchange Between Surfaces with Specular Reflection," *International Journal of Heat Mass Transfer*, vol. 3 (1961), pp. 42–54.
4. EDWARDS, D. K., K. E. NELSON, R. D. RODDICK, and J. T. GIER, "Basic Studies on the Use and Control of Solar Energy," Department of Engineering Report 60-93, University of California at Los Angeles, October 1960.
5. ETEMAD, G. A., Discussion of "Comparison of Total Emittance with Values Computed From Spectral Measurements," by J. T. Bevans, J. T. Gier, and R. V. Dunkle, *ASME Transactions*, vol. 80 (1958), p. 1415.
6. JAKOB, MAX, *Heat Transfer*, vol. 1. New York: John Wiley & Sons, Inc. (1949), p. 44.
7. MOON, PARRY, *The Scientific Basis of Illuminating Engineering*. New York: McGraw-Hill, Inc., 1936.
8. PIVOVONSKY, MARK, and MAX R. NAGEL, *Tables of Blackbody Radiation Functions*. New York: Crowell Collier and Macmillan, Inc., 1961.
9. SPARROW, E. M., E. R. G. ECKERT, and V. K. JONSSON, "An Enclosure Theory for Radiative Exchange Between Specularly and Diffusely Reflecting Surfaces," ASME Paper 61-WA-175 (1961).

CHAPTER 7

Energy Transfer in
Absorbing and Emitting Media

In previous chapters, consideration of energy transfer by radiation through a nonparticipating medium has not involved the problem of interaction. That is, radiation exchange has been treated as a boundary condition for conduction occuring within a system and has been considered separately.

When a medium such as a transparent solid or a participating gas absorbs and emits energy, radiation, conduction—and perhaps convection for the gaseous case—all occur simultaneously. When all modes of transfer occur simultaneously, a nonlinear differential equation results from the typical energy balance. Furthermore, if the medium is a scattering medium, an integro-differential equation results. These mathematically complex systems are presently being studied by various researchers [8, 17, 18] to determine limiting solutions for practical systems.

In order to delineate an area of study for this chapter, the material included will involve only those cases where the radiant mode of transfer is predominate. Most of the discussion will be concerned with gaseous systems that are isothermal. Such systems obviously do not occur in the real world; however, the study of energy exchange in these ideal cases is necessary to understand some of the difficulties in analyzing energy exchange in gas or transparent media.

Initially, energy exchange from isothermal nongray gases will be considered. It is felt that an understanding of this system will lead to more complete appreciation of the simplicity of the gray gas system. If the gray gas system is discussed first, the empirical relationships necessary for its analysis do not lead to a complete understanding of the problems involved. After the discussion of nongray and gray gas systems, the limited information available for radiation from flames will be presented.

155

Typical Gaseous Emission and Absorption

Gases that exhibit energy transformations in the wavelengths of thermal radiation are gases with polar molecular form. In the terms of the physicist, these gases have an *electric moment*. In some cases this is a dipole moment, and in more complex molecules a quadrupole moment. Regardless of the terminology, the molecules are always asymmetric in some mode of vibration. For example, H_2O, CO_2, CO, or CN are asymmetric in one or more modes of vibration; O_2, N_2, H_2, and A are not asymmetric in any mode of molecular vibration. It should be understood that electronic energy transformations (which are essentially line or monochromatic phenomena) may occur in thermal radiation wavelengths, but the energy associated with these transformations is generally very small when compared to energies in thermal analysis.

The typical thermal energy transformation occurs as a result of changes in vibrational frequency and rotation. This is manifested in a strong peak of energy emitted at a wavelength corresponding to the vibrational transformation, with multiple rotational energy emissions at wavelengths slightly different than the wavelength for vibrational energy. For this reason, the energy emitted is usually described as a band of energy over a group of wavelengths from a rotation-vibration transformation.

The result of this type of energy interaction is that gaseous absorption or emission occurs in discrete bands, as shown in Figure 7.1. It is important

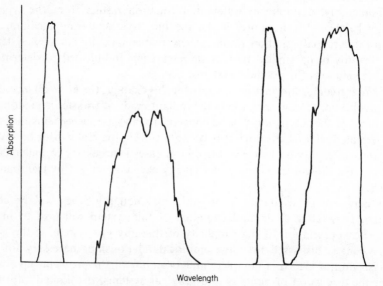

Figure 7.1   Typical Gas Absorption.

to notice that the behavior of gases results in a system that is highly nongray. That is, the possibility of simply assuming either the monochromatic emission or absorption independently of the wavelength is precluded.

7.1 Mathematical Expressions for Gas Properties

Properties of gases are normally reported in terms of monochromatic absorption, since this is the type of data obtained from experimental apparatus. Also, the data is frequently reported on the basis of frequency or its equivalent, wave numbers. For this reason the following discussion will use the symbol v to indicate wave number, and dv to describe the interval v to $(v + dv)$.

In a typical experimental evaluation of gaseous properties, a beam of energy with the measurable intensity $I_v(O)$ is directed onto the face of a finite isothermal gas layer as shown in Figure 7.2. The intensity $I_v(L)$ emerging from the gas layer of thickness L is measured experimentally. Considering only the energy proceeding in the direction of the original intensity $I_v(O)$, we get the following differential equation for the change in the intensity [1]:

$$dI_v(x) = \kappa_v I_{bv} \gamma \, dx - \kappa_v I_v(x) \gamma \, dx \tag{7.1}$$

where I_{bv} is the intensity of a black surface at T_g
  κ_v is the mass absorption coefficient
  γ is the density.

The first term to the left of the equality in Equation 7.1 represents the energy emitted by the gas in the direction of the original intensity $I_v(O)$, and the second term represents the energy absorbed from the local intensity $I_v(x)$ in the

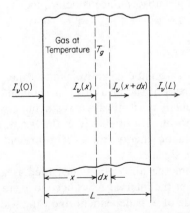

Figure 7.2   System for Gas Property Definition.

interval dx. Integrating Equation 7.1 results in

$$I_v(L) = I_v(0)e^{-\kappa_v \gamma L} + I_{bv}(1 - e^{-\kappa_v \gamma L}) \qquad (7.2)$$

It is important to note that this integration is possible only if κ_v, γ, and I_{bv} are constant over the length of the gas considered. For a system in which the values are variables, an entirely different result occurs. Another assumption which is made is that local thermodynamic equilibrium exists. If equilibrium does not exist, the mass absorption coefficient κ_v is not the same for both emission and absorption.

Equation 7.2 is usually written as

$$I_v(L) = \tau_v(T_g, \gamma, L)I_v(0) + \alpha_v(T_g, \gamma, L)I_{bv}(T_g) \qquad (7.3)$$

where

$$\tau_v(T_g, \gamma, L) = e^{-\kappa_v \gamma L}$$

$$\alpha_v(T_g, \gamma, L) = 1 - \tau_v(T_g, \gamma, L)$$

Equation 7.3 shows the transmittance and absorptance or emittance of the gas in a fairly recognizable format. In general, for an isothermal gas system or a system which has local thermodynamic equilibrium,

$$\alpha_v(T_g, \gamma, L) = \varepsilon_v(T_g, \gamma, L).$$

If the energy emerging in the experimental gas measurement consists of both energy emitted and energy transmitted, it would seem impossible to identify the source of the energy. However, this can be accomplished by chopping the incident beam $I_v(0)$. If $I_v(0)$ is chopped, the emerging beam consists of a continuous beam resulting from the energy emitted, and a chopped beam resulting from the energy transmitted. By using a detection system that is insensitive to the continuous beam, the transmittance of the gas layer can be measured. By definition, the gas absorptance is $1 - \tau_v(T_g, \gamma, L)$; thus, monochromatic gas absorptance is determined.

7.2 Band Absorption

In measuring monochromatic gas absorptance, the absorptance indicated depends on the bandpass of the measuring instrument. This occurs because the measuring instrument must always have a finite-width bandpass Δv in order to obtain a finite amount of energy in the beam. If the beam consisted of strictly monochromatic energy, the energy present would be too small to cause a measurable signal.

With this restriction, the absorption measured is always an average of the real absorption over the interval Δv. Since the average value is measured, the absolute magnitude of α_v is dependent upon the width of the interval Δv. This means that α_v cannot be reported as a function of wave number unless the wavelength interval Δv is also reported. For this reason the band absorption is reported where it is defined as

$$\mathscr{A}_i = \int_{v_1}^{v_2} \alpha_v \, dv \tag{7.4}$$

In Equation 7.4, v_1 and v_2 are chosen such that the monochromatic absorptance is zero for each value. Of course, this implies that $\mathscr{A}_i$ is the total absorptance in the absorption band. Band absorption $\mathscr{A}_i$ is independent of the bandpass Δv of the measuring instrument [1]; therefore, these values can be reported without specifying the bandpass Δv of the measurements.

In the measurement of band absorption, the variables that can be controlled for any given gas are temperature T_g, partial pressure p_g, total pressure P, and the mass path length γL. With this many independent variables, it is imperative that some sort of correlation be developed. Correlations for band absorption have been the concern of a number of research groups for several years [6, 7, 16]. In general, they are still being developed, but certain correlations can be presented from the literature now.

The correlations for carbon dioxide given in Table 7.1 were determined by a UCLA group under the direction of D. K. Edwards. In this tabulation two basic correlation equations were used:

$$\mathscr{A} = B \cdot P_E{}^n \cdot w^m \tag{7.5}$$

and

$$\mathscr{A} = B + C \log w + D \log P_E \tag{7.6}$$

where P_E is the equivalent broadening pressure $P(1 + x + 0.5x^2 P)$ in which P is the total pressure in atmospheres and x is the mole fraction of CO_2 present, w is the mass path length γL in which γ is the mass density in milli-pounds per cubic foot and L is the path length in feet, and B, C, D, n, and m are the correlation constants given in Table 7.1.

An arbitrary expression of the absorptivity of each band listed is also given in Table 7.1. These are S (strong), MS (medium strong), M (medium), and W (weak) for each band fit. In the table the limits of the equivalent broadening pressure and mass path length are indicated by the subscripts L (lower) and U (upper) on P_E and w. Additional correlations for CO_2 have been published by Edwards in [6, 7].

Energy-Exchange Expressions for Enclosures

7.3 Basic Geometric Considerations

In this section equations will be developed for radiant energy exchange in an enclosure that includes an isothermal gas. The energy exchange between the walls and the gas by either conduction or convection is not considered.

TABLE 7.1†

Band-absorption Correlations for Carbon Dioxide in Nitrogen

Band	Fit	P_{E_L} (atm)	P_{E_U} (atm)	T_g (°R)	w_L (mlb/ft²)	w_U (mlb/ft²)	Correlation for $\mathscr{A} \pm \Delta\mathscr{A}$ (cm⁻¹)	(cm⁻¹)
15μ	S	2.5	70	530	400	5000	$82w^{0.11}p_E^{0.03}$	6
				1000	80	740	$121w^{0.11}p_E^{0.02}$	6
				1500	80	500	$147w^{0.11}p_E^{0.01}$	6
				2000	75	380	$166w^{0.11}p_E^{0.01}$	7
				2500	60	310	$182w^{0.11}$	7
	MS	0.1	1.0	530	4	3300	$36 + 55\log w + 47\log P_E$	
		1.0	10	530	13	400	$20 + 51\log w + 22\log P_E$	5
				1000	4	80	$20 + 82\log w + 19\log P_E$	5
				1500	3	80	$20 + 112\log w + 12\log P_E$	4
				2000	2	75	$20 + 135\log w + 7\log P_E$	4
				2500	2	60	$20 + 152\log w$	
10.4μ	M	0.1	1.0	530		3	$30.3w^{0.50}p_E^{0.44}$	
	M	20	70	1000	380	750	$2.1w^{0.50}$	2
				1500	260	510	$4.4w^{0.50}$	2
				2000	190	390	$6.1w^{0.50}$	3
				2500	150	310	$7.1w^{0.50}$	3
	W	1.0	20	530	0	5000	$4 \times 10^{-3}w$	2
				1000	0	380	$9 \times 10^{-2}w$	2
				1500	0	260	$0.30w$	2
				2000	0	190	$0.50w$	3
				2500	0	150	$0.69w$	3
9.4μ	M	20	70	1000	380	750	$1.9w^{0.50}$	2
				1500	260	510	$3.4w^{0.50}$	2
				2000	190	390	$4.5w^{0.50}$	3
				2500	150	310	$5.3w^{0.50}$	3

Band	Structure	p_E (min)	p_E (max)				Correlation	Ref.
	W	1.0	20	530	0	5000	$5 \times 10^{-3}w$	2
				1000	0	380	$0.10w$	2
				1500	0	260	$0.31w$	2
				2000	0	190	$0.50w$	3
				2500	0	150	$0.65w$	3
7.5μ	W	6	70	530	0	5000	$1.0 \times 10^{-3}wP,\ x = 1.00$	4
5.2μ	M	0.1	1.0	530	30	30000	$0.18w^{0.50}p_E^{0.40}$	2
	W	6	70	530–2500‡	400	5000	$0.2w^{0.50}p_E^{0.10}$	2
4.8μ	M	1	10	530–2500‡	0	400	$8 \times 10^{-3}w$	2
	W	6	70	530	30	7000	$0.73w^{0.50}p_E^{0.37}$	2
	M	1	10	530–2500‡	400	5000	$0.62w^{0.50}p_E^{0.1}$	2
	W	0.1	1.0	530–2500‡	0	4000	0.040	
4.3μ	S	0.1	1.0	530	30	7000	$99 + 34\log w + 31.5\log p_E$	7
	S	0.5	70	530	13	5000	$89w^{0.11}p_E^{0.08}$	7
				1000‡	8	750	$111w^{0.11}p_E^{0.05}$	5
				1500‡	3	500	$142w^{0.11}p_E^{0.03}$	5
				2000‡	4	390	$171w^{0.11}p_E^{0.02}$	5
				2500‡	2	310	$209w^{0.11}p_E^{0.01}$	
2.7μ	S	0.1	1.0	530	40	6500	$15 + 77\log w + 68\log p_E$	22
	S	1	70	530	60	5000	$107w^{0.12}p_E^{0.06}$	22
				1000	50	750	$143w^{0.12}p_E^{0.02}$	17
				1500	50	510	$179w^{0.12}$	17
				2000	50	390	$205w^{0.12}$	17
				2500	50	310	$239w^{0.12}$	
	M	0.1	1.0	530		3	$28.3w^{0.5}E^{0.43}$	
	M	0.5		530	13	60	$24w^{0.50}p_E^{0.4}$	22
	M	1	10	1000	4	50	$30w^{0.50}p_E^{0.06}$	22

† D. K. Edwards [4]

‡ An arbitrary separation of the 4.3, 4.8, and 5.2μ bands, which overlap at high temperatures, was made by taking the 530°R correlations of the latter two bands to be valid at all temperatures.

TABLE 7.1 (Continued)

Band	Fit	P_{E_L} (atm)	P_{E_U} (atm)	T_g (°R)	w_L (mlb/ft²)	w_U	Correlation for $\mathscr{A} \pm \Delta \mathscr{A}$ (cm⁻¹)	(cm⁻¹)
2.0μ	S	0.1	1.0	530	400	32000	$-286 + 138 \log w + 114 \log P_E$	
		20	70	530	1400	5000	$39w^{0.20}p_E^{0.06}$	15
	M	0.1	1.0	530	200	500	$3.4w^{0.50}p_E^{0.39}$	15
		1	70	530	380	1400	$3.2w^{0.50}p_E^{0.15}$	15
				1000	260	750	$3.4w^{0.50}p_E^{0.15}$	8
				1500		510	$3.9w^{0.50}p_E^{0.15}$	15
2.0μ	W	1	70	530	0	200	$0.34w$	15
				1000	0	150	$0.40w$	8
2.0μ	W	1	70	1500	0	100	$0.50w$	9
				2000	0	400	$0.53w$	9
				2500	0	310	$0.53w$	
1.6μ	M	0.1	1.0	530	400	32000	$0.41w^{0.50}p_E^{0.38}$	8
	1	70	70	530	290	5000	$0.40w^{0.50}p_E^{0.1}$	
1.4μ	M	0.1	1.0	530	400	32000	$0.46w^{0.50}p_E^{0.41}$	8
		1	70	530	290	5000	$0.45w^{0.50}p_E^{0.1}$	
				1500	3	50	$37w^{0.50}p_E^{0.06}$	16
				2000	4	50	$45w^{0.50}p_E^{0.06}$	16
				2500	2	50	$53w^{0.50}p_E^{0.06}$	16

The basic equation to be used for radiant exchange is the same as used previously, that is, the radiant energy exchange q'' is equal to the difference between the energy absorbed by a surface and the energy emitted by a surface. With this general concept, energy-exchange calculations reduce to an evaluation of the irradiation of any particular surface in an enclosure.

Figure 7.3   Geometry for Energy-Exchange in a Gas-filled Enclosure.

For example, consider the irradiation of surface 1 by energy from the direction of surface 2 as shown in Figure 7.3. The irradiation of surface 1 by energy from surface 2 and the intervening gas is given from Equation 7.3 as

$$G_{1 \text{ from } 2}A_1 = \int_0^\infty \int_{A_2} \int_{A_1} \tau_v I_{v2} \frac{\cos \phi_1 \cos \phi_2 \, dA_1 \, dA_2 \, dv}{r^2}$$

$$+ \int_0^\infty \int_{A_2} \int_{A_1} \alpha_v I_{bv}(T_g) \frac{\cos \phi_1 \cos \phi_2 \, dA_1 \, dA_2 \, dv}{r^2} \qquad (7.7)$$

In Equation 7.7 the first term to the right of the equality represents the irradiation of surface 2 by energy that leaves surface 1 and is transmitted through the gas. This is recognizable as the same term used when energy transfer occurred without a gas present, that is, if τ_v is equal to unity, this is exactly the same as the previously obtained expression. The second term on the right-hand side of the equality represents the energy emitted by the gas between surfaces 1 and 2 that is incident upon surface 1. In this term $I_{bv}(T_g)$ is the intensity of a Plankian or black body evaluated at the gas temperature T_g. When surface 1 is one surface of an n surface enclosure, n expressions like Equation 7.7 are required to express the total irradiation of the surface, that is

$$G_1 A_1 = \sum_{k=1}^n \left[\int_0^\infty \int_{A_k} \int_{A_1} \frac{\tau_v I_{vk} \cos \phi_1 \cos \phi_k \, dA_1 \, dA_k \, dv}{r^2} \right.$$

$$\left. + \int_0^\infty \int_{A_k} \int_{A_1} \frac{\alpha_v I_{bv}(T_g) \cos \phi_1 \cos \phi_k \, dA_1 \, dA_k \, dv}{r^2} \right] \qquad (7.8)$$

If we assume that each of the surfaces in the enclosure are diffuse emitters and reflectors, I_{vk} can be replaced with J_{vk}/π, and similarly, $I_{bv}(T_g)$ by $E_{bv}(T_g)/\pi$.

$$G_1 A_1 = \sum_{k=1}^{n} \left[\int_0^\infty \int_{A_k} \int_{A_1} \frac{\tau_\nu J_{\nu k} \cos \phi_1 \cos \phi_k \, dA_1 \, dA_k \, d\nu}{\pi r^2} \right.$$

$$\left. + \int_0^\infty \int_{A_k} \int_{A_1} \frac{\alpha_\nu E_{b\nu}(T_g) \cos \phi_1 \cos \phi_k \, dA_1 \, dA_k \, d\nu}{\pi r^2} \right] \quad (7.9)$$

Since the energy exchange can be immediately evaluated if the irradiation of a surface is known, the problem of energy exchange with a gas present is reduced to the evaluation of Equation 7.9 for each surface in the enclosure.

7.4 The Inherent Difficulty of Evaluation

In order to show the inherent difficulty of the evaluation of Equation 7.9, we shall examine the first term on the right-hand side of the equality. Since this discussion is to indicate the basic problem, only the $k = 2$ term will be considered.

$$\int_0^\infty \int_{A_2} \int_{A_1} \frac{\tau_\nu J_{\nu 2} \cos \phi_1 \cos \phi_2 \, dA_1 \, dA_2 \, d\nu}{\pi r^2}$$

From our definition, $\tau_\nu = e^{-\kappa_\nu \gamma r}$ for the path from dA_1 to dA_2; thus, this term can be expressed as

$$\int_0^\infty \int_{A_2} \int_{A_1} \frac{e^{-\kappa_\nu \gamma r} J_{\nu 2} \cos \phi_1 \cos \phi_2 \, dA_1 \, dA_2 \, d\nu}{\pi r^2}$$

Since the functional dependence of the geometric terms A_1 and A_2 can be evaluated, it would appear that this term could be evaluated if the functional dependence of $J_{\nu 2}$ and κ_ν could be determined. The radiosity $J_{\nu 2}$ can be evaluated in a manner similar to the methods used for systems without a gas; therefore, this leaves κ_ν variations with ν as the only variable. Thus, if the variation of κ_ν can be determined, it is possible, at least in principle, to evaluate this term. Actually, the variation of κ_ν is not known, since the experimental procedure results in values of band absorption $\mathscr{A}$ rather than κ_ν. For this reason it is practically impossible to evaluate terms of this nature.

7.5 Practical Approximations

The practical approach to the solution of this problem involves the judicious use of several approximations. First, the enclosure is divided into surface elements small enough that $J_{\nu 2}$ may be assumed to be independent of location over the area A_2. Secondly, the evaluation is carried out over finite-width wavelength bands, and these bands are assumed to be so narrow that $J_{\nu 2}$ does not vary over the wavelength bands. With these two approximations,

$$\int_{\Delta v_i} \int_{A_2} \int_{A_1} \frac{\tau_v J_{v2} \cos \phi_1 \cos \phi_2 \, dA_1 \, dA_2 \, dv}{\pi r^2}$$

$$= J_{v2} \int_{A_2} \int_{A_1} \frac{\cos \phi_1 \cos \phi_2 \, dA_1 \, dA_2}{\pi r^2} \int_{\Delta v_i} \tau_v \, dv$$

Substituting $\tau_v = 1 - \alpha_v$ and using band absorption notation gives

$$\int_{\Delta v_i} \int_{A_2} \int_{A_1} \frac{\tau_v J_{v2} \cos \phi_1 \cos \phi_2 \, dA_1 \, dA_2 \, dv}{\pi r^2}$$

$$= J_{v2} \Delta v_i F_{12} A_1 - J_{v2} \int_{A_2} \int_{A_1} \frac{\mathscr{A}_i \cos \phi_1 \cos \phi_2 \, dA_1 \, dA_2}{\pi r^2}$$

With these two assumptions, an extremely difficult expression has been reduced to the evaluation of a double integral:

$$\int_{A_2} \int_{A_1} \frac{\mathscr{A}_i \cos \phi_1 \cos \phi_2 \, dA_1 \, dA_2}{\pi r^2}$$

If band-absorption correlations are available, this term can be integrated [19]. Such a procedure is usually not justified, since the accuracy of the solution resulting is not any better than the accuracy of the band-absorption data.

7.6 Mean Beam Length

If the term

$$\int_{A_2} \int_{A_1} \frac{\mathscr{A}_i \cos \phi_1 \cos \phi_2 \, dA_1 \, dA_2}{\pi r^2}$$

is expanded to include a typical correlation for band absorption, the result is

$$\int_{A_2} \int_{A_1} \frac{\mathscr{A}_i \cos \phi_1 \cos \phi_2 \, dA_1 \, dA_2}{\pi r^2}$$

$$= B \cdot P_E{}^n \cdot \gamma^m \int_{A_2} \int_{A_1} \frac{r^m \cos \phi_1 \cos \phi_2 \, dA_1 \, dA_2}{\pi r^2}$$

This expression may be satisfactorily approximated by using the geometric mean beam length [3] defined as

$$\bar{r}_{12} = \frac{1}{F_{12} A_1} \int_{A_2} \int_{A_1} r \frac{\cos \phi_1 \cos \phi_2 \, dA_1 \, dA_2}{\pi r^2}$$

Thus

$$\int_{A_1} \int_{A_1} \frac{r^m \cos \phi_1 \cos \phi_2 \, dA_1 \, dA_2}{\pi r^2} \simeq \bar{r}_{12}^m F_{12} A_1$$

This last approximation has been examined for the case of $m = 0.12$ and

$m = 0.50$, but it has not been examined for logarithmic band-absorption correlations. For the cases where the correlation equations are of the form $B \cdot P_E{}^n \cdot w^m$, this will result in approximations as accurate as the usual band-absorption data.

To recap, the expressions on the right-hand side of Equation 7.9 have been approximated for an index equal to 2 as

$$Gv_{i1}\Delta v_i A_1 \simeq \bar{J}_{v2}\Delta v_i F_{12}A_1 - \bar{J}_{v2}F_{12}A_1 B \cdot P_E{}^n(\gamma \bar{r}_{12})^m +$$

$$\bar{E}_{bv}(T_g)F_{12}A_1 B \cdot P_E{}^n(\gamma \bar{r}_{12})^m$$

In order to specify which terms are the average values over the band Δv_i, the symbol with a bar over it is desirable, that is,

$$\bar{J}_{v2} = \frac{\displaystyle\int_{\Delta v_i} J_{v2}\,dv}{\Delta v_i}$$

Similarly, a single symbol is desirable for the band absorption; thus, if

$$\bar{\alpha}_{\Delta v_i} = \frac{B \cdot P_E{}^n(\gamma \bar{r}_{12})^m}{\Delta v_i} = 1 - \bar{\tau}_{\Delta v_i}$$

we have

$$\bar{G}_{v_i1}A_1 \simeq \bar{J}_{v2}F_{12}A_1\bar{\tau}_{\Delta v_i} + \bar{E}_{bv}F_{12}A_1\bar{\alpha}_{\Delta v_i} \tag{7.10}$$

Equation 7.10 represents the irradiation of surface 1 by energy from surface 2 and the gas between the surfaces only in the frequency band Δv_i. Thus, if the total irradiation of surface 1 is to be evaluated, terms of this type must be evaluated for the entire frequency spectrum of importance.

7.7 Summary of the Nongray Isothermal Gas Solution

To summarize the requirements and methods of analysis for energy exchange in an enclosure that contains a nongray gas, we shall consider a gas with absorption characteristics similar to those in Figure 7.4. The frequency band of interest is divided into absorption regions and window regions. In the window regions, the gas is totally transparent. This causes two different types of expressions for energy transfer: one for the regions of absorptance and another for the window regions.

If we are to consider an enclosure consisting of n surfaces, each of which is assumed to have a uniform radiosity, the following sets of equations must be solved: For the i absorption regions,

$$\bar{G}_{vij}A_j = \sum_{k=1}^{n} \bar{J}_{vik}F_{kj}A_k\bar{\tau}_{v_i} + \sum_{k=1}^{n} \bar{E}_{bvi}(T_g)F_{kj}A_k\bar{\alpha}_{\Delta v_i}$$

$$j = 1, 2, 3, \dots n \tag{7.11}$$

For the l window regions,

$$\bar{G}_{v_l j} A_j = \sum_{k=1}^{n} \bar{J}_{v_l k} F_{kj} A_k \qquad j = 1, 2, 3, \dots n \qquad (7.12)$$

Equations 7.11 and 7.12 are written for the irradiation of the jth surface for compactness; actually, the solution must be obtained for the radiosities

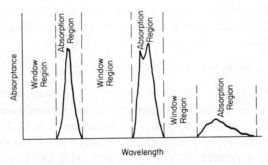

Figure 7.4   Band Division for Energy Exchange Calculations.

from the standard radiosity equation for a surface, $J_j = \rho_j G_j + E_j$. Comparison of the two equations indicates that the only items different from the expressions used previously are the average transmittance or absorptance and, although not explicitly, the bandwidths Δv_i and Δv_l.

For certain cases these expressions can be evaluated with close approximation by using band-absorption correlations and geometric mean beam lengths. In these cases, the bandwidths Δv_i and Δv_l may have to be estimated from experimental data; that is, the tabulations of band-absorption do not indicate bandwidth to be used with the values. Such information is obviously necessary in order to evaluate average values for use in the equations. Thus, the solution for energy exchange in enclosures using nongray gas assumptions is presently very arbitrary in nature. For this reason a method for solution presented by Edwards will be discussed in Section 7.13, after the gray gas discussion that follows.

Gray Gas Approximations for Energy Exchange

The technique of solution by assuming gray gases was introduced many years ago by H. C. Hottel [14]. In the gray gas method, it is understood that most engineering problems involving radiant energy exchange with a gas present occur only in high-gas-temperature apparatus. Frequently, these apparatus have highly oxididized or contaminated walls with very high emittance or absorptance. For this reason, the gray gas techniques which were developed are mainly applicable to energy exchange in systems where the walls are either black or nearly black.

7.8 Method of Approach

If an enclosure with black walls exchanges energy with an enclosed radiating gas, the energy exchange consists of energy emitted by a wall at some temperature T_w and transmitted through a gas at T_g, plus energy emitted by the gas. Since the walls do not reflect energy, no interreflections are involved. If we consider two walls in such a system, we can write the energy incident upon one wall from the other wall and the gas between as

$$G_1 A_1 = E_{b_2}(T_w) F_{21} A_2 \tau_g + E_b(T_g) F_{21} A_2 \varepsilon_g \tag{7.13}$$

In Equation 7.13, $A_2 E_{b_2}(T_w)$ is the energy emitted by black wall 2, of which F_{21} is directed toward wall 1. The symbol τ_g, the transmittance of the gas between the walls, is the main new variable to be evaluated in this term. The second term on the right-hand side of Equation 7.13 is the energy emitted by the gray gas, expressed as $\varepsilon_g E_b(T_g) A_2$, and since the gas considered is between surfaces 1 and 2, F_{21} is the fraction of the energy emitted by the gas incident upon surface 1.

At this point the question may arise why the total emissive power of the gas is multiplied by the area A_2. Suffice it to say that the energy emitted from the volume between surfaces 1 and 2 may be artificially represented by the terms used. Once again, the emittance ε_g of the gas between the surfaces is the primary new variable to be evaluated.

7.9 Evaluation of Gas Emittance and Transmittance

Experimentally, the total transmittance of any given gas composition at some given state can be measured by comparing the energy emitted by a black source either having the gas in the path or out of the path. If the black source is maintained at the temperature of the surroundings, the emittance can be measured; if the source is at a temperature above the gas temperature, the transmittance can be measured indirectly.

In any experiment, a definite gas path L must be maintained, with total

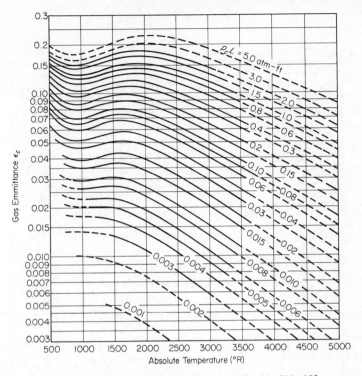

Figure 7.5   Emittance of Carbon Dioxide [11, 12].

and partial pressures and gas temperature as variables. Usually, the energy received by the detector is unidirectional and represents either the emittance or transmittance for a single direction. For this reason the emittance and transmittance values described in Equation 7.13 must be evaluated for some mean beam length when surfaces 1 and 2 are finite.

Typically, emittance is a function of gas temperature, mass path length, gas total pressure, and active gas partial pressure. Tabulations of experimental results must allow consideration of all of these variables. The results of Hottel and Egbert [10, 11], presented in Figures 7.5, 7.6, 7.7, 7.8, and 7.9, are designed to allow this consideration.

In Figures 7.5 and 7.6, the reduced emittance ε_g' of CO_2 and H_2O are presented as a function of the absolute temperature of the gas and the product of the mean beam length and partial pressure. These values are called the *reduced emittance* because they are plotted for a reduced pressure; that is, in order to obtain smooth presentation of the data, all data is reduced to an equivalent partial pressure of zero.

The effect of total pressure is given in Figures 7.7 and 7.8. These figures give the ratio of the actual emittance at the state being considered to the

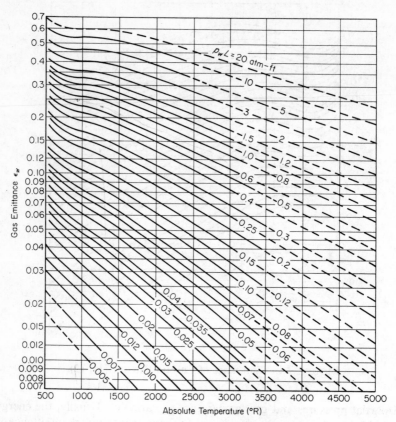

Figure 7.6   Emittance of Water Vapor [11, 12].

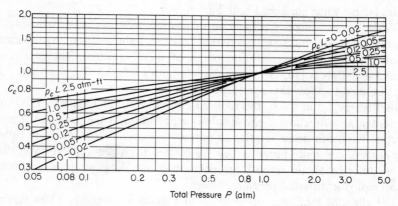

Figure 7.7   Correction Factor for CO_2 Emittance [10].

reduced emittance values of Figures 7.5 and 7.6. The variables for this ratio are the total pressure and the product of partial pressure times mean beam length. When both water vapor and carbon dioxide are present in the gas, a correction for the mixture composition may be made from Figure 7.9. The values of $\Delta\varepsilon$ in these figures are subtracted from the sum of the emittances of each component, as determined from Figures 7.5, 7.6, 7.7, and 7.8.

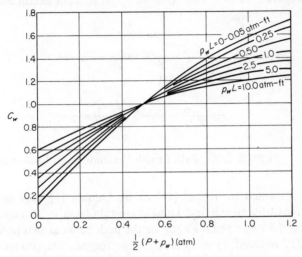

Figure 7.8   Correction Factor for H_2O Emittance [10].

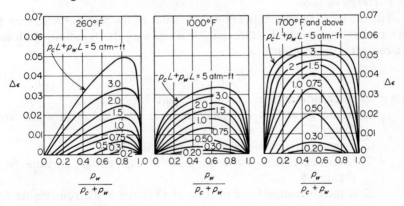

Figure 7.9   Correction Factor for Band Overlap when CO_2 and H_2O Are Present in an Enclosure [10].

7.10 Calculation of Energy Transfer for Black-Wall Enclosures

The clearest presentation of the technique of energy transfer calculation is by example. Consider two infinite flat plates with an isothermal radiating gas between them. Since data is available for CO_2 or H_2O, assume the active gas present to consist of either or both of these gases.

The first problem that arises in calculating energy transfer through gray gas is to deduce what path length to use in evaluating the emittance from Figures 7.5 through 7.9. In the case of infinite plates, the path through the gas varies from a minimum of L to a maximum of ∞; two such paths are shown in Figure 7.10 as l_1 and l_2. Since a mean beam length must be used,

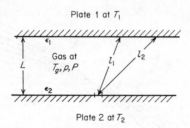

Plate 1 at T_1

Gas at T_g, p, P

Plate 2 at T_2

Figure 7.10   Path Length Variation in an Enclosure.

the values presented by Hottel [14] or by Dunkle [3] may be used. The results obtained by Hottel and Dunkle are tabulated in Appendix 6. From these values, the mean beam length for the path between two parallel infinite planes is $2L$, reduced by a suitable factor for pL, the product of partial pressure times mean beam length. Assuming that pL is rather large, a value of $1.7L$ may be used.

With the mean beam length known, the value of the gas emittance may be obtained from Figures 7.5 through 7.9. Following the notation of Hottel, we can write the emittance as

$$\varepsilon_g = \varepsilon_c' C_c + \varepsilon_w' C_w - \Delta\varepsilon \tag{7.14}$$

where ε_c' is the emittance of CO_2 from Figure 7.5
$\quad C_c$ is the correction for total pressure and partial pressure from Figure 7.7
$\quad \varepsilon_w'$ is the emittance of the H_2O from Figure 7.6
$\quad C_w$ is the correction for total pressure and partial pressure from Figure 7.8
$\quad \Delta\varepsilon$ is the correction for a mixture of CO_2 and H_2O from Figure 7.9.

Referring back to Equation 7.13, we see that the value of $F_{21}A_2\varepsilon_g$ is simply $A_2\varepsilon_g$ for the infinite parallel plate system. When Hottel's values for the mean beam length are used, the energy emitted by the gas is given as $E_b(T_g)A\varepsilon_g$. Dunkle's tabulation for mean beam length is strictly a geometric value and must be used when an enclosure is divided into subareas. All of Hottel's values are for radiation from the entire enclosure. In Equation 7.13 the term

$F_{21}A_2\tau_g$ is evaluated from $\tau_g = 1 - \alpha_g$ where

$$\alpha_g = \alpha_c + \alpha_w - \Delta\alpha \tag{7.15}$$

in which

$$\alpha_c = \varepsilon_c'\left(\frac{T_g}{T_w}\right)^{0.65} C_c \tag{7.16}$$

$$\alpha_w = \varepsilon_w'\left(\frac{T_g}{T_w}\right)^{0.45} C_w \tag{7.17}$$

$$\Delta\alpha = \Delta\varepsilon_{\text{eval at } T_w}$$

In the evaluation of ε_c' or ε_w' in Equations 7.16 and 7.17, the value is obtained by using $pL(T_w/T_g)$ and T_w rather than pL and T_g. This is done to account for the nongrayness of the real gas. The empirical relationships used for these evaluations are understandable when it is recognized that all of the gray gas assumptions have a wide range of error.

7.11 Numerical Example

As a numerical example of problem solution using gray gas assumptions, consider the infinite plate system of the previous section, with a spacing of 1 ft. Assume the gas between the plates to be an isothermal mixture consisting of 25 percent by volume CO_2, 25 percent by volume H_2O, and 50 percent by volume N_2, with a total pressure of 1 atm and a temperature of 1500°R. Considering the upper and lower plates to be isothermal at 500°R and 2500°R respectively with black surfaces, we can calculate the energy exchange per square foot as follows:

For the top plate:

$$G_1 = \varepsilon_g E_{bg} + (1 - \alpha_g)E_{b2}$$

The gas emittance is calculated from equation 7.14, where the mean beam length is 1.7 ft. Thus

$$p_c L = 0.425 \text{ atm-ft} \qquad p_w L = 0.425 \text{ atm-ft} \qquad T_g = 1500°R$$

From Figures 7.5 through 7.9,

$$\varepsilon_c' = 0.116$$

$$\varepsilon_w' = 0.167$$

$$C_c = 1.0$$

$$C_w = 1.1$$

$$\Delta\varepsilon = 0.033$$

$$\varepsilon_g = (0.116)(1.0) + (0.167)(1.1) - 0.033$$

$$= 0.266$$

Similarly, the gas absorptance is calculated from Equation 7.15, where $p_cL(T_2/T_g) = 0.709$ and $p_wL(T_2/T_g) = 0.709$, by

$$\varepsilon_c'(0.709,\ 2500°R) = 0.122$$

$$\varepsilon_w'(0.709,\ 2500°R) = 0.145$$

$$C_c = 1.0$$

$$C_w = 1.1$$

$$\Delta\varepsilon(2500°R) = 0.04$$

$$\alpha_g = (0.122)(1.0)\left(\frac{1500}{2500}\right)^{0.65} + (0.145)(1.1)\left(\frac{1500}{2500}\right)^{0.45} - 0.04$$

$$= 0.174$$

The irradiation of the upper surface (surface 1) is

$$G_1 = (0.266)(0.1713)\left(\frac{1500}{100}\right)^4 + (1.0 - 0.174)(0.1713)\left(\frac{2500}{100}\right)^4$$

$$G_1 = 5.77 \times 10^4\ \text{Btu per hr-ft}^2$$

of which 23,000 Btu per hr-ft^2 comes from the gas and the remainder is transmitted through the gas. This results in a net heat transfer rate for surface 1 of

$$q_1'' = G_1 - J_1 = G_1 - E_{b_1}$$

$$= 5.77 \times 10^4 - 107.0$$

$$= 5.77 \times 10^4\ \text{Btu per hr-ft}^2$$

In a similar manner, the net heat transfer rate for surface 2 is

$$\varepsilon_g = 0.266$$

For the gas absorptance:

$$p_cL(T_1/T_g) = 0.1417$$

$$p_wL(T_1/T_g) = 0.1417$$

$$\varepsilon_c'(0.147,\ 500°R) = 0.096$$

$$\varepsilon_w'(0.1417,\ 500°R) = 0.39$$

$$C_c = 1.0$$

$$C_w = 1.1$$

$$\Delta\varepsilon(500°R) = 0.003$$

$$\alpha_g = (0.096)(1.0)\left(\frac{1500}{500}\right)^{0.65} + (0.39)(1.1)\left(\frac{1500}{500}\right)^{0.45} - 0.003 = 0.896$$

Thus, the irradiation of surface 2 is

$$G_2 = (0.266)(0.1713)\left(\frac{1500}{100}\right)^4 + (1.0 - 0.896)(0.1713)\left(\frac{500}{100}\right)^4$$

$$G_2 = 2.31 \times 10^3 + 11.18 = 2.31 \times 10^3 \text{ Btu per hr-ft}^2$$

The net heat transfer rate q_2'' is

$$q_2'' = 2.31 \times 10^3 - (0.1713)\left(\frac{2500}{100}\right)^4 = -6.47 \times 10^4 \text{ Btu per hr-ft}^2$$

Since surface 1 gains 5.77×10^4 Btu per hr-ft^2 and surface 2 loses 6.47×10^4 Btu per hr-ft^2, the gas gains 0.7×10^4 Btu per hr-ft^2, where the area is the area of one of the plates.

It is important to notice that the emittance of the gas is the same for energy emitted to either surface, but the absorptance, which is used to calculate the transmittance, is different for each emitting surface. This occurs because the gas is not gray, and therefore the nongrayness must be considered in an empirical manner.

7.12 Calculation of Energy Transfer for Gray or Nongray Wall Enclosures

The method presented in Sections 7.11 and 7.12 is applicable only when the gas enclosure has walls that are black. For the case where walls are nearly black, Hottel [14] presents an approximation useful in evaluating irradiation. When surface emittance is above 0.8, calculating irradiation will involve only a small error if it is expressed as

$$G_2 A_2 = \varepsilon_g A_1 E_b(T_g) + (1 - \alpha_g) A_1 \left(\frac{\varepsilon_1 + 1}{2}\right) E_b(T_w) \tag{7.18}$$

This approximation is only valid when the emittances of the walls ε_1 and ε_2 are quite large.

When the enclosure walls have small emittances, specified as either gray or nongray, the gray gas method is not applicable. In this case a method presented by Edwards and Nelson [45] may be used. Basically, the technique assumes a nongray gas system that allows more accurate evaluation of energy absorption in multiple reflections.

In the analysis of systems with gases present, the typical irradiation equation for a two-surface system is

$$\bar{G}_{vki} A_k \Delta v_i = \bar{J}_{vji} A_j F_{jk} \bar{\tau}_{vi} \Delta v_i + \bar{E}_{bvgi} A_j F_{jk} \bar{\varepsilon}_{vi} \Delta v_i \tag{7.19}$$

where $\bar{G}_{vki}$ is the average monochromatic irradiation of the kth surface element for the ith band in Btu per hr-ft^2-wave number

$\bar{J}_{vji}$ is the average monochromatic radiosity of the jth surface
  element for the ith band in Btu per hr-ft^2-wave number
$\bar{E}_{bvgi}$ is the average monochromatic emissive power of a black body
  evaluated at the temperature of the gas T_g for the ith band in
  Btu per hr-ft^2-wave number
$\bar{\tau}_{vi}$ is the average transmittance of the gas between surface elements
  j and k for the ith spectral band
$\bar{\varepsilon}_{vi}$ is the average emittance of the gas between surface elements
  j and k for the ith spectral band
Δv_i is the width of the ith spectral band in wave number.

Equation 7.19 is the basic equation to be used in solving for the energy
exchange in a finite band Δv_i; the total energy exchange is obtained by
evaluating the energy exchange in each of the i bands and summing the
values. Since the energy exchange equations for any system may be evaluated
if the irradiation equations can be evaluated, the other equations will not be
repeated.

The technique of approximation of Edwards and Nelson is based on the
use of fractional band absorption. The band absorption $\mathscr{A}_i$, defined as

$$\int_{\Delta v_i} \alpha_v \, dv$$

represents only a fraction of the total energy absorbed, or, since the gas is
considered nongray, the total energy emitted. Hottel's total emittance of a
gas represents the total energy emitted. With this in mind, the fractional band
emittance is defined as

$$b_i = \frac{\mathscr{A}_i \bar{E}_{bvgi}}{\varepsilon_g \sigma T_g^4} \tag{7.20}$$

where $\mathscr{A}_i$ is the band absorption
$\bar{E}_{bvgi}$ is the average monochromatic emissive power of a black body
  evaluated at the gas temperature for the ith band
ε_g is the total gas emittance evaluated from Hottel's work.

Since both $\bar{E}_{bvgi}$ and σT_g^4 depend on gas characteristics, the value

$$a_i = \frac{\bar{E}_{bvgi}}{\sigma T_g^4} \tag{7.21}$$

may be calculated for each band of interest. Thus

$$b_{i\varepsilon} = \frac{\mathscr{A}_i a_i}{\varepsilon_g} \tag{7.22}$$

The method is successful because the fractional band emittance $b_{i\varepsilon}$ is relatively
insensitive to the mass path length of the gas.

The transmittance or absorptance of the gas is obtained in a similar manner, that is, the fractional band absorptance is defined as

$$b_{i\alpha} = \frac{\mathscr{A}_i \bar{E}_{bvwi}}{\alpha_g \sigma T_w^4} = \frac{\mathscr{A}_i a_i}{\alpha_g} \tag{7.23}$$

where $\bar{E}_{bvwi}$ is the average monochromatic emissive power of a black body evaluated at the temperature of the emitting wall T_w for the ith spectral band

α_g is the toal absorptance of the gas for energy emitted from a wall at T_w.

In Equation 7.23, $b_{i\alpha}$ values should be evaluated at the wall temperature and gas mass path length. An alternate method of evaluation is shown by Edwards and Nelson as

$$\mathscr{A}_i(T_g, W_g)\bar{E}_{bvwi} = b_i(T_g, W_g)\varepsilon_g(T_g, W_g)\left[\frac{a_i(T_w)}{a_i(T_g)}\right]\sigma T_w^4 \tag{7.24}$$

Either Equation 7.23 or 7.24 may be used to obtain the quantity required. The values of the fractional band absorption and the computation quantity a_i are presented in Figures 7.11, 7.12, 7.13, and 7.14 for the two important gases CO_2 and H_2O.

Using these figures, the band absorption values $\mathscr{A}_i$ may be determined for energy emitted or absorbed by the gas. In the cases where reflections are important or where enclosure walls have various temperatures, the values of Δv_i, $\bar{\tau}_{vi}$, and $\bar{\varepsilon}_{vi}$ must be obtained separately. These are obtained from the recommended band limits given in Tables 7.2 and 7.3. Consideration of the values in these tables indicates that either band limits or $\bar{\tau}_{vi}$ are obtained from

$$\mathscr{A}_i = \bar{\alpha}_{vi}\Delta v_i = \bar{\varepsilon}_{vi}\Delta v_i \tag{7.25}$$

where $\bar{\alpha}_{vi} = 1 - \bar{\tau}_{vi}$.

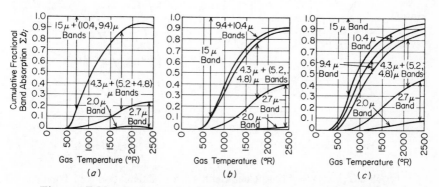

Figure 7.11 Fractional Band Absorption for Carbon Dioxide (a) $p_cL = 0.1$ atm-ft (b) $p_cL = 1.0$ atm-ft (c) $p_cL = 10$ atm-ft [5].

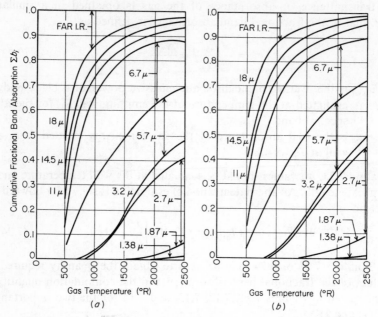

Figure 7.12 Fractional Band Absorption for Water Vapor (a) $p_wL = 1.27$ atm-ft (b) $p_wL = 2.54$ atm-ft [5].

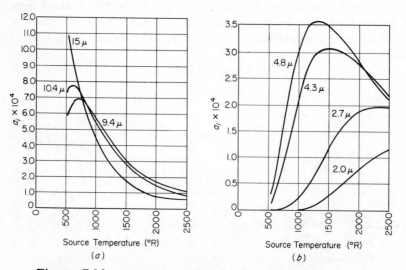

Figure 7.13 Weighting Coefficient a_i for Calculation of Total Absorption (a) 15, 10.4, and 9.4μ Bands of CO_2 (b) 4.8, 4.3, 2.7, and 2.0μ Bands of CO_2 [4].

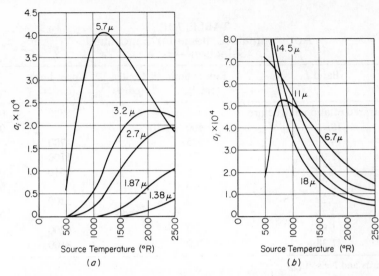

Figure 7.14 Coefficient $a_i(T)$ for (a) 5.7, 3.2, 2.7, 1.87, and 1.38μ Bands of H_2O (b) 18, 14.5, 11, and 6.7μ Bands of H_2O [5].

TABLE 7.2†
Approximate Criteria for Band Limit
Selection—CO_2

Band i	Lower limit (cm^{-1})	Center (cm^{-1})	Upper limit (cm^{-1})	τ_{gj}
15μ		667		0.11
10.4μ	849		1013	
9.4μ	1013		1141	
7.5μ	1141		1485	
5.2μ	1830		1995	
4.8μ	1995		2169	
4.3μ			2460	0.11
2.7μ			3830	0.12
2.0μ	4400		6000	

†Edwards and Nelson [5]

7.13 Numerical Example of Nongray Analysis

In order to illustrate the nongray method without getting involved in calculations for numerous bands, a three-surface system will be examined for a single absorption band. The transparent bands are not handled any differently than in the previous examples; therefore, they will not be considered.

TABLE 7.3†
Approximate Criteria for Band Limit
Selection—H_2O

Band i	Lower limit (cm⁻¹)	Center (cm⁻¹)	Upper limit (cm⁻¹)	τ_{gi}
Far infrared rotational structure	Say 0		500	0
18μ	500			0.2
14.5μ	625		700	
11.0μ	770		1100	
6.7μ			1610	0.2
5.7μ	1610			0.3
3.2μ	2650		3300	
2.7μ		3800		0.3
1.87μ	4620		6200	
1.38μ	6200		8100	

†Edwards and Nelson [5]

For this example consider a cubic furnace enclosure with 18-in. internal dimensions, as shown in Figure 7.15. The three surfaces of interest are Surface 1 (door), surface 2 (floor), surface 3 (remaining walls and top).

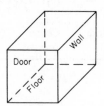

Figure 7.15   Geometry for Nongray Example.

Since only one band is to be considered, the surface properties are specified for the 2.7-μ bands as

$$\bar{\varepsilon}_{v1} = 0.4$$

$$\bar{\varepsilon}_{v2} = 0.8$$

$$\bar{\varepsilon}_{v3} = 0.8$$

The furnace enclosure is heated by coils in the floor; thus, surface 2 has the highest temperature. Assume 1500°R. The door is cooler than the walls or floor; assume its temperature to be 1200°R. Assume the walls to be at 1400°R. During operation the furnace is flooded with CO_2 at a pressure of 1 atm, and this gas is supplied continuously. Assume the temperature of the gas to be 1000°R.

The 2.7-μ band is an important band for CO_2; therefore, this band will be the one considered. The procedure used for this band would simply be repeated for each of the other absorption and transparent bands.

In the heat transfer analysis, the following three equations must be used:

$$\bar{G}_{v1}A_1\Delta v = \bar{J}_{v2}A_2F_{21}\bar{\tau}_{v21}\Delta v + \bar{J}_{v3}A_3F_{31}\bar{\tau}_{v31}\Delta v$$
$$+ \bar{E}_{bvg}A_2F_{21}\bar{\varepsilon}_{v21}\Delta v + \bar{E}_{bvg}A_3F_{31}\bar{\varepsilon}_{v31}\Delta v \quad (7.26)$$

$$\bar{G}_{v2}A_2\Delta v = \bar{J}_{v1}A_1F_{12}\bar{\tau}_{v12}\Delta v + \bar{J}_{v3}A_3F_{32}\bar{\tau}_{v32}\Delta v$$
$$+ \bar{E}_{bvg}A_1F_{12}\bar{\varepsilon}_{v12}\Delta v + \bar{E}_{bvg}A_3F_{32}\bar{\varepsilon}_{v32}\Delta v \quad (7.27)$$

$$\bar{G}_{v3}A_3\Delta v = \bar{J}_{v1}A_1F_{13}\bar{\tau}_{v13}\Delta v + \bar{J}_{v2}A_2F_{23}\bar{\varepsilon}_{v23}\Delta v + \bar{J}_{v3}A_3F_{33}\bar{\tau}_{v33}\Delta v$$
$$+ \bar{E}_{bvg}A_1F_{13}\bar{\varepsilon}_{v13}\Delta v + \bar{E}_{bvg}A_2F_{23}\bar{\varepsilon}_{v23}\Delta v + \bar{E}_{bvg}A_3F_{33}\bar{\varepsilon}_{v33}\Delta v \quad (7.28)$$

Each of these equations expresses the irradiation of a surface by the other surface in the enclosure, plus the irradiation of the surface by the gas between the surfaces. In order to keep the transmittance and emittance values separate for the various surfaces, we use the notation $\bar{\tau}_{vjk}$, where the jk subscript indicates which surfaces are involved. In each of the equations, the irradiation due to the gas between surfaces—the terms multiplied by $\bar{E}_{bvg}$—occurs for each surface in the enclosure. For this reason it is somewhat easier to combine these into a single term. For example, Equation 7.25 may be written

$$\bar{G}_{v1}A_1\Delta v = \bar{J}_{v2}A_2F_{21}\bar{\tau}_{v21}\Delta v + \bar{J}_{v3}A_3F_{31}\bar{\tau}_{v31}\Delta v$$
$$+ \bar{E}_{bvg}A_1[F_{12}\bar{\varepsilon}_{v12} + F_{13}\bar{\varepsilon}_{v13}]\Delta_v$$

or

$$\bar{G}_{v1}A_1\Delta v = \bar{J}_{v2}A_2F_{21}\bar{\tau}_{v21}\Delta_v + \bar{J}_{v3}A_3F_{31}\bar{\tau}_{v31}\Delta v + E_{bvg}A_1[\bar{\varepsilon}_{v\,encl-1}]\Delta v$$

where $\bar{\varepsilon}_{v\,encl-1}$ is used to represent the emittance of the entire enclosed gas body to surface 1. Use of this term reduces the apparent complexity of the irradiation equations, but it does not actually change the problem.

The next step in the evaluation of the energy transfer is the evaluation of the mean beam lengths. These can be taken from the geometric mean-beam-length tables and figures in Appendix 6. For surface 1 (door) to surface 2 (floor), $r_{12} = 0.835$ ft. For surface 1 to surface 3 (the walls) flux algebra methods [3] may be used. Using the subscripts s for the side wall, b for the back wall, and t for the top, we get

$$A_1F_{13}\bar{r}_{13} = A_1F_{1s}\bar{r}_{1s} + A_1F_{1s}\bar{r}_{1s} + A_1F_{1b}\bar{r}_{1b} + A_1F_{1t}\bar{r}_{1t}$$

$$\bar{r}_{13} = 1.04 \text{ ft}$$

For surface 2 to surface 3, by symmetry,

$$\bar{r}_{23} = \bar{r}_{13} = 1.04 \text{ ft}$$

By reciprocity, from the definition of geometric mean beam lengths,

$$\bar{r}_{21} = \bar{r}_{12} = 0.835 \text{ ft}$$

$$\bar{r}_{31} = \bar{r}_{13} = 1.04 \text{ ft}$$

$$\bar{r}_{32} = \bar{r}_{23} = 1.04 \text{ ft}$$

For surface 3 to itself, by flux algebra,

$$A_3 F_{33} \bar{r}_{33} = A_3 F_{3s} \bar{r}_{3s} + A_3 F_{3t} \bar{r}_{3t} + A_3 F_{3s} \bar{r}_{3s}$$

$$\bar{r}_{33} = 1.11 \text{ ft}$$

For one side to the entire enclosure

$$A_s F_{s\text{-encl}} \bar{r}_{s\text{-encl}} = 4 A_3 F_{ss} \bar{r}_{ss} + A_b F_{bs} \bar{r}_{bs}$$

$$\bar{r}_{s\text{-encl}} = 1.00 \text{ ft}$$

After evaluating the geometric mean beam lengths, the various mass path lengths may be evaluated:

$$(xPL)_{12} = 0.835 \text{ atm-ft}$$

$$(xPL)_{13} = 1.04 \text{ atm-ft}$$

$$(xPL)_{23} = 1.04 \text{ atm-ft}$$

$$(xPL)_{33} = 1.11 \text{ atm-ft}$$

$$(xPL)_{s\text{-encl}} = 1.00 \text{ atm-ft}$$

From Figures 7.11 and 7.13, using Equation 7.24 modified, we get

$$\bar{\alpha}_{vjk} \Delta v = \frac{b_i(T_g, w_g) \varepsilon_g(T_g, w_g)}{a_i(T_g)}$$

$$\bar{\alpha}_{v12} \Delta v = 246 \text{ cm}^{-1} \qquad \bar{\varepsilon}_{v12} \Delta v = 246 \text{ cm}^{-1}$$

$$\bar{\alpha}_{v13} \Delta v = 258 \text{ cm}^{-1} \qquad \bar{\varepsilon}_{v13} \Delta v = 258 \text{ cm}^{-1}$$

$$\bar{\alpha}_{v23} \Delta v = 258 \text{ cm}^{-1} \qquad \bar{\varepsilon}_{v23} \Delta v = 258 \text{ cm}^{-1}$$

$$\bar{\alpha}_{v33} \Delta v = 260 \text{ cm}^{-1} \qquad \bar{\varepsilon}_{v33} \Delta v = 260 \text{ cm}^{-1}$$

$$\bar{\varepsilon}_{v \, \text{encl-}s} \Delta v = 256 \text{ cm}^{-1}$$

Table 7.1 suggests a value of $\bar{\tau}_v$ for the 2.7-mu band of 0.12, with an upper limit on the band of 3830 cm^{-1}. Since five values of band absorption were obtained and only one value of Δv is possible, the values of $\bar{\tau}_{vjk}$ must vary. Choosing the largest value of $\mathscr{A}_i$ or 260 cm^{-1}, $\Delta v = 296$ cm^{-1}. Using this value, we get the following transmittance and emittance values:

$$\bar{\tau}_{v12} = 0.167 \qquad \bar{\varepsilon}_{v12} = 0.833$$

$$\bar{\tau}_{v13} = 0.126 \qquad \bar{\varepsilon}_{v13} = 0.874$$

$$\bar{\tau}_{v23} = 0.126 \qquad \bar{\varepsilon}_{v23} = 0.874$$

$$\bar{\tau}_{v33} = 0.120 \qquad \bar{\varepsilon}_{v33} = 0.880$$

$$\bar{\varepsilon}_{v\,encl\text{-}1} = 0.867$$

Using these values, we get the following three linear algebraic equations for the solution:

$$\bar{J}_{v1} = \bar{E}_{bv1} + \rho_1[\bar{J}_{v2}F_{12}\bar{\tau}_{v12} + \bar{J}_{v3}F_{13}\bar{\tau}_{v13} + \bar{E}_{bvg}\bar{\varepsilon}_{v\,encl\text{-}1}]$$

$$\bar{J}_{v2} = \bar{E}_{bv2} + \rho_2[\bar{J}_{v1}F_{21}\bar{\tau}_{v21} + \bar{J}_{v3}F_{23}\bar{\tau}_{v23} + \bar{E}_{bvg}\bar{\varepsilon}_{v\,encl\text{-}2}]$$

$$\bar{J}_{v3} = \bar{E}_{bv3} + \rho_3[\bar{J}_{v1}F_{31}\bar{\tau}_{v31} + \bar{J}_{v2}F_{32}\bar{\tau}_{v32} + \bar{J}_{v3}F_{33}\bar{\tau}_{v33} + \bar{E}_{bvg}\bar{\varepsilon}_{v\,encl\text{-}3}]$$

All of the quantities in these equations except $\bar{J}_{v1}$, $\bar{J}_{v2}$, and $\bar{J}_{v3}$ are known or may be obtained. The average monochromatic emissive power quantities, such as $\bar{E}_{bv1}$, are easily obtained from Figure 7.13. Only $\bar{\varepsilon}_{v\,encl\text{-}3}$ has not been calculated previously, and this is obtained from

$$\bar{\varepsilon}_{v\,encl\text{-}3} = F_{31}\bar{\varepsilon}_{v31} + F_{32}\bar{\varepsilon}_{v32} + F_{33}\bar{\varepsilon}_{v33}$$

Inserting the known quantities and solving the three equations simultaneously, we get

$$\bar{J}_{v1} = 0.267 \text{ Btu per hr-ft}^2\text{-cm}^{-1}$$

$$\bar{J}_{v2} = 1.065 \text{ Btu per hr-ft}^2\text{-cm}^{-1}$$

$$\bar{J}_{v3} = 0.782 \text{ Btu per hr-ft}^2\text{-cm}^{-1}$$

From the average monochromatic radiosity values, the irradiation of each surface may be calculated as follows:

$$\bar{G}_{v1} = F_{12}\bar{\tau}_{v12}\bar{J}_{v2} + F_{13}\bar{\tau}_{v13}\bar{J}_{v3} + \bar{\varepsilon}_{v\,encl\text{-}1}\bar{E}_{bvg}$$

$$\bar{G}_{v1} = (0.2)(0.167)(1.065) + (0.8)(0.126)(0.782) + (0.867)(0.041)$$

$$= 0.150 \text{ Btu per hr-ft}^2\text{-cm}^{-1}$$

$$\bar{G}_{v2} = 0.123 \text{ Btu per hr-ft}^2\text{-cm}^{-1}$$

$$\bar{G}_{v3} = 0.126 \text{ Btu per hr-ft}^2\text{-cm}^{-1}$$

These values of irradiation and radiosity result in net heat transfer rates in the band of

$$q''_{net_1} = (\bar{G}_{v1} - \bar{J}_{v1})\Delta v = (0.15 - 0.267)(296)$$

$$q''_{net_1} = -34.6 \text{ Btu per hr-ft}^2$$

$$q''_{net_2} = -279 \text{ Btu per hr-ft}^2$$

$$q''_{net_3} = -194.5 \text{ Btu per hr-ft}^2$$

Since each surface is losing energy, the heat transfer rate to the gas is

$$q_g = (2.25)(34.6) + (2.25)(279) + 4(2.25)(194.5)$$

$$q_g = 2456 \text{ Btu per hr}$$

The energy gain by the gas can also be calculated from the following equation:

$$q_g = [(\bar{J}_{v1} - \bar{E}_{bvg})(\bar{\varepsilon}_{v\,\text{encl-1}})A_1 + (J_{v2} - E_{bvg})(\bar{\varepsilon}_{v\,\text{encl-2}})A_2$$

$$+ (\bar{J}_{v3} - \bar{E}_{bvg})(\bar{\varepsilon}_{v\,\text{encl-3}})A_3$$

$$q_g = (0.267 - 0.041)(0.867)(2.25) + (1.065 - 0.041)(0.867)(2.25)$$

$$+ (0.782 - 0.041)(0.878)(9.00) = 2460 \text{ Btu per hr}$$

This technique is used in each band and the results summed. As can be seen from this example for a single band, the analysis of the heat transfer rates for a nongray isothermal gas-filled enclosure is a formidable problem. Unfortunately, whenever the walls of an enclosure are particularly reflective, this technique is the only practical approach to analysis.

7.14 Nonisothermal Gas Systems

In any real gas heat-transfer system, the gases present in an enclosure are not isothermal. The gas temperature gradient depends on the dynamic and static properties of the gas. If the gas is moving, convection and radiation modes of heat transfer may occur simultaneously. If the gas is stationary, conduction and radiation may occur simultaneously. As indicated by Viskanta [18], when radiation and conduction occur simultaneously, the dimensionless group $N = (k\kappa\gamma)/(4\sigma T^{*3})$—where k is the thermal conductivity, κ is the mass absorption coefficient, γ is the density, and T^* is a reference temperature (generally the highest gas temperature encountered)—is important. For large values of N, conduction is dominant; for small values, radiation is dominant.

Viskanta examined the particular case of heat transfer between two infinite parallel plates enclosing a nonscattering medium. A large variety of cases were examined to show the effects of the variables. The solution is complex and, therefore, is not considered practical for engineering approximations, but the results indicate the effects of certain parameters for energy transfer.

The dimensionless temperature distribution T/T^* is plotted in Figures 7.16, 7.17, and 7.18, versus the optical thickness $(\kappa\gamma y)$, where y is the distance from one of the infinite parallel black plates. The values of the dimensionless group N are used as parameters. As may be noted from Figure 7.18, when the maximum optical thickness $\kappa\gamma h$ is small, the dimensionless temperature

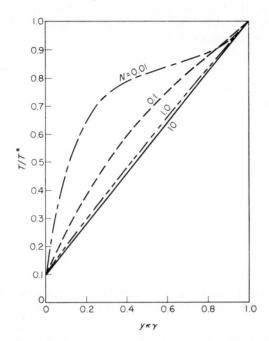

Figure 7.16   Dimensionless Temperature Distribution for Infinite Parallel Plate System with Spacing $h\kappa\gamma = 1.0$ and $T/T^*(0) = 0.1$ [18].

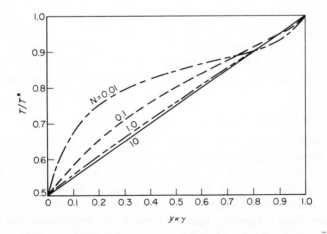

Figure 7.17   Dimensionless Temperature Distribution for Infinite Parallel Plate System with Spacing $h\kappa\gamma = 1.0$ and $T/T^*(0) = 0.5$ [18].

profile is a straight line; that is, conduction predominates. For small values of $\kappa\gamma h$ or for large values of N, conduction effects are much larger than radiation effects. For large values of the maximum optical thickness ($\kappa\gamma h$) or small values of N, radiation effects predominate.

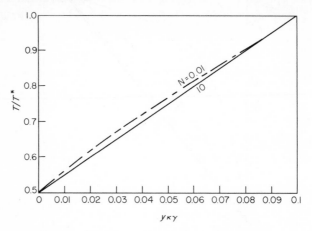

Figure 7.18 Dimensionless Temperature Distribution for Infinite Parallel Plate System with Spacing $h\kappa\gamma = 0.1$ and $T/T^*(0) = 0.5$ [18].

When radiation effects predominate, a gray gas approximation may be possible using the methods presented by Hottel [14]. These techniques are not well developed for the case of a bounded gas, but may be applicable for gases that are nearly opaque to radiation. If a nongray gas approximation is desired, the method used by de Soto [2] may be useful. This method is laborious, requiring a digital computer and band-shape information that is not generally available for gases. The system examined by de Soto involves CO_2 only and uses three absorption bands to represent the radiation characteristics of the gas. In general, the de Soto technique is the most satisfactory, but the data required for such a solution is very difficult to obtain.

Radiation from Luminous Flames

The radiant energy emitted from luminous flames is considered to be caused by very small particles formed in the flame. When flames have the characteristic blue color of well-adjusted gas flames, the radiant energy leaving the flames is very much less than when the flames are luminous. Since high-temperature water vapor and/or carbon dioxide is always present in gaseous flames, energy is radiated away from these flames, but the energy leaving luminous flames cannot be attributed to high-temperature gas emission. For this reason, the concept of energy emission from very small soot or carbon particles in luminous flames has been widely accepted [12, 14]. Since radiation from small particles involves scattering, absorption, and conduction transfer, the problem of luminous flame radiation has been approached through empirical methods. The prediction of energy transfer from luminous flames by using first principles is practically impossible; however, certain empirical methods may be used for engineering approximations.

7.15 Luminous Gas Properties

According to the work of many investigatiors [12, 14] the properties of a luminous gas may be expressed in the following form:

$$\varepsilon_\lambda = 1 - \exp(-\kappa_\lambda L) \tag{7.29}$$

where ε_λ is the monochromatic emittance of the luminous gas
κ_λ is the absorption coefficient for the luminous gas
L is the equivalent length of the radiating system.

According to Hottel [9] the absorption coefficient κ_λ can be represented by either

$$\kappa_\lambda = \frac{Ck_1}{\lambda^{0.95}} \text{ (in the infrared region, } 0.8\text{--}10\mu)$$

or

$$\kappa_\lambda = \frac{Ck_2}{\lambda^{1.39}} \text{ (in the visible region, } 0.3\text{--}0.8\mu)$$

where C is the soot concentration, and k_1 and k_2 are constants. A similar approach to evaluating the absorption coefficient is given by Shack [12]:

$$\kappa_\lambda = \frac{k_1}{\lambda^{0.90}}$$

where k_1 is a constant equal to κ_λ when the wavelength is 1 μ. In either case, the values of the constants k_1 and k_2 must be determined for a particular flame by experimental methods.

More recent data available in German literature and cited by Kutateladze and Borishanskig [13, 15] indicates that

$$\kappa_\lambda = Ck(\lambda^{-n+m\log})$$

where n and m are dependent upon the diameter of the soot particles.

Since none of these methods can be applied *a priori* for a proposed radiation transfer system, engineering methods have been developed for approximating the energy transfer from a given system [12, 14]. All these methods involve the measurement of flame temperatures by using either total or optical pyrometers. Only the method presented by Hottel can be extrapolated to different flame shapes.

7.16 Experimental Measurements of Luminous Flame Temperatures

All the experimental techniques for determining energy exchange from luminous flames require the measurements of two or more temperatures. These temperatures are

T_f the true flame temperature

T_r the apparent temperature of the flame measured optically through a red ($\lambda = 0.665\mu$) filter

T_g the apparent temperature of the flame measured optically through a green ($\lambda = 0.555\mu$) filter.

The true flame temperature (which may be misnamed because thermal equilibrium obviously does not exist in flames) may be measured by a high-velocity suction pyrometer or by extrapolating temperature measurements made with thermocouples of progressively smaller wire diameter [12]. These methods are difficult to apply except in a laboratory.

Apparent flame temperatures, either red or green, are measured by using an optical pyrometer (see Chapter 8) with a red or green filter in the optical path. These measurements are made by matching the brightness of the flame under observation to the brightness of an electrically heated filament. The technique described in the following discussion assumes that the pyrometer has been sighted through the flame onto a cold black background. When the background can be seen through the flame and is hot, modifications for the energy emitted by the background should be made.

In temperature measurement using an optical pyrometer, the intensity of the observed sample may be very closely matched to the brightness of the heated wire [12]. By calibrating it with the standard strip lamp of a laboratory black body, the pyrometer will read an equivalent black-body temperature. Since the basic match is intensity, the intensity indicated by the optical pyrometer reading may be equated to the equivalent black-body temperature, or

$$I_{b\lambda}(T_p) = \varepsilon_\lambda I_{b\lambda}(T_f) \tag{7.30}$$

where T_p is the temperature indicated by the calibrated optical pyrometer, and ε_λ is the emittance of the flame at the equivalent wavelength of the filter system.

Expressing the intensity of a black body from Wien's distribution (Equation 3.1) since the λT product is quite small for the visible region and the flame temperatures, we get the following result:

$$\frac{1}{T_p} - \frac{1}{T_f} = -\frac{\lambda}{C_2} \ln \varepsilon_\lambda \tag{7.31}$$

Then if an optical pyrometer with two filters, one red and one green, is used, two equations like (7.31) may be written:

$$\frac{1}{T_r} - \frac{1}{T_f} = -\frac{\lambda_r}{C_2} \ln \varepsilon_{\lambda r} \tag{7.32}$$

$$\frac{1}{T_g} - \frac{1}{T_f} = -\frac{\lambda_g}{C_2} \ln \varepsilon_{\lambda g} \tag{7.33}$$

where λ_r is the equivalent wavelength of the red filter

λ_g is the equivalent wavelength of the green filter

$\varepsilon_{\lambda r}$ is the emittance of the flame at the equivalent wavelength of the red filter

$\varepsilon_{\lambda g}$ is the emittance of the flame at the equivalent wavelength of the green filter.

If the monochromatic emittance of the flame in the visible region is given by [9]

$$\varepsilon_\lambda = 1 - \exp(KL/\lambda^{1.39}) \tag{7.34}$$

Equations 7.32, 7.33, and 7.34 may be solved simultaneously for the flame temperature T_f and the product KL, which Hottel calls the *absorption strength*. A plot presented in [9] for the rapid evaluation of T_f and KL is shown in Figure 7.19.

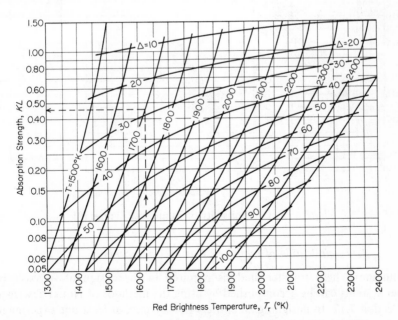

Figure 7.19   Absorption Strength KL of Luminous Flames [9].

Assuming that the absorption strength KL is not a function of wavelength, and using

$$\varepsilon_\lambda = 1 - \exp(KL/\lambda^{1.39}) \qquad \text{for } \lambda = 0\text{--}0.8\mu$$

and

$$\varepsilon_\lambda = 1 - \exp(KL/\lambda^{0.95}) \qquad \text{for } \lambda = 0.8\text{--}10\mu$$

we can calculate the total emittance of the flame. The results obtained by Hottel using these relationships are plotted in Figure 7.20. In order to use the curves for absorption strength and flame temperature presented by Hottel, the red and green filters used should have the same equivalent wavelength of transmittance as were used in the preparation of the curves. If filters with transmittances at different equivalent wavelengths are used, Equations 7.32, 7.33, and 7.34. should be solved simultaneously for absorption strength and flame temperature.

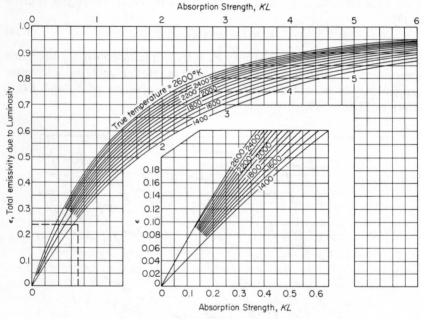

Figure 7.20   Emissivity of Luminous Flames [9].

7.17 Application of Luminous Gas Measurements

Luminous heat transfer analysis required in the design of furnaces or other systems can be accomplished by using the methods of Hottel described in Section 7.17. In designing an entirely new system, at least one experiment must be run in order to characterize the flame.

As an example, assume that a proposed furnace has burners arranged such that a long cylindrical flame roughly 4 ft in diameter will be produced. Since it is assumed that the system is unique, at least to the designer, some sort of model must be built, perhaps a smaller burner with all conditions controlled to make its flame as similar as possible to the design flame.

If the state of the flame produced by the small burner is identical to the state of the large flame, measurement of the temperatures T_r and T_g will give sufficient information to design the large system. For example, if the small flame is 1 ft in diameter where T_r and T_g are measured, the value of KL for the large flame will be four times the absorption strength for the small flame.

In a heat transfer analysis of the large flame some sort of mean beam length L_e may be required. If this is the case, the value of K obtained by experiment from the small flame can be assumed to be constant for both flames. In this manner, KL_e and T_f may be obtained for the flame of the system to be designed; from this information the gas emittance for the large flame may be determined.

7.18 Numerical Example of Flame Heat Transfer Analysis

A proposed furnace design for experimental transfer of heat to boiling water is a high-pressure oil-fired system expected to produce a cylindrical flame 4 ft in diameter and 12 ft long. Since the design is for a new system, a model that produces a flame 1 ft in diameter is constructed. The model is arranged so that the flame produced will approximate the proposed flame as closely as possible. The apparent flame temperature measured while looking through the 1 ft flame is $T_r = 2780°F$ and $T_g = 2870°F$. From this information, an estimate can be made of the heat transfer by radiation in the proposed furnace.

From T_r and T_g, and Figure 7.19, $KL = 0.26$ and the flame temperature $= 3528°R$ for the 1 ft flame. In the proposed flame, 4 ft in diameter and 12 ft long, the mean beam length as given from Hottel's information in Appendix 6 is between 4 and 2.66 ft. Assuming the mean beam length to be the average, 3.33 ft, will not introduce a large error. KL_e for the proposed furnace will be approximately $(0.26)(3.33/1.0) = 0.866$. Using this value of KL and a flame temperature of $3528°R$, the flame emittance from Figure 7.20 is 0.38. The total energy emitted from the flame by the luminous gas is given by $\varepsilon_f A_f \sigma T_f^4$, where A_f is the area of the flame envelope. In this case the total energy emitted would be approximately

$$(0.38)(56\pi)(0.1713)(3528/100)^4 = 1.43 \times 10^7 \text{ Btu per hr}$$

Energy would also be emitted by the CO_2 and H_2O present in the gases, This energy could be estimated if the fuel and the fuel-air ratio were known that is, if the composition of the flame could be estimated. It is not correct to include all of the energy emitted by the hot gases, since part of the energy would be counted twice. Jakob [12] reports a procedure suggested by Schack which may be used if a reasonable estimate of the gas composition can be determined.

After determining the flame's total emissive power, the techniques described previously can be used to calculate energy transfer. Of course, the energy transfer depends upon the wall temperature and location in the furnace. Since no method is presented to calculate the absorptance of the luminous flame, only total enclosures may be examined. However, by assuming the absorptance of the flame to equal the emittance, an estimate may be obtained for multinode analysis of systems.

Exercises

7.1 Two sample low-resolution absorption curves for pure CO_2 at 10 atm, 2500°R, and 12.7 atm-ft are shown in the accompanying figures. From these two curves, determine the band absorptions, and compare the values obtained to the values obtained from the correlations in Table 7.1.

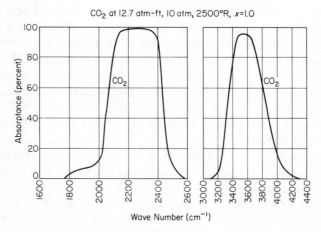

CO_2 at 12.7 atm-ft, 10 atm, 2500°R, $x=1.0$

Exercise 7.1

7.2 Calculate the geometric mean beam length for a gas in a rectangular parallelepiped which has relative dimensions of $1 : 2 : 6$ radiating to a 1×6 face. Use the geometric mean beam length tables of R. V. Dunkle in Appendix 6. Compare this value to the H. C. Hottel value given in Appendix 6.

7.3 For the rectangular parallelepiped of Problem 7.2, calculate the mean beam length for the radiation of the gas between a 1×6 face and the opposing 1×6 face plus the adjacent 2×6 face.

7.4 Two parallel opposed plates are 1 ft × 1 ft in size and are spaced 1 ft apart. A mixture of 50 percent CO_2 and 50 percent N_2 by volume, with a total pressure of 10 atm and a temperature of 1000°R, is between the two plates. Determine the band absorption for the gas mixture in the 2.7-μ region.

7.5 Calculate the energy transfer by radiation from superheated steam carried in an 8-in. diameter steam line if the steam temperature is 2500°R, the pressure is 10 atm, and the pipe inner wall is black, with a temperature of 2000°R. Use gray gas assumptions. (This problem is more instructive if the radiant transfer is compared to the convective transfer, assuming the steam average velocity to be 150 ft per sec.)

7.6 Two infinite parallel plates 1 ft apart have between them a 50–50 mixture by volume of CO_2 and N_2, at a total pressure of 10 atm and temperature of 1000°R. Assuming the plates to be black with temperatures of 1500°R and 2000°R respectively, (a) calculate the net energy loss per square foot for each plate using gray gas assumptions, (b) calculate the energy exchange using the rapid calculation method of Edwards [5].

7.7 Repeat Problem 7.6, except in this case assume the plates to have emittance values of 0.7 for the 1500°R plate and 0.8 for the 2000°R plate.

References

1. BEVANS, J. T., and R. V. DUNKLE, "Radiant Interchange within an Enclosure," *Journal of Heat Transfer*, vol. 82 (February 1960), p. 1.

2. DE SOTO, SIMON, "The Radiation from an Axi-Symmetric, Real Gas System with a Non-Isothermal Temperature Distribution," AIChE Paper, Presented at the 7th Annual Heat Transfer Conference, Cleveland, Ohio, August 1964.

3. DUNKLE, R. V., "Geometric Mean Beam Lengths for Radiant Heat Transfer Calculations," ASME Paper No. 62-WA-120 (1962).

4. EDWARDS, D. K., "Radiation Interchange in a Non-gray Enclosure Containing an Isothermal Carbon–Dioxide–Nitrogen Gas Mixture," ASME Paper No. 60-WA-210 (1960).

5. —— and K. E. NELSON, "Rapid Calculation of Radiant Energy Transfer Between Non-gray Walls and Isothermal H_2O or CO_2 Gas," ASME Paper No. 61-WA-175 (1961).

6. —— and W. A. MENARD, "Comparison Models for Correlation of Total Band Absorption," *Applied Optics*, vol. 3, no. 5, May 1964.

7. —— and ——, "Correlations for Absorption by Methane and Carbon Dioxide Gases," *Journal of Applied Optics*, vol. 3, no. 7, July 1964.

8. HOWELL, J. R., "Determination of Combined Conduction and Radiation of Heat Through Absorbing Media by the Exchange Factor Approximation," AIChE Paper No. 2, Presented at the 7th National Heat Transfer Conference, Cleveland, Ohio, August 1964.

9. HOTTEL, H. C., and F. P. BROUGHTON, "Determination of True Temperature and Total Radiation from Luminous Gas Flames," *Industrial and Engineering Chemistry*, vol. 4 (1933), pp. 166–175.

10. —— and R. B. EGBERT, "Radiant Heat Transmission from Water Vapor," *AIChE Transactions*, vol. 38 (1942), p. 531.

11. —— and ——, "The Radiation of Furnace Gases," *ASME Transactions*, vol. 63 (1941), p. 297.

12. JAKOB, MAX, *Heat Transfer*, vol. 2. New York: John Wiley & Sons, Inc., 1957.

13. KUTATELADZE, S. S., and V. M. BORISHANSKIG, *Handbook of Heat Transfer* (Translation). ASTIA Document 284118 (1958).

14. MCADAMS, W. H., *Heat Transmission*. New York: McGraw-Hill Book Company, Inc. (1954), chap. 4 (by H. C. HOTTEL).

15. PEPPERHOFF and A. BAHR, "Zur Optik leuchtender Flammen," *Archiv fur das Eisenhuttenwesen*, vol. D, No. 382 (September–October 1952), p. 335.

16. STULL, R. V., P. J. WYATT and G. N. PLASS, "The Infrared Transmittance of Carbon Dioxide," *Journal of Applied Optics*, vol. 3 (1964), p. 243.

17. VISKANTA, RAYMOND, "Heat Transfer by Conduction and Radiation in Absorbing and Scattering Materials," *ASME Transactions*, no. 64-HT-33, 1964.

18. ——, "Heat Transfer in Thermal Radiation Absorbing and Scattering Media," ANL-6170. Argonne, Illinois: Argonne National Laboratory, 1960.

19. WIEBELT, J. A., "Comparison of Geometric Absorption Factors with Geometric Mean Beam Lengths," *Journal of Heat Transfer*, vol. 85 (August 1963), p. 287.

CHAPTER 8

Radiation Equipment

The purpose of this chapter is to introduce various practical radiation apparatus and to discuss their characteristics. Since radiation measurements are generally much less familiar to experimentalists than the measurements involved in other types of heat transfer, the chapter will include discussions of the more important measuring systems. In general, the physics of the radiation detection apparatus will not be considered. Both of these topics are very well covered in several books presently available [6, 7].

Detectors

1.8 Mechanisms of Detector Operation

The spectrum of wavelengths important in thermal radiation is so extensive that several different types of detectors are required. These detectors must react to wavelengths from ultraviolet, about 0.3 μ to far infrared, about 100 μ. Such a wide range of wavelengths cannot be detected efficiently with a single detector system. For this reason it is normal to use three or four separate detectors for the measurement of thermal radiation.

These detectors are different in their basic mechanism of operation. One type of detector, which depends on the heating effect of the incident radiation, is called a *thermal* detector. Thermal detectors are normally used in the infrared wavelength region. A second basic type of detector is the *photon counter*, which operates when energetic photons react with electrons, causing a shifting of the electron orbits. Since photons have appreciable energy only when wavelengths are short, the photon counter detector is useful primarily in the visible and near infrared wavelength regions.

8.2 Comparison Parameters for Detectors

Certain basic information is necessary in considering detectors. This includes (1) the minimum radiant flux incident on the detector that will result in a useful signal, (2) the signal voltage that may be expected per unit of radiant flux incident, (3) the wavelength region in which the detector is useful, and (4) the time required for the detector to respond to a step change in the incident radiant flux [7]. Each of these four characteristics requires a separate defined parameter for specification.

In any detection system a certain basic noise level exists. This noise is electrical noise generated by the random movement of the molecules and electrons in the detector element. Noise may also be generated in any electronic system used in the amplification or display of the signals. These basic noise signals depend upon the frequency bandpass of the entire system; that is, since they are generated by thermal disturbances, if a large frequency interval is passed through the system, the noise level will be higher. Furthermore, the noise level depends on the basic frequency of amplification, and, for calibration purposes, on the temperature of the calibrating source.

Considering these variables, the most typical detector parameter used to describe the minimum detectable radiant flux is the *noise equivalent power*, or NEP. NEP is defined as *the root-mean-square value of the radiant flux that causes a signal equal to the noise signal* [7]. Also, since the signals are normally electrical voltages, NEP is the radiant flux that will cause a voltage equal to the natural noise voltage from the detector. Obviously, if the signal voltage is only equal to the noise voltage, the accurate evaluation of the signal is not possible. It is important to notice that the detector is better when the NEP is smaller.

Since detectors are better with small NEP values—contrary to normal interpretation—an equivalent parameter called *detectivity* is sometimes used. The detectivity D is defined as the reciprocal of the NEP, $D = 1/\text{NEP}$. Both the detectivity and the NEP are dependent upon the area of the detector. In most detectors the NEP is directly proportional to the square root of the area of the detector. In order to eliminate the detector area from the expressions of merit, we can define a special detectivity $D^* = (A_d)^{1/2}/\text{NEP}$.

These figures of merit are normally expressed as $D^*(500°\text{K}, 1000, 1)$ where the three values in the parentheses are the temperature of the calibration source, the basic frequency of amplification (or chopping rate), and the bandpass of the calibrating amplifier system. Typical values for D^* and NEP are

$$D^*(500°\text{K}, 1000, 1) = 4 \times 10^7 \text{ cm-cps}^{1/2} \text{ per watt}$$

and

$$\text{NEP}(500°\text{K}, 1000, 1) = 2 \times 10^{-9} \text{ watts-rms}$$

These values were taken from a manufacturer's specifications for an indium-antimony photoconductive detector. In this case the detector-element temperature was specified as 25°C; this is very important because the element is capable of better performance when cooled to cryogenic temperatures.

The second important figure of merit is the signal voltage, which can be obtained from the detector directly, or in the case of detectors which change resistance upon being irradiated, from a suggested preamplifier input network. This figure of merit is the responsivity R, expressed in units of volts per watt. In the case of a thermoelectric type of detector, this can be specified directly for a given system, but for the photoconductive type, such as the indium-antimony detector mentioned previously, a suggested circuit must be given. For example, a 12-junction bismuth-silver thermopile may have a specified responsivity of 3 volts per watt, which may be detected directly with a voltage-sensitive galvanometer, whereas the indium-antimony detector has a responsivity of 0.5 volts per watt, which can only be detected with an a–c amplification system.

The third item of interest is the spectral characteristics of the detector. A typical method of reporting spectral characteristics is to supply a curve of spectral responsivity R_λ as a function of the wavelength λ, or a curve of the spectral detectivity D^*_λ as a function of wavelength λ. These are illustrated for typical photoconductive types of detectors in Figure 8.1 and Figure 8.2. In Figure 8.1 the specific spectral responsivity, or spectral responsivity per unit area of detector element, is plotted rather than the over-all spectral

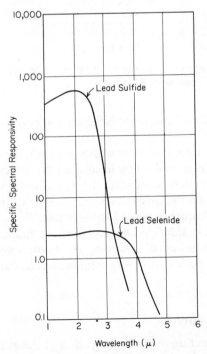

Figure 8.1   Spectral Responsivity of Photoconductors (Eastman-Kodak *Infrared Components Manual*).

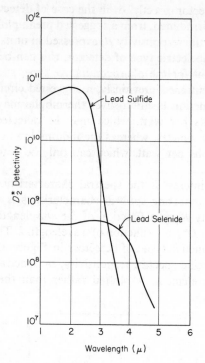

Figure 8.2   Spectral Detectivity of Photoconductors (Eastman-Kodak *Infrared Components Manual*).

responsivity. This is done because manufacturers supply detector elements in a variety of sizes.

Finally, the rate of response for detectors is specified by a time constant. The time constant τ is determined by irradiating the detector element with a sinusoidal, or approximately sinusoidal, varying radiant power of frequency f. Beginning at a low point the frequency is increased until the signal begins to drop. This value of frequency is used to determine the time constant from the basic expression $\tau = 1/2\pi f$. Since many detector applications require a-c amplification, the frequency of chopping or modulation of the incident beam should always be less than the frequency calculated from the time constant.

8.3 Thermal Detectors

Detectors that depend upon the heating effect of the radiant energy being measured are classed as thermal detectors. The most frequently used detectors of this class are the *thermopile*, or *thermocouple*, and the *bolometer*. In the thermocouple detector, a thermocouple or thermocouples are arranged in a suitable case, as shown in Figure 8.3. In this figure a blackened low-mass receiver is shown as the element irradiated by the radiant power to be measured. This receiver has a thermocouple junction attached to the back, and is supported by very fine wires or fibers. The second thermocouple junction, or *cold* junction, is attached to the case of the detector such that it never "sees" any of the radiant energy to be measured.

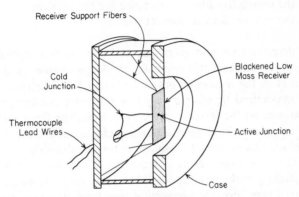

Figure 8.3   Thermopile Detector.

In operation, the receiver is heated by the incident radiant energy until thermal equilibrium is established with the surroundings. This change in temperature causes a measurable voltage, due to the temperature difference between the receiver thermocouple junction and the thermocouple junction mounted on the case. The signal generated depends on the thermoelectric constant of the thermocouple wires and the temperature difference at thermal equilibrium for the two junctions.

In the design of thermocouple detectors, the important heat transfer parameters are associated with the equilibrium temperature of the receiver. This temperature may be estimated by making an energy balance on the receiver:

$$q_{rad_{in}} = q_{rad_{out}} + q_{cond \, (lead \, wires)} + q_{cond \, (support \, wire)} + q_{conv} \qquad (8.1)$$

If each of the energy-loss terms on the right-hand side of Equation 8.1 are expressed as temperature difference divided by resistances, the result is

$$q_{rad_{in}} = \frac{T_r - T_s}{R_{rad}} + \frac{T_r - T_c}{l_w/(k_w A_w)} + \frac{T_r - T_c}{l_{supp}/(k_{supp} A_{supp})} + \frac{T_r - T_a}{l/(hA_r)} \qquad (8.2)$$

where T_r is the temperature of the receiver

T_s is the temperature of the radiation surrounds

T_c is the temperature of the case

T_a is the temperature of the gas around the receiver

R_{rad} is the resistance to radiant energy flow

l_w is the equivalent length of the thermocouple wire

k_w is the thermal conductivity of the thermocouple wire

A_w is the equivalent area of the thermocouple lead wires

l_{supp} is the equivalent length of the support fibers

k_{supp} is the thermal conductivity of the support fibers

h is the convective film conductance for the receiver

A_r is the receiver area in contact with the gas.

For a given detector case and given gas and surrounds temperatures, the highest receiver temperature will occur for the largest values of the thermal resistance values in the denominators of Equation 8.2. The radiation resistance can be maximized by using a very low emittance coating on the back of the receiver and on the interior of the case. Since the front surface must be blackened in order to have good absorbing characteristics for the incident radiation, nothing can be done to reduce the loss on this side.

Examination of the other terms in Equation 8.2 shows that the thermocouple wires leading to the receiver should be long, very fine wires, as should be the support fibers. For the convection loss term, the film conductance should be as small as possible. This may be accomplished by removing the gas, or by evacuating the case.

All of these procedures tend to increase the resistance for heat flow from the receiver, in an attempt to obtain a large temperature difference between the measuring thermocouple junctions. This is important if very small irradiation values are expected; however, the large resistances may be undesirable if the detector is to be used in a system that has a-c amplification. This is so because the time constant is increased by large resistance values. Actually, the time constant for the receiver is RC, where R is the effective resistance for all paths of energy loss and C is the thermal capacity of the receiver.

The thermal capacity (the product of mass times specific heat) may be minimized by using very-low-mass foil strips for the receiver, but this will not overcome the high resistance values. For this reason the usual design compromise of two divergent functions must be made in the selection of materials that affect resistance values.

Another popular thermal detector is the bolometer, which consists of a material with a very large change in resistance with a change in temperature. Modern bolometers use semiconductor materials for the active element. Since the physical change occurring in the bolometer is a resistance change, a supplementary bridge circuit is required to give a signal voltage. Typically, the bolometer is used in an a-c amplification scheme, and the bridge circuit used is similar to the circuit shown in Figure 8.4. As indicated in the figure, an active and a compensating element are used in a bridge circuit. Irradiation of the active element results in a small temperature change, which in turn causes a corresponding resistance change. The bridge unbalance caused by the resistance change is applied to the grid of the preamplifier tube as shown in the circuit diagram. Bolometers generally have a larger responsivity than thermocouple detectors, but, since they have higher resistance, they usually have a lower detectivity.

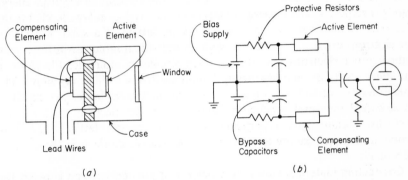

Figure 8.4 (a) Thermistor Bolometer (b) Thermistor Bolometer Circuit.

In both thermocouple and bolometer detectors, the response depends upon heating. If the windows have a constant transmittance independent of wavelength, and the receivers have constant absorptance, the detectors will have constant responsivity. This simply means that a given radiant flux irradiation will cause the same heating effect regardless of the spectral distribution of the incident energy. Since no window material or receiver coating is actually independent of the wavelength, no real detector will have constant responsivity, although the responsivity may be nearly constant over a limited range with certain materials. In particular applications it may be feasible to eliminate the window and use a coating which is nearly black over a wide wavelength range. Such modifications are generally not required unless the detector is to be used for absolute measurements.

One other thermal detector in use is the *pneumatic* detector or Golay cell detector. Basically, this detector uses a small gas cell which has a flexible mirror for one wall. When the gas in the cell is heated by incident radiation, the resulting expansion causes movement of the flexible wall. This movement is magnified optically and detected with a photocell. Although these detectors have very high detectivity and responsivity, they are not in general use because of their susceptibility to microphonics and vibrations. Laboratory use may be made of Golay detectors when the vibration level is very low.

8.4 Photon-counting Detectors

An entirely different class of detectors, which have many applications in radiant energy systems, are the detectors that essentially count photons. These detectors all depend upon the interaction of the incident photons with the electrons in the detecting element. The various physical mechanisms involved are called *photoemissive* effect, *photoconductive* effect, and *photovoltaic* effect.

In the discussion of these various effects, the concept of electron energy bands is required. These energy bands are conceived as energy levels for the electrons of materials bound into the crystal lattice of a solid. Certain of the electrons are firmly associated with an individual molecule in the crystal lattice; other electrons may drift from molecule to molecule. Electrons in the outer shells are the less firmly bound electrons which may move. The energy levels available for these electrons in the crystal lattice are classified as *valance* bands and *conduction* bands. When the electrons in the outer shell disassociate from a particular site in the crystal lattice, they have acquired sufficient energy to move from the valance bands into the conduction bands.

Conducting materials have a very narrow, if any, energy gap between the valance band and the conductance band. This results in the free movement of many electrons or electrical conductance. Insulating materials have a large energy gap between the valance and conductance bands and consequently have very few free electrons available for energy transfer. In between conductor and insulator types of materials are semiconductor materials. In semiconductors the energy gap between the valance and conduction bands is much more than in conductors but much less than in insulators. Furthermore, by appropriate seeding of semiconductor materials with other materials, the energy gap between valance and conduction bands can appear to be much less.

If appropriate materials are used, the energy gained by an electron when it interacts with a photon may move the electron into the conduction band. This movement will result in a change of the resistance of the material. Such an interaction is called the photoconductive effect. Similarly, photon-electron interactions may result in the photoemissive effect and the photovoltaic effect. In the case of the photoemissive effect, electrons are moved completely out of the material, and in the photovoltaic effect the electrons are moved across a barrier layer. In either case the basic physical mechanism of the detection is an interaction between photons and electrons.

Since a certain minimum amount of energy is required to move electrons, photon effect detectors will operate only when fairly energetic photons are available. The energy per photon becomes larger as the wavelength of the incident energy becomes smaller. For this reason photon effect detectors are most useful in the short wavelength region or in the visible and near infrared region. However, since the energy per photon increases as the wavelength decreases, the signal, which depends on the number of photon-electron interactions, will decrease as the wavelength becomes shorter if the incident energy is constant. This behavior for a theoretical detector is illustrated in Figure 8.5.

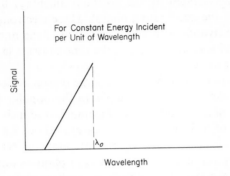

Figure 8.5   Theoretical Behavior of a Photodetector.

As indicated in the figure, a certain threshold wavelength λ_o exists beyond which the energy per photon is too small to cause any movement of the electrons. For energetic photons with wavelengths less than λ_o, interactions occur that result in a signal. Since the total energy is assumed to be constant, as the wavelength decreases the energy per photon increases, and therefore the number of photons decreases, resulting in a decreasing signal. Real detectors exhibit this behavior almost exactly, as shown by Figure 8.6, except that the threshold wavelength λ_o is not abrupt, as in Figure 8.5.

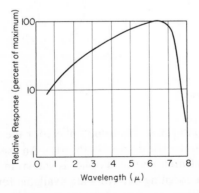

Figure 8.6 Response for an Indium-Antimonide Photoconductive Detector (Block Associates, Inc.: Bulletin KH-51-1).

The second important photon-counting detector in general use is the photo-multiplier. In the photomultiplier an active region, the cathode, is coated with a photoemissive material. This material emits electrons when irradiated with energetic photons. By using a series of secondary plates, a cascade effect is achieved. This is accomplished by maintaining a progressive potential difference between each succeeding stage in the tube. Electrons emitted by the cathode are accelerated by the potential difference to the first *dynode* (the term used for the accelerating plates). These electrons cause secondary emission from the dynode with a multiplication of the number of electrons. An arrangement of several dynodes in the tube causes a large multiplication of the initial electron flow.

For this reason photomultipliers have large responsivities when compared to other types of detectors. For example, in the popular 1P21 photomulti-plier, which has nine dynodes, the maximum responsivity (expressed as amperes per watt of incident flux in this case) is about 7.8×10^4 at a wave-length of 0.4 µ, and has a noise equivalent power of NEP(2870°K, 90, 1) $= 7 \times 10^{-16}$ watts. Since photomultipliers are photon-counting devices, the monochromatic responsivity is typical of such devices. For example see Figure 8.7, which shows the relative responsivity for the 1P21 photomulti-plier. As can be seen from this figure, this photomultiplier is mainly useful

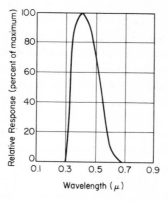

Figure 8.7 Response for a 1P21 RCA Photomultiplier Detector (RCA Tube Manual).

in the visible wavelength range. Photomultipliers for the near infrared range are also available from the DuMont Laboratories. An example of the relative response for a near infrared photomultiplier is shown in Figure 8.8. Several other types of photon-counting detectors are available for special use. For a discussion of these detectors, any of the texts on the physics of infrared technology may be consulted [6, 7].

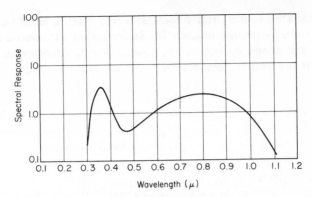

Figure 8.8   Response for DuMont K 2276 Photomultiplier Detector (DuMont Catalog No. T-100).

Radiant Sources

Radiant sources, like detectors, have general wavelength regions of application. If total measurements are being made, the source must be one which emits essentially like a blackbody. This is required for definition of the properties measured. When monochromatic measurements are made, strong sources in the individual wavelength region of interest are required.

8.5 Blackbody or Continuous Sources

Blackbody sources are typically isothermal solid materials with a conical, cylindrical, or cylindrical-conical cavity drilled into them. Several commercial models are available, from the Barnes Engineering Company for example; however, these sources can be readily constructed in the laboratory.

A typical source of this type is shown in Figure 8.9. In the construction of such a source, the main items to be considered are temperature gradients in the source cone and conical angle. By careful heat transfer analysis the temperature gradients in the cone may be maintained at a minimum. From previous considerations, we can observe that small cone angles are required in order to have a nearly black cavity. Typical cone angles are on the order of 20 deg. Although none of these sources have ideal (black) characteristics, many practical designs may approach blackness within less than 1 percent.

Recent literature has indicated that the surfaces of the cone or cylinder may appear blacker if the surfaces are specular reflectors rather than diffuse reflectors [11]. It should be noted that highly absorbent specular surfaces are not as easy to produce as diffuse surfaces. This is because roughened surfaces may have a high apparent absorptance because of multiple reflections at the surface. For this reason most blackbody sources have roughened surfaces coated with a material of large emissivity.

A very intense source, nearly equivalent to a 3800°K blackbody, may be obtained from a carbon-arc system (4). In the carbon-arc source, the positive crater in the anode is used as the source object. Commercial models of convenient arc sources are available, which may be used as laboratory tools [1].

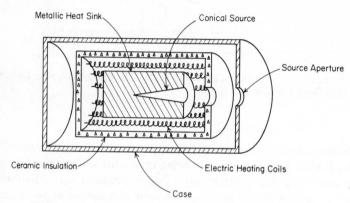

Figure 8.9 Moderate Temperature Blackbody Source.

8.6 Sources for Monochromatic Measurements

When monochromatic measurements require sources, several different types are practical. For the infrared region, the most common source is a Globar heated element. Globar elements are sintered tungsten carbide rods that can be heated electrically in air to temperatures up to 1500°K. These rods can be obtained in a variety of sizes from the Carborundum Division of the General Electric Company. Since they may be operated in air, no intervening window is required which would reduce the beam intensity. For this reason they are very popular sources in the longer wavelength regions where window materials are expensive and difficult to handle.

For shorter wavelength regions near the visible region, tungsten strips can be operated at a higher temperature than globars, but the glass envelope required to maintain a protective atmosphere will not transmit well in the longer wavelength regions. These sources are available commercially from the General Electric Company or the Perkin–Elmer Company.

When the wavelength region of interest is in the ultraviolet region, gas discharge tubes made with quartz envelopes are frequently used. Several different types of tubes are used, but high-pressure deuterium or high-pressure mercury are popular sources. Information on these two sources may be obtained from the Bausch and Lomb Company.

Radiation Pyrometers

8.7 Optical Pyrometers

As implied by the name, optical pyrometers are temperature-measuring instruments which depend upon optical-sensing methods. The easiest way to understand the operation of an optical pyrometer is to examine Figure 8.10. Basically, the optical pyrometer consists of a telescope with two additional features. One is a filter introduced into the optical path, and the second is a

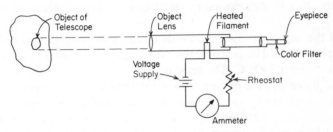

Figure 8.10   Schematic of an Optical Pyrometer.

wire filament which may be heated electrically. By proper choice of a lens system, the heated wire is superimposed on the image of the target as seen by the observer. Both the target object and the wire filament are seen through a filter, usually a red filter, such that the energy incident on the observer's eye is essentially a narrow wavelength band centered around some chosen value.

In operation, the heated wire brightness is controlled by the current flow through the electrical circuit. By placing the wire image on the target image, the observer matches the brightness of the wire to the brightness of the target object. Since wire brightness is a function of current flow through the electrical system, any given brightness match will be indicated by a corresponding ammeter reading.

From our analysis of the intensity of radiation of a black body (brightness is equivalent to intensity), we observe that the absolute temperature of a test object is a function of its brightness, or vice versa. With this information, the ammeter readings may be calibrated with a blackbody source, so that any given reading corresponds to a particular temperature of the source. For exacting work, the blackbody cavity may be maintained at the melting point of gold, resulting in a primary standard for temperature.

After calibration, an optical pyrometer may be used to measure the temperature of black bodies with surprising accuracy [8]. That is, the normal observer may match brightness within 1 percent, which corresponds to an error of about 1.5°C at 1800°K. This accuracy does not extend to measurements of real bodies, since emittance must be known for such measurements. Normally there are uncertainties in emittance, which reduce the precision of real-body measurement.

Inaccuracy is particularly noticeable when the human eye is used as a detector. In this case, monochromatic response is a variable that cannot be predicted, resulting in a variation of wavelength range reported by various observers for the same body. Since the emittance required to determine temperature is the average monochromatic emittance over the wavelength band examined, a human factor is introduced. It is possible for this error, plus other human errors, to result in temperature errors of 10 to 20 deg [12].

One of the important applications of optical pyrometers is in establishing a temperature scale. The practical limit for a gas thermometer in temperature definition is about 1000°C. The scale of temperatures above this value must be defined by an optical pyrometer. On the international temperature scale, all temperatures above the freezing point of gold are determined by an optical pyrometer. The technique for relating current flow through the pyrometer filament (the ammeter reading in Figure 8.10) to temperature is as follows:

The pyrometer is sighted on a black-body cavity immersed in freezing gold. The ammeter reading at this point represents the gold-point temperature. Then a neutral density filter with transmittance τ is imposed between a black object (usually a separate black-body source) and the object lens. This neutral density filter is frequently a rotating sector disk [12]. If the black object is heated to a temperature such that the ammeter reading corresponds to the gold-point temperature, the black object temperature is determined from

$$\tau E_{b\lambda e(\text{object})} = E_{b\lambda e(\text{gold point})}$$

$$\tau \frac{C_1}{\lambda_e{}^5(\exp C_2/\lambda_e T - 1)} = \frac{C_1}{\lambda_e{}^5(\exp C_2/\lambda_e T - 1)}$$

or

$$\exp C_2/\lambda_e T_{\text{object}} - 1 = \tau(\exp C_2/\lambda_e T_{\text{gold point}} - 1) \qquad (8.3)$$

Notice that the effective wavelength of observation λ_e must be known for the red-filter human-eye combination. This wavelength cannot be determined exactly; therefore, Equation 8.3 cannot be evaluated exactly.

Generally, a more accurate procedure would be to integrate over a wavelength band as shown in Equation 8.4, although this also requires knowledge of the eye response:

$$\int_{\Delta\lambda} (\exp C_2/\lambda T_{\text{object}} - 1)\, d\lambda = \int_{\Delta\lambda} \tau(\exp C_2/\tau T_{\text{gold point}} - 1)\, d\lambda \qquad (8.4)$$

A more realistic approach to establishing a temperature scale is to use a series of test-object temperatures, using a black cavity as the test object. Marking these temperatures on the ammeter calibrates the optical pyrometer for black-surface temperatures at the selected values. If these are fairly close together, interpolation may be used for other temperatures from the Planck equation or Wien's law, with small error.

8.8 Total Radiation Pyrometers

Radiation pyrometers that react to all wavelengths of incident radiant energy or react equivalently are called *total radiation* pyrometers. These pyrometers consist of an optical system to define the target area, a detector, and a temperature-compensating system. A typical system is shown in Figure 8.11.

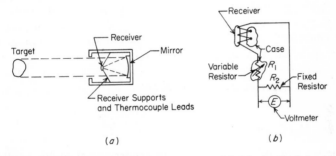

(a)   (b)

Figure 8.11   Total Radiation Pyrometer (a) Mechanical Arrangement (b) Thermopile Arrangement.

The case serves to hold the mirror (optical system) and the receiver. It is also used as the cold junction for the thermopile and as a heat sink for a variable resistor. During operation, the thermopile hot junctions respond to the energy flux incident upon the receiver. If the thermopile cold junctions are maintained at a constant temperature, the pyrometer can be calibrated directly in millivolt output versus source or target temperatures.

Normally, the pyrometer case temperature is not constant, causing the cold-junction temperature to vary, and resulting in a signal variation. In order to avoid this problem, a thermally sensitive resistor (R_1 in Figure 8.11) is mounted in thermal contact with the case. By proper choice of resistor material, the effect of the variation in the cold-junction temperature can be reduced. This can be seen from the following equation for the potential E on the voltmeter:

$$E = \frac{\text{emf}(T_{hj}) - \text{emf}(T_{cj})}{(R_1(T_{cj})/R_2) - 1}$$

where $\text{emf}(T_{hj})$ is the thermoelectric potential of the hot-junction thermo-couples

$\text{emf}(T_{cj})$ is the thermoelectric potential of the cold-junction thermo-couples

$R_1(T_{cj})$ is the resistance of the thermally sensitive resistor connected to the case

R_2 is the resistance of a load resistor across the output terminals

E is the output potential.

With this arrangement, the resistor R_1 must be a material that has a negative temperature coefficient of resistance. For a material such as this, proper choice of resistance value allows compensation of the pyrometer for a limited range of case temperatures.

In some of the commercial pyrometers available, the mirror optical system is replaced with a lens. The lens material chosen is usually calcium fluoride, since this material has good long-wavelength transmission. If the targets are assumed to be black, systems which do not pass all wavelengths may be calibrated, as well as a truly black energy-responding system. However, if the target is nonblack, the emittance correction factor must be evaluated with the transmittance of the nonideal lens system if meaningful temperature measurements are to be made.

8.9 Multicolor Pyrometers

Pyrometers may be made more or less independent of the emittance of the radiating object by using two or more wavelength regions of examination. In the typical two-color pyrometer the monochromatic emittance is assumed to be constant over the wavelengths used for observation. The two-color pyrometer consists of two detectors with optical systems such that both detectors "see" the same area of the object for which the temperature is being measured. In the optical path of each detector a bandpass filter is introduced such that the detectors are irradiated by energy bandwidths $\Delta\lambda_1$ and $\Delta\lambda_2$.

In a typical arrangement, shown in Figure 8.12, the solid angle of observation for the two detectors is varied by a diaphragm. For each detector the signal is given by

$$S_i = \int_{\Delta\lambda_i} \varepsilon_{\lambda i} B_i \frac{\tau_{\lambda i} C_1}{\lambda^5 (\exp C_2/\lambda T - 1)} \, d\lambda \tag{8.5}$$

where $\varepsilon_{\lambda i}$ is the monochromatic emittance of the test object, and B_i is an optical constant dependent upon the diaphragm position. By moving the diaphragm, the detector signals may be adjusted in magnitude.

With a design such as the one shown, a movement of the diaphragm results

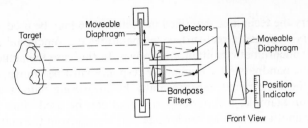

Figure 8.12 Two-color Pyrometer.

in an increase of one signal and a decrease in the other signal. By such a movement the detector signals may be adjusted to be equal to each other. If these
signals are arranged electrically to be of opposite polarity, the net signal
can be nulled. At the null position

$$S_1 - S_2 = 0 = \int_{\Delta\lambda_1} \varepsilon_{\lambda 1} B_1 \frac{\tau_{\lambda 1} C_1}{\lambda^5 (\exp C_2/\lambda T - 1)} \, d\lambda$$

$$- \int_{\Delta\lambda_2} \varepsilon_{\lambda 2} B_2 \frac{\tau_{\lambda 2} C_1}{\lambda^5 (\exp C_2/\lambda T - 1)} \, d\lambda \quad (8.6)$$

Since B_1, B_2, $\varepsilon_{\lambda 1}$, $\varepsilon_{\lambda 2}$ are assumed to be independent of wavelength, and
$\varepsilon_{\lambda 1} = \varepsilon_{\lambda 2}$,

$$0 = \varepsilon_{\lambda 1} B_1 \int_{\Delta\lambda_1} \frac{\tau_{\lambda 1} C_1}{\lambda^5 (\exp C_2/\lambda T - 1)} \, d\lambda - \varepsilon_{\lambda 2} B_2 \int_{\Delta\lambda_2} \frac{\tau_{\lambda 2} C_2}{\lambda^5 (\exp C_2/\lambda T - 1)} \, d\lambda$$

$$0 = B_1 f(\Delta\lambda_1, T) - B_2 f(\Delta\lambda_2, T) \quad (8.7)$$

where

$$f(\Delta\lambda, T) = \int_{\Delta\lambda} \frac{\tau_\lambda C_1}{\lambda^5 (\exp C_2/\lambda T - 1)} \, d\lambda$$

Equation 8.7 indicates that the temperature T is a function of the two optical
constants B_1 and B_2, and of the wavelength pass of the filters $\Delta\lambda_1$ and
$\Delta\lambda_2$. In practice this equation does not have to be used. Rather than
determine the actual $\Delta\lambda$'s and optical constants, the pyrometer is calibrated
by focusing it on a black-body cavity with measured temperature. With the
signals set at null by moving the diaphragm, a mark is made on the position
indicator representing the calibrated temperature. Repeating this procedure
at a variety of temperatures results in a calibrated temperature scale on the
diaphragm-position indicator.

The same basic technique as described for the two-color pyrometer may
be used for a three-color pyrometer. In the three-color pyrometer the monochromatic emittance may be assumed to be a linear function of wavelength
rather than a constant.

In theory the technique described in Section 7.16 may be used with optical pyrometers to measure real-surface temperatures if a functional relationship for the monochromatic emittance is known. In this case the actual transmittance of the bandpass-filter human-eye response must be known. Practically, this may be determined experimentally by measuring with a well-defined source. For example, a tungsten strip lamp can be used since the monochromatic emittance of tungsten is quite well known from the many measurements available in the literature. In this case an empirical formulation of monochromatic emittance as a function of wavelength is possible.

Property Measurement Apparatus

The methods presently available for measuring thermal radiation properties are conveniently classified as total or monochromatic. A subclassification is required for conductors and nonconductors, and in some cases for nonopaque systems. Methods presently available are described, and some of the advantages or disadvantages of each method are discussed. Many people are presently working in this area, and better methods will doubtless soon become available.

8.10 Total Radiation Property Measurement

From a consideration of the independent variables for total emittance, reflectance, and absorptance it is immediately apparent that total emittance is the most desirable property to use as a basis for measurement, because emittance is a function of the radiating system temperature only. Both reflectance and absorptance are functions of two temperatures, the radiating system temperature T_s and the radiating surrounds temperature T_s^*. For this reason most measurement data available for total properties are total emittance values measured calorimetrically.

Basically the calorimetric method of measurement consists of placing a sample of the material to be tested in an environment where all of the sample's energy losses are by radiation. A typical scheme for this is shown in Figure 8.13.

The purpose of this system is to allow the emittance to be derived from the equation, power $= \varepsilon A_s \sigma T_s^4$. In order to fulfill this purpose, all the power entering must leave by radiation, and the cooled sphere walls must be at absolute zero. However, neither of these criteria can be fulfilled, since (1) energy is conducted along the power and thermocouple leads, and (2) the walls cannot be maintained economically much below liquid nitrogen temperatures. In a typical system, energy loss by conduction may be evaluated quite accurately and the wall temperature error may be made quite small by using a small sample in a large sphere. Thus measurements of this type are generally accepted as very accurate if sufficient care is taken to control experimental conditions.

Calorimetric methods can be used for either conducting or nonconducting

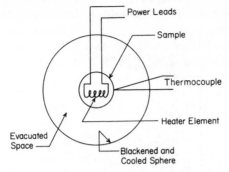

Figure 8.13   Calorimetric Total Emittance Measurement System.

materials. If the material is an electrical conductor, the sample is usually heated by resistance heating of the sample itself. For nonconductors, an electrical heater is embedded within the sample.

8.11 Monochromatic Property Measurement

As in the case of total property measurements, it would appear that monochromatic emittance is the most desirable property to measure. Once again, this is because monochromatic emittance is a function of only one temperature. However, in many cases, monochromatic reflectance is measured instead, since the heating of samples to very high temperatures may change their physical characteristics.

Another reason for measuring reflectance is the necessity for short-wavelength data. In emittance-measuring apparatus, the available energy level is very low for measurements of low-temperature samples at shorter wavelengths. This energy level may be so low that meaningful measurements are not possible.

A typical method of measuring monochromatic emittance is shown in Figure 8.14. In this system an optical arrangement alternately focuses an image of the heated sample surface, or an image of the black-body cavity at the same temperature, onto the slit of an monochromator. The particular system shown alternately traverses the sample and the black-body cavity into the optical path.

This monochromator detector consists basically of a system that filters out all wavelengths except a specified narrow bandwidth. This is accomplished by using a prism, a grating, or bandpass filters. The energy in the wavelength band that passes through the monochromator is focused upon a detector. This gives a signal, which is due to the energy image on the slit, in the narrow band of wavelengths passed. Thus, if the system alternately views a sample at temperature T and a black body at temperature T, the ratio of the two signals is the monochromatic emittance in the wavelength band passed by the monochromator.

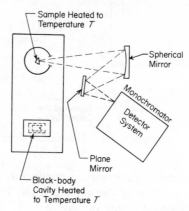

Figure 8.14 Monochromatic Emittance Measuring System.

Many varieties of this basic system have been proposed and used. Normally, when the sample is metal, it is possible to use a slit in a tubular sample as the black body. This eliminates the separate black body and removes one of the experimental variables.

The main difficulty with this system is in maintaining a sample at high enough temperature to give reasonable signal levels. When materials are heated in the presence of oxygen, their surface usually changes. Even if a nonoxidizing atmosphere is used, the samples may change crystal structure. In any case, the samples tend to change with heating except for certain particular materials. This results in a measurement for samples with different physical characteristics than anticipated.

Generally speaking, thermal radiation data, regardless of the method of measurement used, suffers from the lack of sample description. As has been observed, nearly any physical or chemical change will change the properties of samples. If a careful description of samples is not made by the experimenter, the property data he has obtained is practically useless.

To avoid heating samples and causing surface changes, experimenters often measure monochromatic reflectance values. The advantage of reflectance measurements is that a high-temperature source may be used, rather than a high-temperature sample. In a typical system, the samples are held at essentially room temperature. Such an arrangement results in the monochromatic reflectance $\rho_\lambda(T)$, where the temperature T is room temperature. As was explained in Section 2.3, this value may be used to determine total reflectance or total emittance, for surface temperatures other than room temperature, with acceptable engineering accuracy for most applications. In the few cases for which this accuracy is not sufficient, measurements at other temperatures are required.

Monochromatic measurements of reflectance are made most accurately with two separate types of reflectometers, the *hohlraum* reflectometer [4] and the *integrating sphere* reflectometer [5]. A sketch of the hohlraum reflectometer is shown in Figure 8.15. In this type of reflectometer, a heated

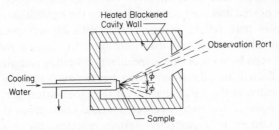

Figure 8.15　Hohlraum Reflectometer

wall is used to produce near isotropic or diffuse irradiation of a sample within a cavity. The sample is mounted on the front of a cooled sample holder. As indicated, a port in the heated cavity wall is used to observe the energy being reflected from the sample surface. In a typical measuring system, a monochromator detector is used to alternately observe the sample and a spot on the heated cavity wall.

If the cavity walls are maintained at a constant and uniform temperature and the port in the cavity is small compared to the cavity, the irradiation within the cavity will be constant. (This was proved in Chapter 2.) An observation of any point on the heated wall results in a signal proportional to the irradiation, or monochromatic irradiation for a monochromator detector system. When the optical system is changed to place the cooled sample under observation, the signal is proportional to the sum of the reflectance irradiation product and the emitted energy.

If the walls of the cavity are maintained at a temperature very much higher than the sample temperature, the emitted energy will be small compared to the ρG product. In practice, the walls are maintained above 1000°F and the sample is cooled to near room temperature. In this case, the ratio of the two signals obtained is the directional reflectance ρ_ϕ or $\rho_{\lambda\phi}$. This result is due to the reciprocity relationships discussed in [9].

The hohlraum reflectometer is considered to be best for measuring monochromatic reflectance in wavelengths longer than about 1 mu. Unfortunately, this type of reflectometer does not operate well at short wavelengths because of the lack of sufficient energy for short-wavelength measurements. This, of course, is due to the relatively low temperature at which the cavity walls can be maintained.

Another difficulty of this type of reflectometer is the unknown error that may be introduced by both sample heating and the observation port. Sample heating may become a very important problem if the sample is not a very good thermal conductor. In this case, the outer surface will be at a temperature considerably above the temperature of the cooling fluid. This results in emitted energy added to the signal from the sample.

The second important error involves the observation port. This port is obviously not heated and does not contribute to the irradiation of the sample. Certain samples may reflect energy neither diffusely or specularly [2]. In these cases, the observation port may introduce very large errors.

This can be seen by considering a specularly reflecting sample. In this case, the energy reflected into the observation beam comes entirely from a spot on the wall located at the polar angle ϕ'. If the observation port were located at this angle, none of the energy reflected would come from the cavity.

When the sample is a perfectly diffuse reflector, the energy reflected comes from the entire hemisphere over the sample. Since the energy is diffusely reflected, the relative effect of a band of the source located at polar angle ϕ is dependent upon the cosine of ϕ. Thus, if the observation port is large and located at a small angle ϕ, the energy assumed to have come from the direction of the observation port may become a significant fraction of the total energy reflected.

In the case of a diffusely reflecting sample a calculable error is introduced in the reflectances measurement; however, if the sample is neither perfectly diffusing nor specular an unknown error is introduced by the observation port. Because of these factors and the inherent difficulty of maintaining constant known temperatures for the cavity wall and sample, a considerable research effort is now underway to develop an improved long-wavelength reflectometer.

For short wavelength measurements, 1.5–0.3 μ, the *integrating sphere* reflectometer is used. Several types of these reflectometers are presently available. A particularly convenient type is shown in Figure 8.16.

In this type of reflectometer a sample is suspended in a sphere by a sample holder that can be revolved. A beam of monochromatic energy from a monochromator is directed into the sphere onto the sample as indicated. By means of an external control, the polar angle ϕ may be varied. Energy reflected away from the sample is diffused by the reflecting inner wall of the sphere.

For the particular geometry of a sphere, a diffusing surface results in uniform irradiation of the sphere wall, except for the portion irradiated

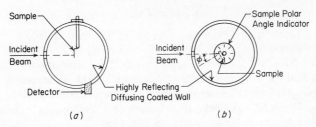

Figure 8.16   Integrating Sphere Reflectometer (a) Side View
(b) Top View.

directly by the first reflection from the sample [2]. If a detector is positioned in the wall such that the first reflected energy does not strike the detector, the signal from the detector is proportional to a constant times the sample reflectance times the sample irradiation. This signal is compared to the signal received when the incident beam is directly incident on the wall of the sphere. This signal is proportional to the irradiation times a constant.

By consideration of the geometry of the system, the constant multiplier in the case of wall irradiation can be shown to be the same as the constant multiplier when the sample is irradiated. A comparison of the two signals then results in the monochromatic directional reflectance of the sample, or $\rho_{\lambda\phi}$. In this case it is not necessary to consider reciprocity, since the entire reflected energy is integrated by the sphere system.

In the integrating sphere reflectometer the only error, other than some minor errors due to polarization, results from energy lost out of the hole through which the incident beam is directed. By proper sizing this error can be minimized, and the reflectance values obtained are generally considered to be very accurate [3].

Except for the low efficiency of the sphere-detector system, the integrating sphere offers many advantages over other systems: (1) Samples may be maintained at any temperature desired without affecting the results; (2) delicate power adjustments to maintain wall temperatures are not required; (3) samples may be either metallic or nonmetallic—there is no problem of sample heating.

One important difficulty with this type of integrating sphere is the detector response. The detector should have a response that is not a function of the local polar angle; that is, the detector should be diffusely reacting.

A diffuse reactor type of detector is not generally available, although a detector may be modified to respond as a diffuse surface if a semitransparent cover is supplied. For example, a milk-glass cover with a roughened upper surface can be used to convert a nondiffuse detector system into a nearly diffuse system. This particular problem has been examined in detail, and, practically speaking, the difficulty has been circumvented [5, 13].

References

1. "A Reproducible High Temperature Radiation Standard at 3800°K," Bulletin 2371. Hollywood, Cal.: Mole-Richardson Company.

2. BIRKEBAK, R. C., "Monochromatic Directional Distribution of Reflected Thermal Radiation from Roughened Surfaces," Ph.D. Dissertation 64-3830. Ann Arbor, Michigan: University Microfilms, Inc., September 1962.

3. CLAYTON, W. A., "Comment on Measurement Techniques," Proceedings, Symposium on Thermal Radiation of Solids, 1964.

4. DUNKLE, R. V., D. K. EDWARDS, J. T. GIER, K. E. NELSON, and R. D. RODDICK, "Heated Cavity Reflectometer for Angular Reflectance Measurements," *Progress in International Research on Thermodynamic and Transport Properties.* New York: American Society of Mechanical Engineers, 1962.

5. EDWARDS, D. K., K. E. NELSON, R. D. RODDICK, and J. T. GIER, "Basic Studies on the Use and Control of Solar Energy," Department of Engineering Report No. 60-93, University of California at Los Angeles, 1960.

6. HOLTER, M. R., S. NUDELMAN, G. H. SUITS, W. L. WOLFE, and G. J. ZISSIS, *Fundamentals of Infrared Technology.* New York: Crowell Collier and Macmillan, Inc., 1962.

7. KRUSE, P. W., L. D. MCGLAUCHLIN, and R. B. MCQUISTAN, *Elements of Infrared Technology.* New York: John Wiley & Sons, Inc., 1962.

8. MCADAMS, W. H., *Heat Transmission.* New York: McGraw-Hill, Inc. (1954), chap. 4 (by H. C. Hottel).

9. MCNICHOLAS, H. J., "Absolute Methods in Reflectometry," *Bureau of Standards Research Journal,* vol. 1 (March 1928), pp. 29–73.

10. NULL, M. R., and W. W. LOZIER, "Carbon Arc as a Radiation Standard," *Journal, Optical Society of America* vol. 52, No. 10 (October 1962), pp. 1156–1162.

11. SPARROW, E. M., and S. H. LIN, "Absorption of Thermal Radiation in V-Groove Cavities," Heat Transfer Laboratories Report, University of Minnesota, Minneapolis, 1962.

12. THORN, R. J., and G. H. WINSLOW, "Recent Developments in Optical Pyrometry," ASME Paper No. 63-WA-224, 1963.

13. ZERLAUT, G. A., and A. C. KRUPNICK, "An Integrating Sphere Reflectometer for the Determination of Absolute Hemispherical Spectral Reflectance," AIAA Paper No. 64-255, 1964.

APPENDIX 1

Property Data
for Total Emittance

Reprinted from Thermal Radiation Properties Survey, *by G. G. Gubareff, J. E. Janssen, and R. H. Torborg (Minneapolis, Minn.: Honeywell Research Center, Minneapolis-Honeywell Regulator Company, 1960)*

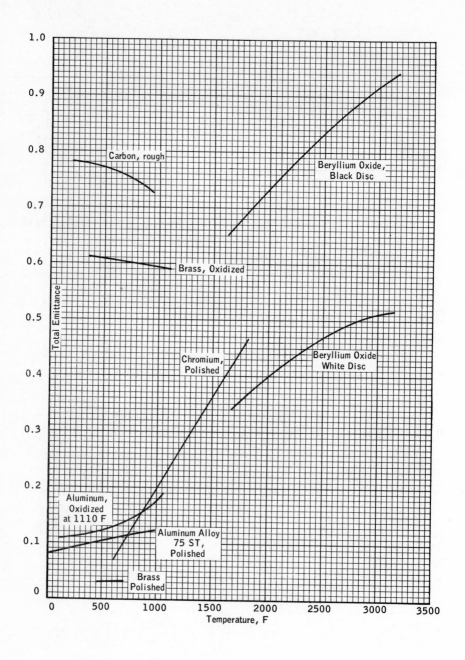

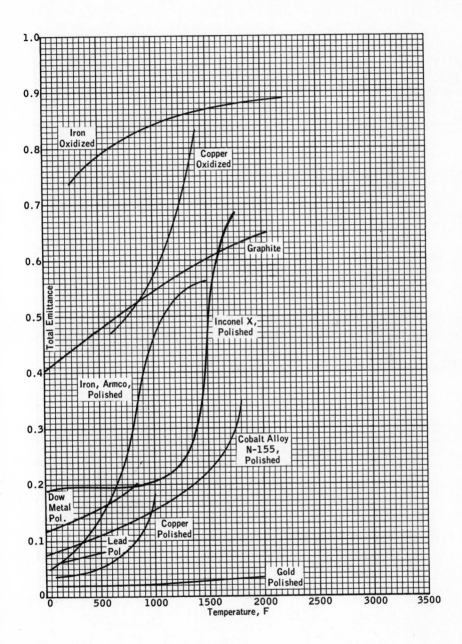

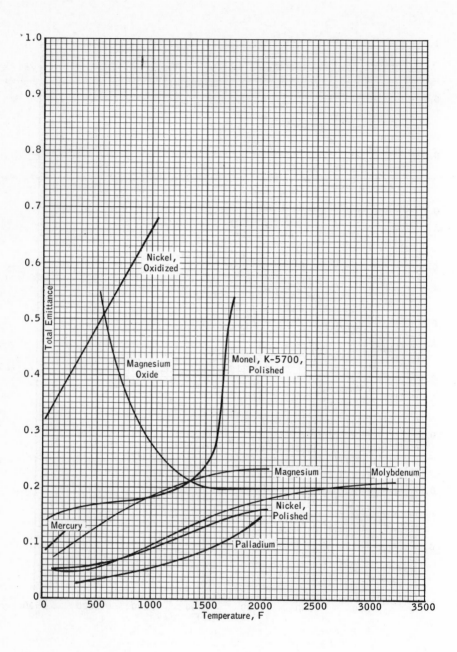

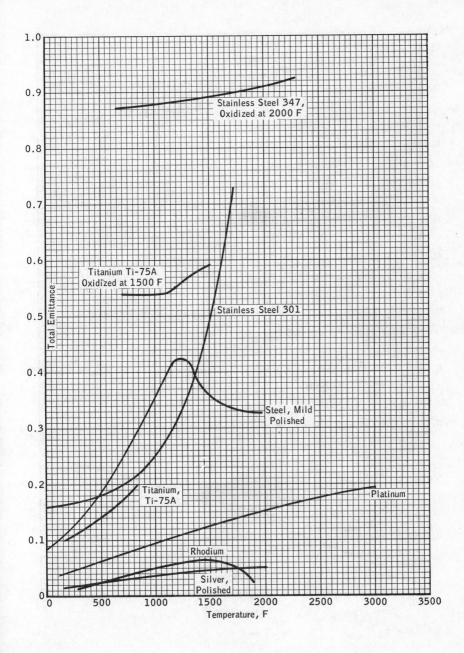

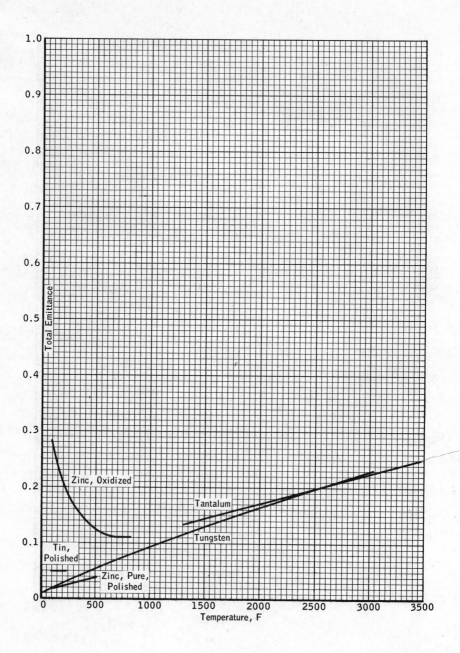

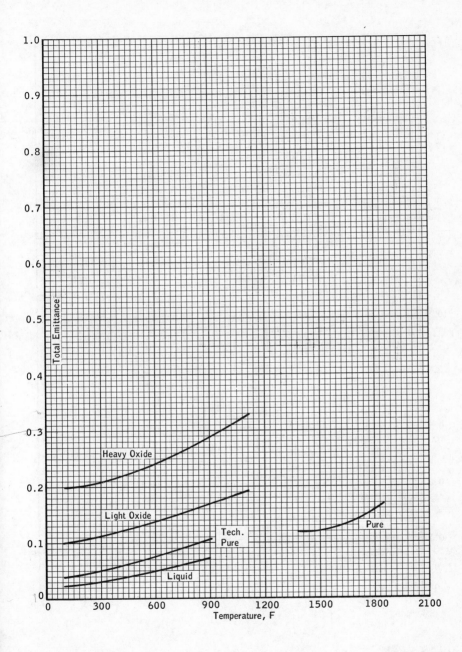

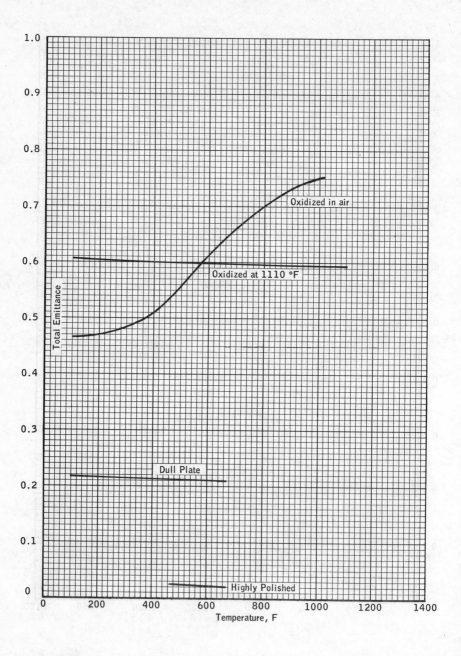

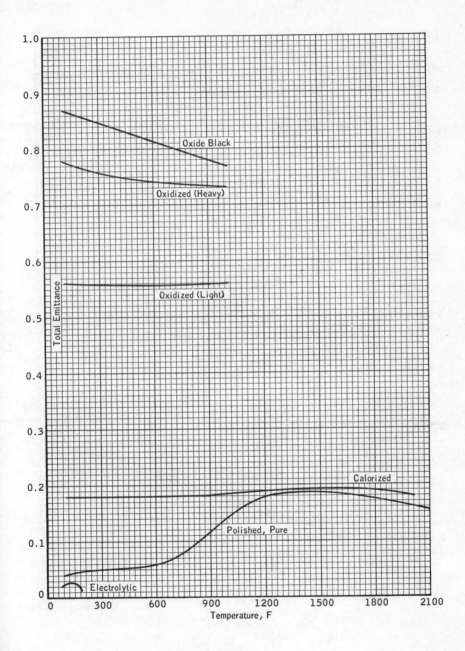

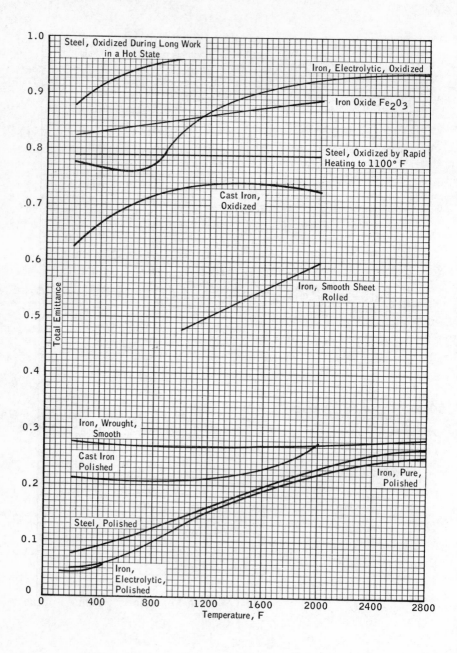

APPENDIX 2

Property Data
for Spectral Emittance

Reprinted from Thermal Radiation Properties Survey, *by G. G. Gubareff, J. E. Janssen, and R. H. Torborg (Minneapolis, Minn.: Honeywell Research Center, Minneapolis-Honeywell Regulator Company, 1960)*

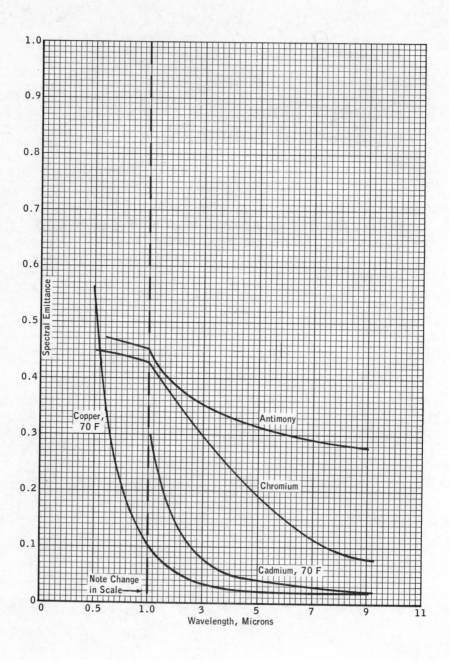

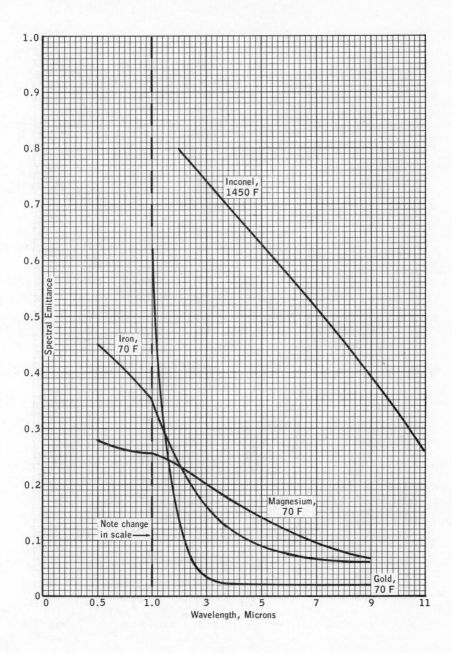

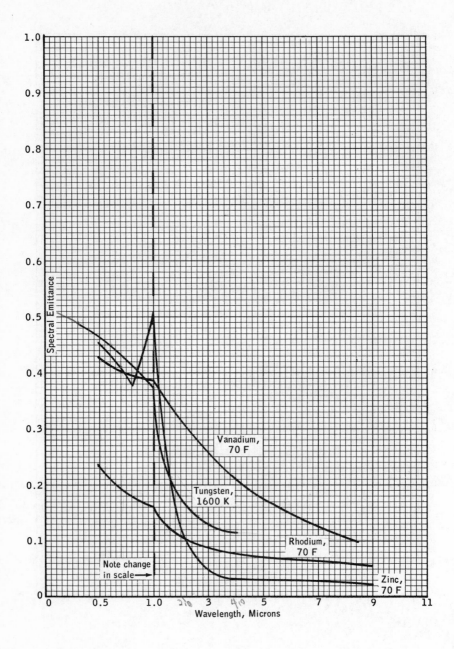

Spectral Emittance

Vanadium, 70 F

Tungsten, 1600 K

Rhodium, 70 F

Zinc, 70 F

Note change in scale→

Wavelength, Microns

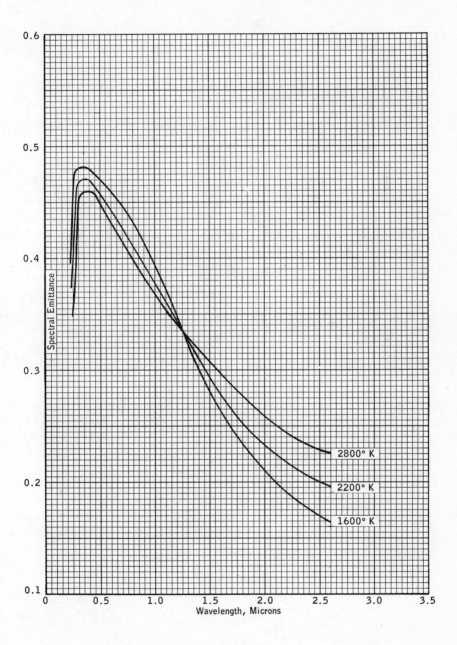

APPENDIX 3

Property Data
for Spectral Reflectance

Reprinted from Thermal Radiation Properties Survey, *by G. G. Gubareff, J. E. Janssen, and R. H. Torborg (Minneapolis, Minn.: Honeywell Research Center, Minneapolis-Honeywell Regulator Company, 1960)*

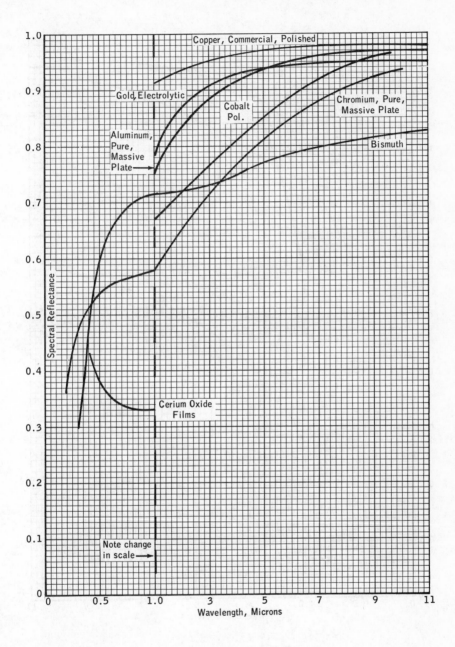

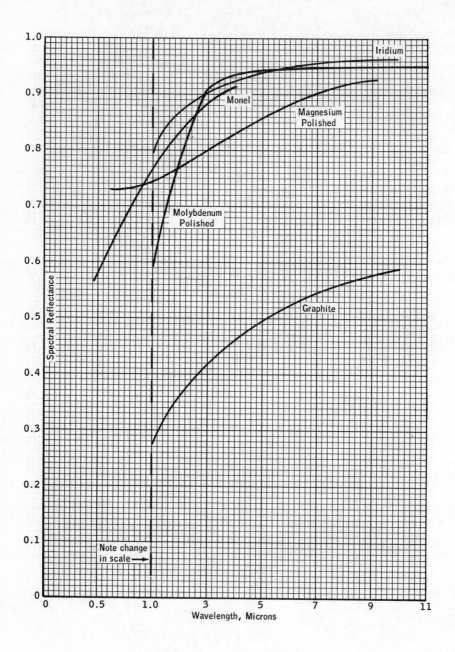

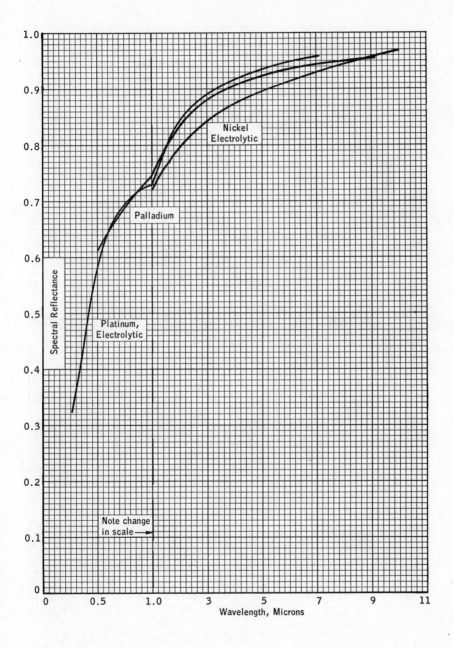

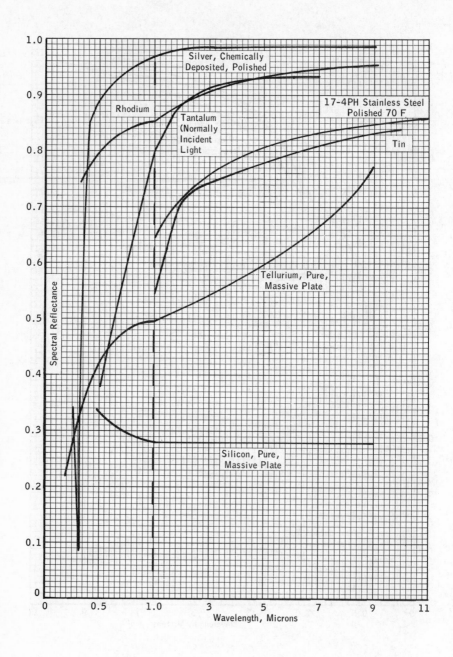

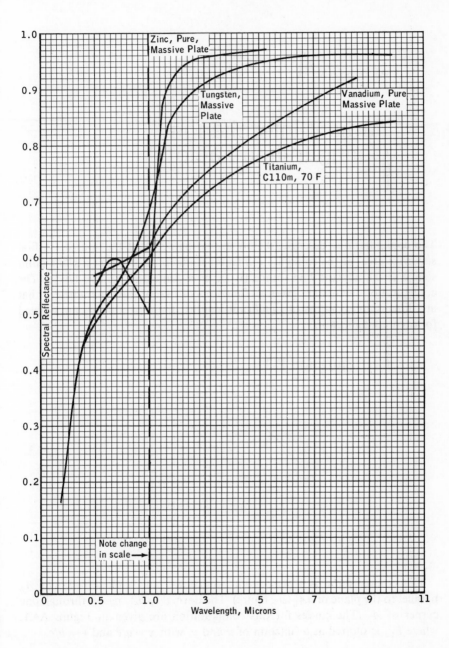

Radiant-Interchange Configuration Factors†

The configurations described below are so named that the source, or first subscript area, of the configuration factor is identified as either a plane point source (P-1), a plane line source (L-1), or a finite-area source (A-1). The configuration factors are given as functions of two or more parameters that are dimensionless ratios of significant lengths; these parameters are defined for each configuration.

Configuration P-1

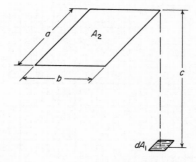

This configuration is a plane point source dA_1 and a plane rectangle A_2 parallel to the plane of dA_1 (see figure). The normal to dA_1 passes through one corner of A_2. The curves for this configuration are given in Figure A4.1, where F_{12} is plotted as a function of x and y, with $x = a/c$ and $y = b/c$.

---

†Adapted from NACA Report No. TN–2836, by D. C. Hamilton and W. R. Morgan.

$$F_{12} = \frac{1}{2\pi}\left[\frac{x}{\sqrt{1+x^2}}\tan^{-1}\left(\frac{y}{\sqrt{1+x^2}}\right) + \frac{y}{\sqrt{1+y^2}}\tan^{-1}\left(\frac{x}{\sqrt{1+y^2}}\right)\right]$$

$$\lim_{x\to\infty} F_{12} = \frac{y}{4\sqrt{1+y^2}}$$

$$\lim_{y\to\infty} F_{12} = \frac{x}{4\sqrt{1+x^2}}$$

Figure A4.1   Configuration-factor Curves for P–1.

Configuration P-2

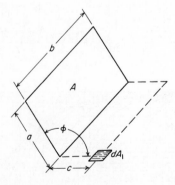

This configuration is a plane point source dA_1 and a plane rectangle A_2, in which the planes of dA_1 and A_2 intersect at an angle ϕ ($0° < \phi < 180°$). The configuration-factor values are given in the curves plotted in Figure A4.2 for various values of ϕ, N, and L, where $N = a/b$ and $L = c/b$ (see figure).

$$F_{12} = \frac{1}{2\pi}\left\{\tan^{-1}\left(\frac{1}{L}\right) + V(N\cos\ - \phi L)\tan^{-1}V\right.$$

$$\left. + \frac{\cos\phi}{W}\left[\tan^{-1}\left(\frac{N - L\cos\phi}{W}\right) + \tan^{-1}\left(\frac{L\cos\phi}{W}\right)\right]\right\}$$

where

$$V = \frac{1}{\sqrt{N^2 + L^2 - 2NL\cos\phi}}$$

$$W = \sqrt{1 + L^2\sin^2\phi}$$

$$\lim_{N\to\infty} F_{12} = \frac{1}{2\pi}\left\{\tan^{-1}\left(\frac{1}{L}\right) + \frac{\cos\phi}{W}\left[\frac{\pi}{2} + \tan^{-1}\left(\frac{L\cos\phi}{W}\right)\right]\right\}$$

$$\lim_{L\to\infty} F_{12} = 0$$

$$\lim_{L\to 0} F_{12} = \frac{1}{4}(1 + \cos\phi)$$

$$\lim_{N,L\to\infty} F_{12} = 0$$

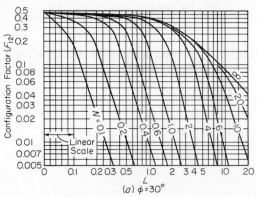

(a) $\phi = 30°$

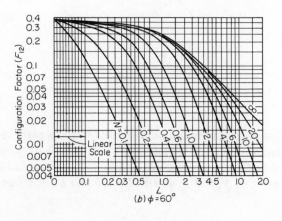

(b) $\phi = 60°$

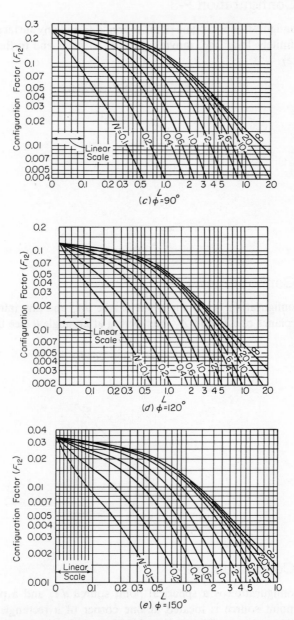

Figure A4.2   Configuration-factor Curves for P–2 at Various Values of Φ
When Φ = 0°, $F_{12} = 0$ for $N < L$ and 0.5 for $N > L$; when Φ = 180°,
$F_{12} = 0$ for all values of N and L.

Configuration P-3

This configuration is a plane point source dA_1 and any surface A_2 generated by an infinitely long line, moving parallel to itself and to the plane of dA_1 (see figure).

$$F_{12} = \frac{1}{2}(\cos\theta - \cos\omega)$$

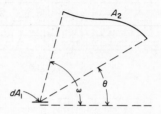

Configuration P-4

This configuration is a plane point source dA_1 and any infinite plane A_2, with the planes of dA_1 and A_2 intersecting at an angle θ (see figure).

$$F_{12} = \frac{1}{2}(1 + \cos\theta)$$

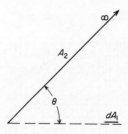

Configuration P-5

This configuration is a spherical point source dA_1 and a plane rectangle A_2; the point source is located at one corner of a rectangle that has one common side with A_2. The planes of the two rectangles intersect at an angle ϕ (see figure). The configuration factor F_{12} is plotted in Figure A4.3 as a function of x and y, where $x = b/c$ and $y = a/c$.

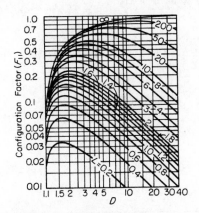

Figure A4.12 Configuration-factor Curves for L–4.

Configuration L-5

This configuration has the same geometry as L-4 (see figure for L-4). The configuration factor from dA_1 to either end can be obtained from Figures A4.11 and A4.12 and the following equation:

$$F_{dA_1-\text{one end}} = \frac{1}{2}(1 - F_{11} - F_{12})$$

Configuration A-1

This configuration consists of identical, parallel, directly opposed rectangles A_1 and A_2 (see figure). The configuration-fact or values are plotted in Figure A4.13 in terms of the parameters x and y, where $x = b/c$ and $y = a/c$.

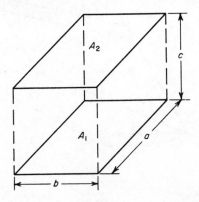

$$F_{12} = \frac{2}{\pi xy} \left\{ \log_e \left[\frac{(1 + x^2)(1 + y^2)}{1 + x^2 + y^2} \right]^{1/2} + y\sqrt{1 + x^2}\, \tan^{-1}\left(\frac{y}{\sqrt{1 + x^2}} \right) \right.$$

$$\left. + x\sqrt{1 + y^2}\, \tan^{-1}\left(\frac{x}{\sqrt{1 + y^2}} \right) - y \tan^{-1} y - x \tan^{-1} x \right\}$$

$$\lim_{x \to \infty} F_{12} = \sqrt{1 + \frac{1}{y^2}} - \frac{1}{y}$$

$$\lim_{y \to \infty} F_{12} = \sqrt{1 - \frac{1}{x^2}} - \frac{1}{x}$$

$$\lim_{\substack{x \to \infty \\ y \to \infty}} F_{12} = 1$$

Figure A4.13   Configuration-factor Curves for A–1.

Configuration A-2

This configuration consists of two rectangles A_1 and A_2, with one common edge and an included angle between the two planes. The configuration factor

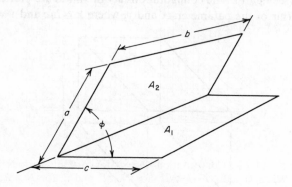

is plotted in Figure A4.14 as a function of N and L for various values of ϕ. $N = a/b$ and $L = c/b$ (see figure). For $\phi = 90°$,

$$F_{12} = \frac{1}{\pi L}\left(L\tan^{-1}\left(\frac{1}{L}\right) + N\tan^{-1}\left(\frac{1}{N}\right) - \sqrt{N^2 + L^2}\,\tan^{-1}\left(\frac{1}{\sqrt{N^2 + L^2}}\right)\right.$$

$$+ \frac{1}{4}\log_e\left\{\left[\frac{(1 + L^2)(1 + N^2)}{(1 + N^2 + L^2)}\right]\left[\frac{L^2(1 + L^2 + N^2)}{(1 + L^2)(L^2 + N^2)}\right]^{L^2}\right.$$

$$\times \left.\left.\left[\frac{N^2(1 + L^2 + N^2)}{(1 + N^2)(L^2 + N^2)}\right]^{N^2}\right\}\right)$$

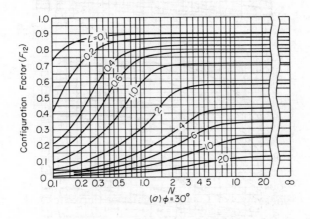

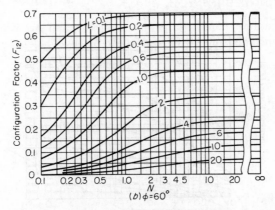

Figure A4.14 Configuration Curves for A–2 at Various Values of ϕ. When $\phi = 0°$, $F_{12} = N/L$ for $N < L$ and 1 for $N > L$; when $\phi = 180°$, $F_{12} = 0$ for all values of N and L.

$$\lim_{N \to \infty} F_{12} = \frac{1}{\pi}\left[\tan^{-1}\left(\frac{1}{L}\right) + \frac{1}{4L}\log_e(1 + L^2) - \frac{L}{4}\log_e\left(\frac{1 + L^2}{L^2}\right)\right]$$

$$\lim_{L \to \infty} F_{12} = 0$$

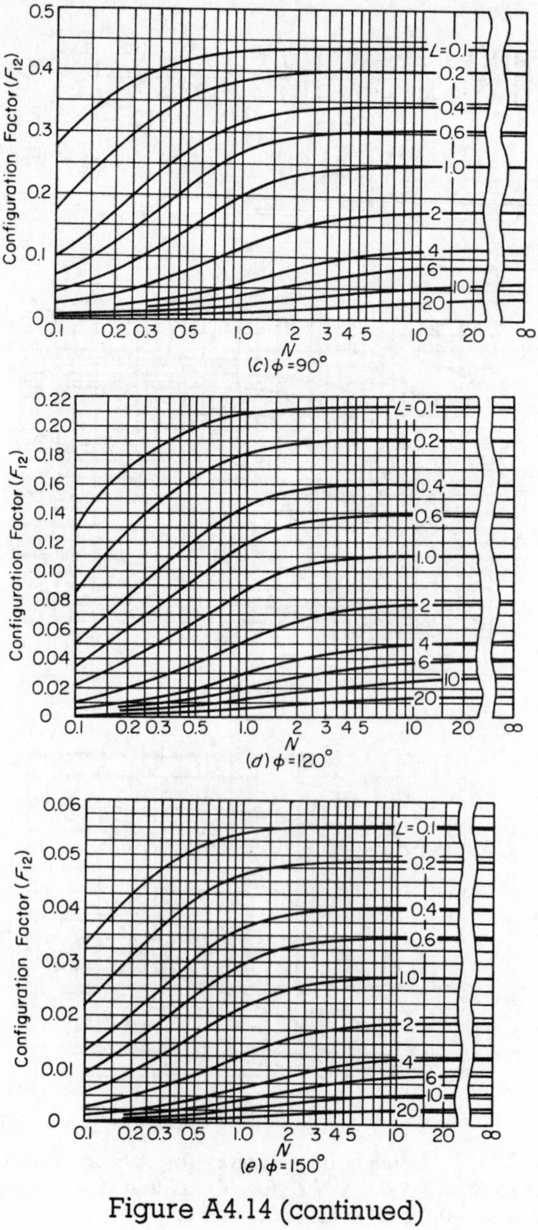

(c) $\phi = 90°$

(d) $\phi = 120°$

(e) $\phi = 150°$

Figure A4.14 (continued)

Configuration A-3

This configuration consists of parallel, directly opposed, plane circular disks (see figure). $E = r_2/d$ and $D = d/r_1$.

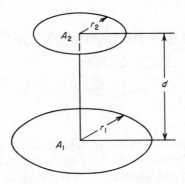

$$F_{12} = \frac{1}{2}(x - \sqrt{x^2 - 4E^2D^2})$$

where $x = 1 + (1 + E^2)D^2$.

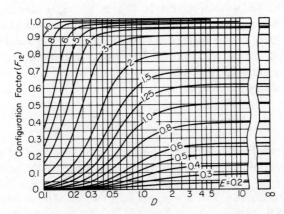

Figure A4.15   **Configuration-factor Curves for A–3.**

APPENDIX 5

Nongray Radiation Exchange in an Enclosure

As discussed in Chapter 6, the solution of the radiant exchange problem for a nongray diffuse surface enclosure involves numerous calculations. The hand labor can be reduced to a minimum by using a digital computer for the solution. The program at the end of this appendix was written in IBM Fortran for the IBM 1620 digital computer, which rapidly evaluates the heat transfer in an enclosure with surface temperatures known. Since the program is written in Fortran it can be easily changed to work on any machine that accepts the Fortran language.

Program Method

The basic solution method used in the program is the relaxation procedure, described for gray system solutions in Section 5.10. However, since the program is for the nongray case, the method is used to determine the energy transfer in specified wavelength bands. That is, for a given enclosure, the gray solution is made m times, where m is the number of wavelength bands to be considered. After all the bands have been relaxed to the required tolerance (the fractional change of radiosity J in one iteration of Equation 5.27), the results are summed to obtain the total radiosity of each node.

Since the energy represented by

$$\int_{\lambda_1}^{\lambda} E_{b\lambda} \, d\lambda$$

must be evaluated for each node, a subprogram is included that performs the necessary integration.† Evaluation was actually done using the integral

---

† This integration was accomplished using the method outlined by Mark Pivovonsky and Max R. Nagel in *Tables of Blackbody Radiation Functions* (New York: Crowell Collier and Macmillan, Inc., 1961).

262

$$\int_{v_1}^{v} E_{bv}\, dv$$

where v is the wave number, since the expressions in Pivovonsky are for wave number independent variables.

Program Input

The best method of understanding the program input is to consider what is required for a given problem definition.

First the number of surface elements in the enclosure N must be known. This is included in the first READ card, statement number 34. From the consideration of the emittance characteristics of all surfaces, the number of wavelength bands m must be chosen. Since the total spectrum runs from zero to infinity wave numbers, the band separations will be $m-1$. The value $J = m-1$ must be given to the program by READ statement 34. In order to specify the minimum number of temperatures for the surface elements, a specification of the number of different temperatures in the enclosure K is required. The value K is also read in by READ statement 34. Finally, the tolerance described previously is given by READ statement 34.

A typical set of data might be as follows:

$$N = 6 \qquad J = 8 \qquad K = 4 \qquad \text{Tolerance } = 0.01$$

READ statement 100 reads into memory the wave numbers that separate the total spectrum into wavelength bands. These J values are written in floating-point arithmetic form and must proceed from small values to large values; that is, $v_1 < v_2 < v_3 \cdots$.

READ statement 101 reads the K temperature values into the memory in floating-point form. The temperatures are identified in the program in order of input; that is, if $K = 4$ and the temperatures are read in as 200.0, 300.0, 400.0, 500.0, the program considers $T_1 = 200.0$, $T_2 = 300.0$, $T_3 = 400.0$, $T_4 = 500.0$.

READ statement 102 identifies the surface element with the proper temperature. For example, if five surface elements are involved that have the temperatures mentioned above,

Surface Element	Temperature	Temperature Symbol
1	200.0	T_1
2	400.0	T_3
3	300.0	T_2
4	400.0	T_3
5	500.0	T_4

the values 1, 3, 2, 3, and 4 in fixed point would identify the surface temperature from the temperature list read in by statement 101.

READ statement 103 reads in the values of the emittance for the surface elements. If ε_{im} is the emittance of the mth surface node in the ith band, for i bands and m nodes, i times m emittance values must be read into the memory. These values are read in row order, one after the other: For $i = 3$, $m = 4$, ε_{11}, ε_{12}, ε_{13}, ε_{14}, ... ε_{33}, ε_{34} is the order of input.

READ statement 104 reads in the configuration factors for the enclosure. For an enclosure of m surface elements, m^2 configuration factors are required. These values are also read in row order, and the order of input is F_{11}, F_{12}, F_{13}, ... F_{1m-1}, F_{1m}.

Program Output

The output device of the program output is controlled by sense switch 1, as indicated by the statement following statement 3. In either case the output, as given by statements 19 or 314, is in the following order:

> Surface element number
> Heat flux in Btu per hr-ft^2
> Irradiation of the surface element in Btu per hr-ft^2
> Radiosity of the surface element in Btu per hr-ft^2

For each surface element the IBM 1620 will print on one line a series of numbers as indicated above. After the completion of one set of data the program will automatically return to read the next set of data, if it is present.

Program Limitations

For the 2000-word IBM 1620 the program is limited to 9 surface elements and 20 wavelength bands. This limitation is shown in the dimension statements (note that 20 bands require only 19 separations). If a larger storage were available, problems of any size could be solved.

Program accuracy is under the control of the user, since the basic error involved is the tolerance of relaxation. In general, the smaller the tolerance, the longer the running time for a problem. Normally, emittance values near 1.0 result in the shortest running time, and small emittance values require a long running time. Tolerance values of 0.001 have been used without excessive running time on the 1620. Unfortunately, each individual problem requires a different running time, since the rate of convergence depends upon the individual variables read into the program.

Program

```
C     NONGRAY RADIATION SOLUTION
      DIMENSION XNU(19),TEMP(9),EPSL(20,9),NDTM(9),XP(9,9)
      DIMENSION EBIN(19,9),GMLT(9),EMLT(9),X(J9),XJSM(9)
      DIMENSION GSM(9),EBBN(9),G(9)
   34 READ,NI,J,K,TOL
      DO 100 I=1,J
  100 READI,XNU(I)
      DO 101 I=1,K
  101 READI,TEMP(I)
      DO 102 I=1,N
  102 READI,NDTM(I)
      JI=J+1
      DO 103 I=1,JI
      DO 103 M=1,N
  103 READI,EPSL(I,M)
      DO 104 I=1,N
      DO 104 M=1,N
  104 READI,XP(I,M)
      DO 7 JI=1,J
      DO 7 KI=1,K
      Z=2.5884*XNU(JI)/TEMP(KI)
C     SUBROUTINE
C     EBBNF
      IF(Z−1.E−3)91,91,161
  161 IF(Z−20.0)111,111,71
  111 IF(Z−2.0)21,21,31
   21 COM=Z**3
      COM1=Z**2
      COM2=COM/(3.0)−(COM*Z)/8.0
      COM3=(COM*COM1)/(60.0)−(Z*COM*COM)/5040.0
      COM4=COM**3
      COM5=COM4/(2.716E5)−(COM4*COM1)/1.33056E7
      COM=(15.0/3.14159**4)*(COM2+COM3+COM5)
      RESLT=1.0−COM
      GO TO 81
   31 XM=1.0
      SUM=0.0
  301 COM3=XM*Z
      COM2=XM**4
      COM1=2.71828**COM3
      COM4=(COM3+3.0)*COM3+6.0
      COM4=COM4*COM3+6.0
      COM4=COM4/(COM2*COM1)
      SUM=SUM+COM4
      IF(SUM−COM4)41,41,51
   41 XM=XM+1.0
      GO TO 301
   51 IF(COM4−0.001*SUM)61,41,41
   61 COM=(15.0)/(3.14159**4)
      RESLT=COM*SUM
```

```
        GO TO 81
   71   RESLT = 0.0
        GO TO 81
   91   RESLT = 1.0
   81   FRAC = RESLT
C       END OF SUB PROGRAM
    7   EBIN(JI,KI) = FRAC*0.1714E - 8*(TEMP(KI)**4)
        DO 2 N4=1,N
        XJSM(N4) = 0.0
    2   GSM(N4) = 0.0
        DO 3 J2=1,JI
        DO 4 NI=1,N
        COMI = EPSL(J2,NI)
        RO = 1.0 - COMI
        COM = 1.0 - RO*XP(NI,NI)
        GMLT(NI) = RO/COM
        EMLT(NI) = COMI/COM
        K = NDTM(NI)
        IF(J2 - 1)5,5,6
    5   EBBN(NI) = - EBIN(J2,K) + .1714E - 8*TEMP(K)**4
        GO TO 4
    6   IF(J2 - JI)8,9,9
    9   EBBN(NI) = EBIN(J2 -1,K)
        GO TO 4
    8   EBBN(NI) = EBIN(J2 -1,K) - EBIN(J2,K)
    4   XJ(NI) = EBBN(NI)
   10   INDX =0
        DO 15 N2=1,N
        SUM = 0 0
        DO 11 M=1,N
        IF(M - N2)12,11,12
   12   SUM = SUM + XJ(M)*XP(N2,M)
   11   CONTINUE
        COM = XJ(N2)
        COMI = EMLT(N2)*EBBN(N2) + GMLT(N2)*SUM
        COM28 = COMI - COM
        IF(COM28)32,33,33
   32   COM28 = - COM28
   33   COM27 = COM28 - TOL*COMI
        IF(COM27)13,13,14
   13   INDX = INDX +1
   14   XJ(N2) = COMI
   15   G(N2) = SUM
        IF(INDX - N)16,17,17
   16   GO TO 10
   17   DO 18 N3=1,N
        XJSM(N3) = XJSM(N3) + XJ(N3)
   18   GSM(NS) = GSM(N3) + G(N3)
    3   CONTINUE
        IF (SENSE SWITCH 1)313,310
  313   DO 19 N4=1,N
        QFLX = GSM(N4) - (1. - XP(N4,N4)*XJSM(N4)
```

```
 19 PUNCH1, N4, QFLX, GSM(N4), XJSM(N4)
    GO TO 34
310 DO 312 I=1, K
312 TYPE1, TEMP(I)
    DO 314 N4=1, N
    QFLX = GSM(N4) − (1. − XP(N4, N4))*XJSM(N4)
314 TYPE1, N4, QFLX, GSM(N4), XSJM(N4)
    GO TO 34
    END
```

APPENDIX 6

Geometric
Mean Beam Length
Data

TABLE A6.1

Geometric Mean Beam Lengths L for Isothermal Gas Radiation

Shape	Characterizing dimension X	Factor by which X is multiplied to obtain mean beam length L	
		When $P_G L = 0$	For average values of $P_G L$
Sphere	Diameter	$\frac{2}{3}$	0.60
Infinite cylinder	Diameter	1	0.90
Semi-infinite cylinder, radiating to center of base	Diameter	. . . .	0.90
Right-circular cylinder, height = diameter, radiating to center of base	Diameter	. . . .	0.77
Same, radiating to whole surface	Diameter	$\frac{2}{3}$	0.60
Infinite cylinder of half-circular cross section. Radiating to spot on middle of flat side	Radius	. . . .	1.26

W. H. McAdams, *Heat Transmission*. New York: McGraw-Hill, Inc. (1954), chap. 4 (by H. C. Hottel).

TABLE A6.1 *continued*

Shape	Characterizing dimension X	Factor by which X is multiplied to obtain mean beam length L	
		When $P_GL = 0$	For average values of P_GL
Rectangular parallelepipeds:			
1 : 1 : 1 (cube)...........	Edge	$\frac{2}{3}$	
1 : 1 : 4, radiating to 1×4 face............		0.90	
radiating to 1×1 face............	Shortest edge	0.86	
radiating to all faces...........		0.89	
1 : 2 : 6, radiating to 2×6 face............		1.18	See table below
radiating to 1×6 face............	Shortest edge	1.24	
radiating to 1×2 face............		1.18	
radiating to all faces...........		1.20	
1 : ∞ : ∞ (infinite parallel planes).........	Distance between planes	2	
Space outside infinite bank of tubes with centers on equilateral triangles; tube diameter = clearance.......	Clearance	3.4	2.8
Same as preceding, except tube diameter = one-half clearance..............	Clearance	4.45	3.8
Same, except tube centers on squares; diameter = clearance.................	Clearance	4.1	3.5

Parallelepipeds. Ratio of Mean Beam Length L to L with $P_GL = 0$

P_cL or P_wL.......	0.01	0.1	1
Ratio for CO_2....	0.85	0.80	0.77
Ratio for H_2O....	0.97	0.93	0.85

TABLE A6.2

Geometric Mean Beam Length Ratios and Configuration Factors for Parallel Equal Rectangles

$\beta = b/c$, $\eta = a/c$, $F =$ Configuration Factor, $r =$ Geometric Mean Beam Length

η	β:	0	0.1	0.2	0.4	0.6
0	r/c	1.000	1.001	1.003	1.012	1.025
	F	—	—	—	—	—
0.1	r/c	1.001	1.002	1.004	1.013	1.026
	F		0.00316	0.00626	0.01207	0.01715
0.2	r/c	1.003	1.004	1.006	1.015	1.028
	F		0.00626	0.01240	0.02391	0.03398
0.4	r/c	1.012	1.013	1.015	1.024	1.037
	F		0.01207	0.02392	0.04614	0.06560
0.6	r/c	1.025	1.026	1.028	1.037	1.050
	F		0.01715	0.03398	0.06560	0.09336
1.0	r/c	1.055	1.056	1.058	1.067	1.080
	F		0.02492	0.04941	0.09554	0.13627
2.0	r/c	1.116	1.117	1.120	1.129	1.143
	F		0.03514	0.06971	0.13513	0.19342
4.0	r/c	1.178	1.179	1.182	1.192	1.206
	F		0.04210	0.08353	0.16219	0.23271
6.0	r/c	1.205	1.207	1.210	1.220	1.235
	F		0.04463	0.08859	0.17209	0.24712
10.0	r/c	1.230	1.232	1.235	1.245	1.261
	F		0.04671	0.09270	0.18021	0.25896
20.0	r/c	1.251	1.253	1.256	1.267	1.282
	F		0.04829	0.09586	0.18638	0.26795
∞	r/c	1.272	1.274	1.277	1.289	1.306
	F		0.04988	0.09902	0.19258	0.27698

R. V. Dunkle, "Geometric Mean Beam Lengths for Radiant Heat Transfer

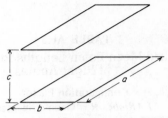

1.0	2.0	4.0	6.0	10.0	20.0
1.055	1.116	1.178	1.205	1.230	1.251
—	—	—	—	—	—
1.056	1.117	1.179	1.207	1.234	1.255
0.02492	0.03514	0.04210	0.04463	0.04671	0.04829
1.058	1.120	1.182	1.210	1.235	1.256
0.04941	0.06971	0.08353	0.08859	0.09272	0.09586
1.067	1.129	1.192	1.220	1.245	1.267
0.09554	0.013513	0.16219	0.17209	0.18021	0.18638
1.080	1.143	1.206	1.235	1.261	1.282
0.13627	0.19341	0.23271	0.24712	0.25896	0.26795
1.110	1.175	1.242	1.272	1.300	1.324
0.19982	0.28588	0.34596	0.36813	0.38638	0.40026
1.175	1.246	1.323	1.359	1.393	1.421
0.28588	0.41525	0.50899	0.54421	0.57338	0.59563
1.242	1.323	1.416	1.461	1.505	1.543
0.34596	0.50899	0.63204	0.67954	0.71933	0.74990
1.272	1.359	1.461	1.513	1.564	1.609
0.36813	0.54421	0.67954	0.7324	0.77741	0.84713
1.300	1.393	1.505	1.564	1.624	1.680
0.38638	0.57361	0.71933	0.77741	0.82699	0.86563
1.324	1.421	1.543	1.609	1.680	1.748
0.40026	0.59563	0.74990	0.86563	0.95125	0.9079
1.349	1.452	1.584	1.660	1.745	1.832
0.41421	0.61803	0.78078	0.84713	0.90499	0.95125

Calculations," ASME Paper No. 62–WA–120 (1962).

TABLE A6.3
Geometric Mean Beam Lengths for Rectangles at Right Angles

$\alpha = a/b$, $\gamma = c/b$, $F =$ Configuration Factor
$\phi = FA/b^2$, $Z_r = FAR/abc$, $R =$ Geometric Mean Beam Length

α	$\gamma:$	0.05	0.10	0.20	0.4	0.6	1.0
0.02	ϕ	0.007982	0.008875	0.009323	0.009545	0.009589	0.009628
	Z_r	0.17840	0.12903	0.08298	0.04995	0.03587	0.02291
0.05	ϕ	0.014269	0.018601	0.02117	0.02243	0.02279	0.02304
	Z_r	0.21146	0.18756	0.13834	0.08953	0.06627	0.04372
0.10	ϕ		0.02819	0.03622	0.04086	0.04229	0.04325
	Z_r		0.20379	0.17742	0.12737	0.09795	0.06659
0.20	ϕ			0.05421	0.06859	0.07377	0.07744
	Z_r			0.18854	0.15900	0.13028	0.09337
0.40	ϕ				0.10013	0.114254	0.12770
	Z_r				0.16255	0.14686	0.11517
0.60	ϕ					0.13888	0.16138
	Z_r					0.14164	0.11940
1.0	ϕ						0.20004
	Z_r						0.11121
2.0	ϕ						
	Z_r						
4.0	ϕ						
	Z_r						
6.0	ϕ						
	Z_r						
10.0	ϕ						
	Z_r						
20.0	ϕ						
	Z_r						

R. V. Dunkle, "Geometric Mean Beam Lengths for Radiant Heat Transfer Calculations,"

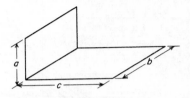

	γ:	2.0	4.0	6.0	10.0	20.0	∞
α							
0.02	ϕ	0.009648	0.009653	0.009655	0.009655	0.009655	0.009655
	Z_r	0.01263	0.006364	0.004288	0.002594	0.001305	
0.05	ϕ	0.02316	0.02320	0.02321	0.02321	0.02321	0.02321
	Z_r	0.02364	0.01234	0.008342	0.005059	0.002549	
0.10	ϕ	0.04376	0.04390	0.04393	0.04394	0.04394	0.04395
	Z_r	0.03676	0.01944	0.01384	0.008018	0.004049	
0.20	ϕ	0.07942	0.07999	0.08010	0.08015	0.08018	0.08018
	Z_r	0.05356	0.02890	0.01972	0.012047	0.006103	
0.40	ϕ	0.13514	0.13736	0.13779	0.13801	0.13811	0.13814
	Z_r	0.07088	0.03903	0.02666	0.01697	0.008642	
0.60	ϕ	0.17657	0.18143	0.18239	0.18289	0.18311	0.18318
	Z_r	0.07830	0.04467	0.03109	0.02025	0.010366	
1.0	ϕ	0.23285	0.24522	0.24783	0.24921	0.24980	0.25000
	Z_r	0.08137	0.04935	0.03502	0.02196	0.01175	
2.0	ϕ	0.29860	0.33462	0.34386	0.34916	0.35142	0.35222
	Z_r	0.07086	0.04924	0.03670	0.02401	0.01325	
4.0	ϕ		0.40544	0.43104	0.44840	0.45708	0.46020
	Z_r		0.04051	0.03284	0.02320	0.01300	
6.0	ϕ			0.46932	0.49986	0.51744	0.52368
	Z_r			0.02832	0.02132	0.01272	
10.0	ϕ				0.5502	0.5876	0.6053
	Z_r				0.01759	0.01146	
20.0	ϕ					0.6608	0.7156
	Z_r					0.008975	

ASME Paper No. 62–WA–120 (1962).

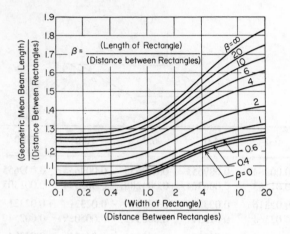

Figure A6.1   Mean Beam Lengths
for Parallel Equal Rectangles

Index